Symposium on the Identity and Dignity
of Man, Boston University, 1969.
Ethical issues in biology and
medicine; proceedings. Edited by
Preston N. Williams. Cambridge, Mass.,
Schenkman Pub. Co.; distributed by
General Learning Press [Morristown,
N.J., 1973]
vii, 296 p. 24 cm.

ETHICAL ISSUES
IN BIOLOGY AND MEDICINE

Proceedings of a Symposium on
The Identity and Dignity of Man

Sponsored by
Boston University, School of Theology
and
American Association for The Advancement of Science

ETHICAL ISSUES
IN BIOLOGY AND MEDICINE

Proceedings of a Symposium on
The Identity and Dignity of Man

Sponsored by
Boston University, School of Theology
and
American Association for The Advancement of Science

Edited by Preston N. Williams

Schenkman Publishing Company
Cambridge, Massachusetts
Distributed by General Learning Press

Schenkman books are distributed by
General Learning Press
250 James Street
Morristown, New Jersey

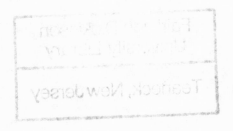

Library of Congress Catalog Card Number: 74-183951
Printed in the United States of America

CONTENTS

v

Preface

The realization of the goal of publishing this provocative material makes me grateful beyond measure for the assistance extended by others in completing this project. I am thankful especially for the aid provided by my co-editors Dean Walter L. Muelder and Professor George P. Fulton, Shields Warren Professor of Biology, and Chairman of the Department of Biology. Dean Muelder helped initiate the project and gave his support at every stage of its development. Professor Fulton elicited the cooperation of the scientific community and took a lively interest in the proper execution of all details, both large and small. Numerous other associates of these men and myself should be mentioned here, for without them there would have been no consultation and, hence, no book. Of these, Drs. Dorothea Roacke and Melvin Ketchel stand out in my memory. The manuscript would still be in a state of unreadiness if Mrs. Carol Moore had not joined me as an executive editor.

Despite the passage of time, the issues discussed and ideas put forth are still timely and relevant, and their implications for the future are only beginning to be understood. The reader will still find our deliberations of two years past immensely worthwhile and rewarding.

Preston N. Williams
Cambridge, Massachusetts

Introduction

The biotechnical revolution raises basic questions of the identity and dignity of man.

On December 28, 29, and 30, 1969 a breakthrough consultation was held at Boston University between theologians and ethicists, on the one hand, and life scientists and physicians on the other. It was held as part of the annual meeting of the American Association for the Advancement of Science and as one of the principal events in the Centennial celebrations of Boston University. Initiation for this conference was by the Faculty of the School of Theology. The faculty planning committee comprised at the outset Professors S. Paul Schilling, H. Neil Richardson, Nils L. Ehrenstrom, and Preston N. Williams. After the retirement of Schilling and Ehrenstrom, Dr. Preston Williams, Martin Luther King, Jr. Professor of Social Ethics at Boston University, became chairman of the theology task force and Dr. Orlo Strunk was added. From the side of the life-scientists the moving spirit was Dr. George P. Fulton, Shields Warren Professor and chairman of the biology department. He was joined by Drs. Dorothea Raacke (molecular biologist), Charles K. Levy (behavioral physiologist), John Mannick (vascular surgeon), and Frank Erwin (physiological psychologist). The National Endowment for the Humanities supported the conference with a substantial grant.

The decision to focus the conference on the identity and dignity of man was a joint decision since many of the bio-technological breakthroughs raised questions on both the meaning of man as an integer and on the quality of life and its value. Three days were devoted to the following topics: "Control of Population and Regulation of Behavior," "Extension of Life Through Organ Replacement," and "Improvement of the Quality of Life through Genetic Manipulation." A theologian and a life scientist or physician each addressed himself to the three general topics.

In developing the three main themes there was first of all a panel of specialists who commented on these papers. Then a more restricted and paired group of ethicists and scientists sought to "zero-in" dialogically on the most focal issues.

The above introduction gives a sense of the structure of this most significant event. I should like to make some general remarks and then to elaborate, however inadequately, on some of the issues.

1

Theology, ethics, and the life-sciences are in a new situation. The conference showed that difficult ethical quandaries provide the meeting ground between theology and the biotechnical practitioners and scientists. In the rapid changes revolutionizing world cultures, presuppositions and priorities in these fields have been challenged by the new powers at man's command. New hopes are linked to great dangers to persons and society.

Within the past two years the ethics debate set off by gains in the life sciences has taken on national and international proportions. Dr. James Watson, Nobel prize-winner in genetics, stresses urgency in the debate and "the possibility [that] our having a free choice will one day suddenly be gone." A bill was introduced into the Senate to establish a two-year National Advisory Commission on Health Science and Society in order to explore the moral, social and legal implications of developments in biology and medicine. Dr. Rene Dubos questions the larger implications than simply those within traditional medicine. Institutes are springing up to consider the relations of human values to the life sciences. Within the National Academy of Sciences a new committee has been set up on Life Sciences and Social Policy. The American Academy of Arts and Sciences devoted a whole number of *Daedalus* to issues relating to experimentation on human beings. The posture of the debate is interdisciplinary.

Theology and ethics do not approach the frontier issues with *a priori* and fixed answers, but are rather concerned about the methods, models, and values in terms of which priorities are set and decisions are made.

Some of the challenges have the magnitude of cumulative forces in the new bio-technology of the preservation and modification of human life. Decision-making of a highly complex order raises new moral, legal, and professional issues. The disciplines of theology, philosophy, and ethics are deeply affected because the assumptions of man's stewardship of human life require re-examination. Established institutions are being attacked and even overthrown. Ultimate issues of life and death affect both leaders and laymen. There is need for a new consensus on the identity and dignity of man.

Human fulfillment is threatened by runaway population growth and its attendant global hunger and by inadequate modes of behavioral control. While the population increases urban density and more people become daily more hungry, the scientific and technological advances extend the average length of life for both the fit and the unfit, polluting the genetic pool as well as conserving the quality of some creative persons who have access to biotechnical resources.

This prolongation depends in part on techniques and mechanisms which necessitate fresh definitions of life and death, personhood, and the identity of the human individual. How far may the interventions go? Who will set the boundaries in law, in medicine, in social control? Who will set the priorities and make the decisions? The problems are not only *quantitative* ones of population size and percentages of hungry people or of prolongation by organ transplants and replacements with mechanical organs, but they are also *qualitative* issues. In the vision of quality control one must now consider interventions in the brain, the use of powerful drugs, and the breakthroughs of genetic manipulation. Power over disease is coupled with power over the irreversible future of mankind. Here particularly one must consider fundamental questions of identity and dignity. Mankind is confronted by the most basic questions of the human use of human beings in part and in whole.

Theologians and scientists must be aware that the variety and complexity of nature does not decrease as they become involved in exploring its depth. Men are not stewards of a *final* boundary of meaning; the mystery increases indefinitely. More questions arise as they become aware of successive emergences of novelty and organization. Nature, including man, may still be in the making. In inquiry of all kinds, the various realms of being are not sacrosanct. Man's response combines wonder and the search for understanding. The mystery of life decreases as knowledge and understanding grow, but it also increases, and with it man's openness to new meaning and value ought to grow. With openness grows the resurgence of the sense of the inexhaustible mystery of God. God acts. We respond to His energizing. In the minds of some men the cultural and historical decisions being made by man are an extension, though on a new level, of the evolutionary thrust that has provided man's genetic construction.

The conference theme proved to be both divisive and unitive. I personally did not expect to find it so divisive, but it was important to become aware of the divisions. Identity and dignity are ascribed to man on all sides, yet these themes exposed (1) how isolated the professionals in theology and ethics have been from the moral thinking of the physicians and life-scientists; (2) how the various disciplines perceive each other and what stereotyped images they have; (3) how different the concerns and fears for the future are on both sides; (4) how they differently interpret the other's role in society and their own definitions of professional responsibility and leadership. Yet it must become clear that none of our neat definitions of morality and ethics will remain fixed. Society will not permit for long a profession to set its priorities in isolation from the community as a whole. The question therefore becomes urgent: how should ethics of life and death be done today? It was a shock to note that some scientists and physicians expected the theologians to be more conservative than they are and that they believed when a biological problem is solved the theological issue disappears.

The theme proved also to be unitive, because both identity and dignity are concerns involving persons, groups, and professions. All stand before common dangers like the population explosion, famine, mounting violence, pollution, manipulative genetic engineering. Extreme solutions are urged involving rejection of voluntarism and the embracing of political coercion. At the same time society demands to be served now and wants solutions to urgent problems. Since theological ministry and medical therapy are complementary professional roles in society, there is need for a comprehensive ethic that will give guidance in the midst of major institutional changes in medicine, education, and the churches.

As this writer sees theological social ethics, the method must be interdisciplinary, and hence the deepest cleavages of the conference only highlight the places where future work should begin. Three disciplines are involved in theological social ethics: the historic, traditional and contemporary values and perspectives of theology; the rational principles of ethical reflection; and the empirical data and findings of the sciences. Hence the theologian needs the ethicist and the life-scientist; the ethicist needs the context of the theologian and the scientist; the scientist needs to face the ultimate assumptions and contexts of his work and the social and historical implications of his "breakthroughs" in knowledge and technology.

To effect the most fruitful dialogue one must be willing to consider a reformation of education, a modification of curricula in universities, and a recomposition of student bodies and of faculties. To work in isolation is dangerous when in fact both faith and science are dimensions in human personality that lie within each other.

Looking now more closely at the issues which were raised, we note that the question of population control and the allowable methods of regulating human behavior drew divergent responses. There is, says Hoagland, a close relation between violent behavior and crowding, and the threat of nuclear war will increase with population growth. Many studies of animals prove that crowding beyond specific limits, either in nature or captivity, results in fighting, collapse of social hierarchies, cannibalism, particularly of the young, and failure of various aspects of reproductive processes. In this way animal societies ranging up from lower invertebrates reduce their populations when they have exceeded a certain number. Thus animal populations tend to grow and decline in regular cycles. War, famine, and disease — the Malthusian factors — cause similar fluctuations in primitive human societies. These cyclic fluctuations of population with crowding have been demonstrated with rats, mice, hares, monkeys, lemmings, deer and many other species, including a host of insect species. Among mammals, the dying off with crowding is characterized by overactivity of the adrenal cortex called upon to meet competitive stresses. This stress response mechanism ultimately breaks down if the stresses of crowding are sufficiently prolonged and severe. The overstressed adrenal system may produce atheroscelerosis, hypertension, enhanced susceptibility to all infectious agents and a variety of other endocrine and metabolic disorders that result ultimately in increased death rates, thus reducing the population.

"In man we know that crowding in concentration camps produced overactivity of the adrenals and deaths from the stress syndrome, even when the prisoners were well fed and housed. Organized social relations among prisoners collapse above certain levels of crowding . . . People with low flash points for violence, of whom there are estimated to be several million, are likely to be triggered off when crowded. When a group of men was penned up together in close quarters for many months on end, its members tended to become hyperirritable, and find each other's small mannerisms positively intolerable."

This problem of population control as a matter of social control proved to be baffling. The political issue was persistent. How far is it permitted for the state to go? No one defended the posture of Pope Paul VI's encyclical on birth control. No one challenged the assumption by all participants that population growth has reached crisis proportions that may require some *involuntary* measures to resolve, and that a "zero growth rate for the human race has become desirable". At the same time, it must be recognized that simple world-wide policy recommendations on birth rates and birth control are unrealistic, because situations vary greatly from region to region, nation to nation, and continent to continent. Perceptions of the population question differ greatly because of "development" issues and protests against crypto-colonialism, when some western countries recommend population control for Asia, Africa, and Latin America.

The danger of political tyranny lurks in all aggressive political intervention. Politics in relation to population control requires thorough ethical consideration.

It is important for the future of interdisciplinary work on population control between theologians and ethicists, on the one hand, and the life scientists, on the other, to recognize: (1) that there is a common sense of urgency and the need of control methods; (2) that the population problem becomes a cluster of other problems when carefully analyzed; (3) that regional differences are particularly important; (4) that enabling methods have to be personally acceptable and capable of being reversed; and (5) in a strategic response different groups have different acceptable processes. It was recognised that religious beliefs play an important role in all aspects of population and behavioral control and hence that theology and religion play an important part in social change precisely for this reason.

The problem of organ transplants and the prolongation of life raised questions and took place in an atmosphere quite different from that of the first day. On population control there was no dramatic confrontation on the part of the disciplines, but rather individual differences which cut across all fields represented by the participants. The atmosphere on the second day was more defensive and conflictful. One might ask: was this inevitable? Do the issues of transplants and the prolongation of life raise questions which lie hidden in some built-in antagonism between the professions of medicine and the ministry? Is this a matter of professional pride and even of arrogance? Does the physician assume that dialogue between himself and a clergyman is really a response to an attack? In many places, not least in the great teaching hospitals of Boston where clinical training of theological students is a lively, well established tradition, the ideas of the teaching team, and of the cooperation of the helping professions are strong. This general situation gave an element of surprise and drama to the tensions which were present at the outset when Dr. Francis Moore defended transplants vigorously, despite the cost in money and to the possible neglect of areas of a city that are not directly involved. This posture raised the question of social strategy in medical development. He seemed to assume that the topic of the dialogue was itself an attack on the ethic of transplants and on the ethics of the medical profession, though this was not intended from the theologians side. He stressed certain criteria that had emerged and had been professionally confirmed in the period covered by the development of kidney transplants. Such are: (a) the physician's role in giving hope to the patient, (b) in assisting the family emotionally, (c) in the matter of the duration of survival, and (d) in the contribution to the quality of life.

The physician tends to be oriented to the traditional patient-physician relationship. He considers himself to be in charge until dismissed. He has a well-developed code of medical ethics. This code has evolved within the profession and its reference points are largely there. For others to raise ethical questions may seem an intrusion, but this situation is changing. Society no longer consents to ethics constructed in isolation.

If there is a conflict, however, it arises only partly because of the above issues. The conflict may arise because the minister and the physician who deal with the same person approach him or her with different value orientations and with different methods of moral decision. The consultation of the Identity and Dignity of Man showed that the ethicists were not confronting the physicians with conflicting ethical answers. They were raising questions of ethical method. How ought choices of transplants and of prolongation of life be made? Theologians were most perturbed by the immunologist who said that when the biological question is solved the theological question disappears.

Given the defensiveness of some medical leaders present, the basic questions raised by Dean L. Harold DeWolf were hardly properly perceived, particularly since he spoke following Dr. Moore. DeWolf raised the question of what principles would illuminate and conserve the greatest values and how choices should be guided by human dignity under God. These questions led to the ethical question of the function of the medical profession in society. Is it, he asked, the all controlling idea of the Hippocratic Oath to *defend the body against death*? Justice to the patient may not always be avoiding death. There are other question on the relation of organ transplants to *fully human living and dying*. Because of scarce resources who gets the benefits? For example, here is a man sixty years old who needs a kidney. Let us say he is a great surgeon. Here is a woman of twenty-five with four children: she also needs a kidney. Assume that the operation will be successful in either case. Who gets the scarce kidney? Who will decide? What are the criteria? When are heart transplants permissible? When is the patient really dead?

Can the nation afford transplants? On this question DeWolf did not simply raise a question but took a position that was in substantial disgreement with that of Dr. Moore. Relatively speaking, according to Dr. DeWolf, some organ transplants are too extravagant. For the population as a whole, medical care is not as good as it should be. Indeed, the communal policies of the profession are in effect a turning of the physicians' backs on the people. Here, then, is a social and a professional question of ethical priorities. Who is entitled to decide? How autonomous should scientists and physicians be?

DeWolf also raised the question of the meaning of death and the rights of the dying. Based on his own pastoral experience, he testified to the repeated situations where the wishes and rights of the patient were in conflict with the medical team. There is often an unwanted prolonging of dying and the attendant loss of personhood. The body is not a person and bodily life is not the highest good. On the other hand, to love the dying is an obligation.

With respect to these latter questions I am led to make several observations on the birth and death of persons.

The question of the identity and dignity of man has to do with levels and quality of life, with the emergence and value of the distinctively human person. The theologian, like the scientist, recognizes that life and death on this planet did not begin with man. Life precedes the emergence of personhood and personhood often ceases before absolute death occurs in the organism as a whole or in organs or in cells. Life is a process, not a single event or entity. When, therefore, we deal with questions like the identity and dignity of man, we note processes which form the antecedent living context as well as the subsequent contexts of essential personality. Persons are dependent on life because personality cannot emerge until certain biological conditions have been met and fulfilled. Consciousness is a key term, and beyond that self-consciousness is an essential criterion of human life. Conscience experience is the mark of a person. The person is the steward of life.

Man as a physiological organism has many analogies and structures comparable to non-human animals and lower forms of life. He is an emergent whole with distinctive qualities, qualities which depend for their appearance and continuity on highly complex orders, levels, and hierarchical systems of life. In his truly human existence, physiological characteristics must be supplemented by psychological, cultural, and historical qualities. Human beings, qua persons, develop out of the matrix of non-human life and may cease to be human beings while sub-personal life continues for a period of time in parts of the body and in the cells of certain organs. It is not the similarities with sub-human life, but the qualities of distinctively human life which should provide the moral guidelines on questions of life and death.

The question of human *life* as a process and human *death* as a process requires further clarification, since the person as the subject of value raises the crucial issues of his identity and dignity. Once conceived and implanted in the womb the embryo has the physiological potentialities of developing into a human being. The tissue of the embryo is unlike that of any other tissue in the mother; it has unique characteristics. Its development is a long process from conception and implantation until adulthood, being completely dependent on the mother within the womb for life itself and subsequently on society for language and socialization. When does the personal integer emerge? The question is difficult to answer, for the unfolding of life is both continuous and by stages and levels. The process is unidirectional and temporal. If the process is interrupted before the brain reaches a certain stage of growth, there is no possibility for consciousness or self-consciousness to arise.

The development of consciousness and of self-consciousness into full personhood is unlike the process of death. Personhood may be experienced along with interruptions of consciousness, but death is a matter of irreversible non-consciousness. Death is not a repetition in reverse order of the stages of life in the body. Still, we can say there is a stage in the life of the fetus when there is not yet a personal consciousness and we can say there is a stage in the death of the body when there is no longer a human being present. It becomes increasingly clear that the death of the brain is a decisive factor, just as the development of the brain is decisive for the emergence of the truly human. For, while consciousness is not the brain and brain is not consciousness, there is a dependence on brain growth and activity for those qualities which characterize a person, such as emotion, communication, understanding and the like. I would propose, therefore, that one criterion for the identity and dignity of the person — whether we deal with questions like abortion, prolongation of life, death in relation to transplants or other related questions of experimentation or therapy — is the stage of fetal brain development when consciousness is possible on the one hand and the stage or brain death when non-consciousness is irreversible.

How do we relate these reflections to the idea of "reverence for life"? Life is a gift. All life has value, but not all life is of equal value. In the very definition of human life a priority of values is given and implied, for all values are *of*, *by* and *for* persons. What is potential human life, e.g., has greater value than what would be, for example, potential mouse life. For this reason experimenting on the human embryo or fetus is of a different order of values from experimenting on the intrauterine life of a mouse. Within the order of human life, the potential personal life of a fertilized ovum is not of the same value as conscious and self-conscious life. All life deserves reverence, and the more the fetus develops the more its potential values become actualized. As the fetus approaches capability of life outside the womb, the more deference should be given to the claims of that life, provided of course, that it has properly developed. On the basis of the above, we cannot in principle rule out experimentation on an embryo or fetus if such experimentation is itself undertaken out of reverence for human life and is controlled by its identity and dignity.

Our approach to death should cohere with the dignity and identity of man, for death has meaning only because life has meaning. We may note the right of a person to die with dignity, recognizing that physiological death may come in stages, the quality of personal life ceasing when certain centers of the brain no longer function. The definition of death as "brain death" or "irreversible coma" is coherent with a sensitive appreciation for personal existence. This definition implies a willingness to think in terms of hierarchies of life and of the integration of organs of life because of the close connection between the brain and emotional and meaningful personal consciousness. The theologian and the ethicists can accept the cessation of the person with "irreversible non-consciousness" as a conception that corresponds to physiological "brain death," though the heart can be kept beating and respiration may continue. In this way the categories of ethics and of the life sciences can be consistent with each other. Brain death is the clinical definition which corresponds to the death of the person as permanent non-consciousness. When there is a flat EEG curve over a sufficient period of time, the human being may be defined as dead, though there is not yet absolute biological death, because there has occurred a terminus to all self-consciousness, emotion, and understanding so far as empirical investigation can determine. When the steward of life has gone, the body is no longer human. The steward of life has the right to decide whether he will or will not receive treatment and to die with dignity. Others may assist in this stewardship.

The mood of the consultation on the third day was unlike that of either the first or the second. Questions of improvement of the quality of life through genetic manipulation are not so immediately urgent as are those of population control nor do they yet involve the physician-patient and the minister-patient relationship as the dramatically publicized transplant operations do. The general mood was more academic and had the air more of the animated dialogue of a seminar. It was not, however, without its dramatic challenges, particularly in view of the work of the Harvard scientists who had just isoloted a gene. Indeed, Dr. James Shapiro, one of the Harvard team, directly challenged the lack of social urgency in Dr. Bernard Davis' keynote presentation.

All genetic information in cells resides in their DNA, which can now be isolated, fractionated, and synthesized in the test tube with increasing precision and versatility. There is, of course, a long trail between the isolation of a single gene and man who is a complex organism with hundreds of thousands of genes. The power to intervene in a single gene is not yet the power to determine human identity. Certain hereditary diseases, Dr. Davis pointed out, are *monogenic* — that is, due to alteration or deficiency of a single kind of protein whose structure is determined by a single gene. The most interesting human traits, however, such as heritable components of intelligence (in its multiple aspects), temperament, physique, resistance to disease, and the like, are highly *polygenic*, and hence show a broad, continuous distribution of values for any variable that can be quantitated.

Genetic engineering does, of course, pose important ethical questions, some more than others. Altering somatic cells, such as installing in an individual's cells a gene that provides a missing product required for health, raises no negative moral problem. At present similar mechanisms for altering polygenic traits do not seem possible. Hence, on this question the matter of identity is not pressing.

In the case of nuclear transplants from somatic cells to egg cells there could arise the formation of limitless numbers of individuals genetically identical with the donor. This is called cloning. For agriculture this development seems inevitable. Two problems are the loss of genetic *variety* and attendant loss of *adaptability*, and the danger of the master-slave issue if such transplants are extended to man.

A further cluster of issues is that of germ cell selection. This has both negative and positive aspects. Any positive eugenic measures raise two problems that seem at the moment insoluble for society as a whole, according to Dr. Davis: (a) agreement on the traits that should be selected and (b) the conflict between such solution and the natural parental pride in progeny that resemble oneself and represent a form of immortality.

It is not too early to face the social ethics problems of a possibly emergent eugenic program. There is the need to stabilize the size of the population and this may press acceptance of restrictions on the freedom to procreate. Then there is the dynamic pressure to advance the scientific knowledge already available by going further regardless of social consequences or priorities that protect personhood. Tomorrow's society may need less aggressive fighters to survive in the evolutionary struggle. "As our technology grows more complex and our planet more crowded the effective adaptation of the species, and perhaps even its survival, may require genetic as well as cultural measures to promote more cooperative social behavior and a greater ability to cope with complexity." Who will decide and according to what criteria?

This last issue leads quite naturally into the theme of genetic engineering and the normative view of the human. Are there some things we value about man that set limits on what we are morally permitted to do in scientific investigation? In posing this question Dr. James Gustafson presented a challenge to Christian ethicists as well as to scientists. Negatively, "a scientist has no right to intervene in the natural processes in such a way that he might alter what men believe to be, and value as the most distinctively human characteristics." Positively, "a scientist has the right to intervene in the courses of human development in such a way that the uses of his knowledge foster growth in those distinctive qualities of life that humans value most highly, and remove those qualities that are deleterious to what is valued."

On this note we may conclude these observations. We are all scientists today. We are all moralists. The potentialities for interdisciplinary dialogue and collaboration are humanly almost unlimited. The urgency of the crises and depth of mutual human respect require that universities carry forward the possible cooperative programs as fully as possible. The humanistic commitment of higher education, not least in theology and the life-sciences, beckons us forward.

We seem to be at the "code" or "resolution" stage in medical ethics as related to the borderland between treatment and experimentation. This stage of ethics development has the following characteristics: (1) there are many generalizations in the range of "middle axioms" but few meaningful proposals that give guidance to all; (2) there are "outsiders" who are telling experimenters how to operate, but many cases where the full story is not disclosed to the public by experimenters; (3) there is little response by those most involved in the ethical questions; (4) when the public is concerned about cases, there is little sustained public interest; (5) there is a small, elite core of "concerned" persons (but few of these have played the role in medical experimentation that Rachel Carson has played in problems of pesticides and the environment); (6) the original situation, consequently, not only continues but intensifies, i.e. it gets worse. Perhaps the field of theological and Christian social ethics should make a much greater external uproar. As a part of this we need a greatly expanded program of mutual indisciplinary work and debate. In all of this we need a clear dedication to the quality of personal life and the improvement of the human community.

Walter G. Muelder
Dean and Professor of Social Ethics
Boston University School of Theology

Papers

BERNARD D. DAVIS

Threat and Promise in Genetic Engineering

The spectacular recent advances of molecular genetics have led to the widespread belief that we will soon be able to alter and to synthesize genes at will, and even to blueprint our progeny. The likelihood and the consequences of this development have already been considered in several essays and symposia,[1] which include some exuberant, Promethean early predictions. Since then most interested geneticists, I believe, have had more restrained second thoughts. However, the threat of nuclear catastrophe, and the deleterious impact of many technological advances on the quality of life, have meanwhile generated wide public suspicion of science in general; and the mass media have accordingly welcomed sensational pronouncements on the dangers of further fundamental research in genetics — especially when such warnings have been used by some young geneticists to dramatize their political convictions, in a juicy, man-bites-dog story. It therefore seems important at this time to try to divorce the assessment of the scientific prospects from any political preferences.

Recent discussions of genetic intervention have focussed primarily on approaches involving laboratory manipulation of genes or of cells — so-called "genetic engineering." And it is true that the possibility of altering or replacing specific genes would significantly broaden our control over the human gene pool, compared with our present dependence on the lottery by which each of us forms an enormous variety of germ cells. Nevertheless, in looking to the future of genetic intervention we should also consider the possibility of extending to man an approach that is already technically feasible: selective breeding, which we have used since Neolithic times in the development of strains of domestic animals. For with this possibilty already at hand, it seems to me that the basic moral question in genetic intervention is not whether or not we dare develop novel techniques, or should apply them to man. Neither is it whether or not we should

17

influence our evolution: we have been doing so for thousands of years, and are still doing so, by changing our environment, since such actions inevitably alter the selective pressures that mold our species. Our fundamental decision, then, is whether or not we should intervene in our own evolution *deliberately*, rather than continue to do so haphazardly; the problems of technique seem secondary.

Indeed, the possibility of using a simple, eugenic technology for this purpose seems to me likely to come up for decision much sooner than the possibility of using genetic engineering. Hence, even though we are far from ready, in terms of either scientific knowledge or social structure, to undertake a eugenic program now, it does not seem too early to encourage social planners to begin to look into the possible good and bad consequences of various approaches. Accordingly, after trying to assess the likelihood and the significance of various developments in genetic engineering I shall consider in more detail some problems of eugenics and human evolution. But first let me review some of the scientific principles that make possible, and also set limits on, genetic engineering.

Relevant scientific principles

a. *The chemistry of heredity.* The genetic information in all cells (ranging from bacterial to human), and also in many viruses, is now known to reside in their DNA (deoxyribonucleic acid). It is only 17 years since Watson and Crick showed that the structure of this substance, consisting of two complementary chains, accounts for the ability of genes to yield identical copies: each chain is used as a template directing the synthesis of its complement. Enormous progress has followed in our understanding of gene action (i.e., the translation of the information of the genes into the structure of the corresponding proteins, on which all cellular activity depends). For our present problem it is particularly relevant that we are developing an increasingly sophisticated ability to copy, and to modify, small blocs of DNA in the test tube.

b. *Gene transfer in the test tube.* While most viruses are lethal to the cells that they infect, others are non-lethal and can incorporate their genes into, and thus modify, surviving host cells — for example, transforming them into tumor cells. Moreover, with bacteria genes can be transferred from one cell to another by means of such "temperate" viruses, and also even as naked DNA added to the surrounding medium. It seems very probable that these techniques will soon be extended to animal cells.

c. *Differentiated cells.* There is now strong evidence that all the differentiated somatic cells of an animal (e.g., muscle cells, skin cells, etc.) contain in their nuclei the same complete set of genes, among which different members are active or inactive in different cells. Hence if the mechanism of differentiation could be reversed, any of the cells in an organism could probably furnish all the genetic information required for copying the whole organism. So far differentiation has been shown to be completely reversible in the cells of plants (as in the transfer of cuttings), but quite irreversible in those of higher animals. However, this stability in animals depends on the interaction of the nucleus with the rest of the cell, and it can be broken down by transplanting the nucleus (by microsurgery or by cell fusion) into a different kind of cell. Specifically, when nuclei from intestinal cells in amphibia are translanted to egg cells they will occasionally support full embryonic development.

In addition to these rather recent developments in molecular and cellular genetics, three principles from classical genetics seem especially relevant.

d. *Interaction of heredity and environment.* In the early years of genetics, after the rediscovery of Mendel's laws in 1900, the existence of a gene could be recognized only through analysis of the Mendelian distribution of its alternative forms from parents to progeny; and this analysis was possible only for those genes that exerted an all-or-none control over the corresponding *monogenic* traits, such as flower color, eye color, or certain hereditary diseases. It was widely believed that other traits, which varied quantitatively rather than in an all-or-none manner, were governed by some other, radically different mechanism of heredity, or else entirely by the environment. Today we have developed a clear general understanding (but not a detailed analysis) of the mechanisms responsible for such continuous variations. First, these traits are *polygenic*, with many genes each contributing to the broad range of values observed. Moreover, each gene is *polymorphic*, i.e., capable of existing, as a result of mutation, in a wide variety of alternative forms (alleles), whose products differ quantitatively in their activity. Finally, with most genes the contribution of the particular alleles present in an individual is not quantitatively fixed but depends on *interaction* with the environment.

The all-or-none effect of certain genes is thus seen to be a special case, which dominated early genetics because of its simplicity. Most genes contribute to determining a *range of potential* in an individual, while his environment, past and present determines his actual state (phenotype) within that range. At a molecular level we now know that each gene, in a given allelic form, specifies a particular structure of a corresponding protein product; while the amount made is determined by the interaction of the gene with subtle regulatory mechanisms, which respond to stimuli from the environment. The important conclusion follows that the prescientific formulation of the question of heredity versus environment in qualitative terms has been false, and has led only to sterile arguments.

e. *Polygenic traits.* For our purposes it is particularly important to note that the most interesting and valuable human traits, related to intelligence, temperament, and physique, are undoubtedly highly polygenic. Indeed, man probably has tens of thousands of genes contributing to polygenic traits, compared with a few hundred recognizable through monogenic traits. Unfortunately, the study of polygenic traits is not yet far advanced; and though everyone now knows that genes are important, recognition of polygenic inheritance has not generally penetrated our culture.

f. *Psychogenetics.* In its application to human behavior, genetics faces not only polygenic traits, intertwined with the most complex environmental influences (i.e., cultural). It also has to contend with strong emotional attitudes, which support a curious relic of metaphysical dualism; for it is still widely believed that genes do not play an important role in determining intelligence and temperament in man. Yet many of those who hold this view will concede that all other traits in man are subject to genetic control, and that mental deficiency is often genetic in origin, and that temperament and intelligence vary widely among different breeds of dogs. I would suggest that in the long term some of the most important contributions to human welfare are likely to come from research in the genetics of behavior (psychogenetics): for example, by tailoring education to individual potential and patterns of response, rather than continuing to build on the naive 18th century concept of the *tabula rasa.* It would be unfortunate if expansion of the under-developed area of psychogenetics should be impeded by environmentalist preconceptions, or by rightist anti-intellectualism, or by leftist mistrust of any increase in our powers.

In this connection it may be useful to recall the consequences of the recent domination of environmentalism over all of biology in the Soviet Union, through Lysenko's insistence that "bourgeois" genetics conflicted with Marxist dogma. Official acceptance of this doctrine completely destroyed genetics in that country, and seriously damaged agriculture, from about 1935 to 1965.[2] This development provides an ironic example of the unstable relation between political and scientific ideas, since much earlier Karl Marx had unsuccessfully requested permission to dedicate "Das Kapital" to Charles Darwin! The moral for our times is obvious.

Major possibilities in genetic engineering

1. *Somatic cell alteration.* It does not seem too unlikely that for some of the diseases that are due to defective formation of a specific protein we will learn, within a decade or so, to replace the defective gene with an effective one, or to add the latter as part of a non-lethal virus that will persist in its host cell. This form of one-shot genetic therapy would be a major improvement over the current practice of continually supplying a missing gene product, such as insulin. Since we may not be able to settle the desired gene in all the cells that could profitably use it, cure may be possible only in those diseases where correction of an occasional cell is sufficient. Of course, it could be argued that improving the soma in this way, without altering the germ cells, would have the dysgenic effect of helping to perpetuate hereditary defectives — but so does conventional medical therapy.

In contrast to monogenic corrections, I very much doubt that such genetic somatotherapy can be used to change personality or intellect in a useful way. The complexity of the brain resides primarily in the network of interconnections of its 10 billion or more nerve cells; and though genes have specified much of this pattern of development, once it has occurred, the later introduction of new DNA would not be expected to alter the network already laid down. The polygenic nature of behavior would also present an obstacle to its alteration by manipulation of DNA, as will be further discussed in the next section.

2. *Germ cell alteration.*

a. *Directed alteration* of the genetic makeup of a cell, by *introducing the desired DNA*, might be easier to accomplish in germ cells than in somatic cells, since the former could be exposed to the DNA in the test tube, and hence in a much more uniform and controllable manner. A related approach would be *directed mutagenesis:* the use of agents that would bring about a specific desired alteration in the DNA, such as reversal of a mutation that made a gene defective. So far, however, efforts to find such agents have not been successful: all known mutagenic agents cause essentially random mutations, of which the vast majority are harmful rather than helpful.

If directed alterations of either kind become possible they will probably find their greatest use in allowing an individual to give rise to his own progeny without condemning them to inherit a particular defective gene that he carries. This development would be a great medical advance, with no significant moral problem that I can see, provided the manipulations carry little risk of harmful side effects. Indeed, replacing a gene for diabetes in a germ cell, and thus in the resulting offspring, would clearly be preferable to replacing it in the somatic cells of a diabetic, whose germ cells could still pass it on.

In contrast, it seems to me extremely unlikely that we will also be able to improve behavioral traits in this way, for the polygenic nature of these traits suggests that they would require extensive replacements of DNA for any substantial and predictable changes. Nevertheless, the possibility of success in this approach cannot be completely excluded, since it is conceivable that a relatively small number of key genes might play an especially large role in determining behavioral potentials. Our present scientific knowledge on this important issue is nil. But whether major retailoring of the psyche would require a great many genes or only a few, this approach seems likely to remain excessively difficult compared with selection, for cloning, from the enormous variety of patterns already displayed in Nature's catalogue.

A major source of concern about genetic engineering arises here from the double-edged nature of increased power: if we could replace defective genes we could also introduce them. And, indeed, although the polygenic nature of the brain presents a serious obstacle to improving it by genetic manipulations, one could more easily impair its function by this approach: for monogenic metabolic defects are already known that can alter the activity of brain cells, without altering their connections. A tyrant could then conceivably use this means for genetic enslavement. Yet such a technical possibility seems to me so far off that we cannot profitably guess what our political structure might then be. Meanwhile, we already have on hand psychological, pharmacological, and nutritional methods that could promote the same horrifying goal, and these tools are rapidly growing more powerful. If we manage to prevent their antihumanitarian applications, we can expect to apply the same controls to any later developments in genetics. And if we fail to solve these earlier problems, and to preserve the ideal of universal human dignity, no anxiety about genetics, or limitations on its progress, will help.

  b. *Reversal of differentiation* of somatic cells (or of their transplanted nuclei) could yield precise genetic copies of the donor, whether the embryo was then developed in the test tube or by implantation into the uterus of a foster mother. This process of asexual reproduction (cloning) would thus produce individuals of strictly predictable genetic endowment, in contrast to the infinite variety generated by sexual reproduction (which more or less randomly selects one of each pair of genes present in each parent). The required complete reversal of differentiation has already been accomplished with transplanted nuclei in adult frogs, as noted above; it seems likely that such reversal will eventually also be accomplished with cells from adult mammals, including man. The use of adults would be important, since by delaying selection of donors until this stage their genetic potentialities can be better assessed.

A less drastic degree of reversal can already be accomplished today in mammals (and hence presumably in man). By removing an early embryo, separating its cells (which are relatively undifferentiated), and using each to start a new embryo, one can produce a large set of identical twins. However, since this procedure copies an embryo of undetermined genetic structure, rather than an already known adult, it yields only uniformity and not predictability. It would thus provide at most an adjunct to eugenics, since it would aim, like all eugenics, to improve the odds in the lottery rather than to eliminate the gamble.

The possibility of cloning mammals seems much closer than the other technical developments that we have been discussing, and so it does not seem too early to begin to consider the moral consequences of its possible extension to man. Our culture could obviously be enormously enriched by a continuous supply, or an expanded supply, of proved geniuses: though even in areas of abstract creativity, such as mathematics and music, a succession of Mozarts and Einsteins might exert an excessively conservative influence, depriving society of the richness that comes from our inexhaustible supply of new combinations of genes. Moreover, how far could we extend the process to "great men" whose outstanding literary, social, or political contributions might depend very much on the interaction of their genetic endowment with a particular culture? The world would probably risk no loss in producing another Tolstoy, Churchill, or Martin Luther King, but it might be disappointed.

A greater danger arises from the fact that there would be no limit, in principle, to the size of a clone derived asexually from cells of the same parent. Cloning could therefore conceivably be extended to the point of markedly homogenizing the population. This development might create an evolutionary danger, since the success of a species depends not only on its degree of adaptation of its present environment but also on its possession of sufficient variety to permit it to adapt to future changes. On the other hand, man is less subject than other species to this danger, because of his control over his environment. But long before we would have to worry about this problem: who would wish to send a child to a school in which most of his class was one set of identical twins?

There will surely be considerable incentive to solve the problem of cloning mammals, since the copying of champion livestock could substantially increase food production. But I do not foresee any strong pressure to extend this achievement rapidly to man, comparable to the economic and military pressures that have led to hasty exploitations of other technological developments without assessment of their social cost. Yet perhaps I underestimate the potential strength of the temptation to inflate one's ego by securing this form of literal immortality. I hope that we will have enough public discussion to provide a consensus on this important issue, well before some geneticist-surgeon team is ready to test its prowess in making 'the new man'.

c. *Predetermination of sex,* by separating the kinds of sperm cells that would give rise to each sex, has not yet been successful, but it may soon be possible. Technically, however, one could even now achieve the same goal in a more indirect manner, by eliminating embryos of the undesired sex. The sex of an embryo can be diagnosed by examining the chromosomes of its cells, and cells that it has released into its surrounding amniotic sac can be recovered without harm by tapping that sac (amniocentesis). Wide use of such methods might cause a marked imbalance in the sex ratio, which would surely lead to changes in our present family structure; or we might create social or legal pressures to prevent such imbalance.[3]

Major possibilities in the selection of parents or of their germ cells (eugenics)

In contrast to the methods described above no new technology would be required to influence the composition of the gene pool by selectively regulating fertility — i.e., by arranging for greater contributions of some potential parents and smaller (or zero) contributions of others. In animal husbandry, where the criteria for selection can be sharply defined and the extent of the selectivity is not limited by social considerations, the efficacy and relative speed of this procedure in influencing evolution have been amply demonstrated. A modern refinement is the long-term preservation of sperm and its widespread distribution by artificial insemination, as already practiced with prize cattle. This method could be extended to man at any time. The parallel preservation and implantation of egg cells is also theoretically possible but would be considerably less convenient.

Certain eugenic patterns have already been extensively pursued in man's past. For example, a polygamous family structure, and special sexual privileges of tribal leaders, accelerated human evolution by amplifying the genetic contribution of the most successful males; and the eugenic intent may have been quite deliberate, since the dynastic character of early political structures clearly reflects great confidence in the force of heredity. In a later pattern, the gene pool of the Jewish race has perhaps been influenced by the tradition, in the medieval ghetto, of having each little community support its most promising scholar not only in his scholarly activity but also in raising a large family.

In general, the process of selection may focus either on particular individuals with outstanding traits or on broad segments of the population. With either focus, the aim may be to increase the fertility of those with especially desirable genes (*positive* eugenics), or to discourage or prevent reproduction of those carrying especially undesirable genes (*negative* eugenics). I shall outline briefly three patterns which could theoretically be used to improve the degree of our genetic adaptation.

a. *Selection against monogenic defects* already constitutes the major task in the medical specialty of genetic counseling. In the past this approach has depended entirely on estimates of probability. However, recently it has become possible, by amniocentesis, to identify in the embryo certain hereditary defects which justify abortion. This procedure is being used increasingly to detect diseases associated with visible abnormalities of the chromosomes (e.g., mongolism = Down's syndrome); and some hereditary diseases with biochemical changes and no visible chromosomal changes are now also becoming detectable in this way.

Though abortion of such defective embryos, and discouragement of their conception, prevent much misery in individual families, the quantitative effect of this type of negative eugenics on the human gene pool is unfortunately miniscule. The reason is that most hereditary diseases are genetically recessive and therefore appear only when both parents have the same rare defective gene; and for each such mating there will be a huge reservoir of carriers of the gene who will not be detected because they did not mate with a similar carrier. The genetic counsellor thus aims at a symptomatic and not a radical approach to the gene pool. To be sure, biochemical tests for the carrier (heterozygous) state have recently been developed for several hereditary diseases, and so a broader base for negative eugenics can now be visualized. However, the utility of any effort to eradicate undesired genes seems highly questionable: for it has been estimated that each of us carries on the average five serious recessive defects. The theologian will recognize the problem of casting the first stone!

b. *Selection of especially desirable germ cells.* For many years H. J. Muller, a distinguished geneticist who received the Nobel Prize for his discovery of the mutagenic action of X-rays, vigorously advocated "germinal choice": the establishment of sperm banks, along with the education of people to the altruistic goal of using these to produce the best possible progeny rather than their own progeny.[4] These views, however, were not taken up favorably either by other geneticists[5] or by the public.

While it is conceivable that Muller was simply ahead of his times, some objections to his scheme seem to me serious. First, there is the difficult problem of securing widespread agreement on the value of the traits that might be selected for: Muller's own beau ideal sounds much like the brilliant, idealistic, scholarly individual that he was. But perhaps a democratic society could solve this problem by providing outstanding representatives of various groups — athletes and movie stars as well as professors and clergymen. Second, evolution has selected not only for love of children but more specifically for parental pride in one's own offspring — no doubt based in part on the image of oneself, and the sense of partial immortality, that they convey. It seems almost certain that in most people this deep-seated trait could not be overcome by theoretical arguments, but would require coercion, and a major advantage of Muller's program — its voluntary nature — would then disappear. Finally, Muller's approach reflects to some extent the notion of the ideal type in a species, and in modern evolutionary thinking his concept has been largely replaced by emphasis on the adaptive value of diversity in the population.

c. *Differential reproduction of large groups.* In general this approach has had little attention, except that many people have expressed concern at the evolutionary consequences of a pattern of differential fertility that has prevailed for some time, as a spontaneous social development, in the more developed countries. For there has been a definite negative correlation between family size and socioeconomic status; and to the extent that our society has become fluid enough to provide a substantial correlation between genetic potential and actual achievement, this reproductive pattern would exert a *dysgenic* effect (i.e., cause deterioration of the human gene pool). Most genetic proposals have aimed at trying to shift the pattern in the opposite direction by enriching the population for the progeny of people with superior achievements, by one or another criterion; but such proposals are hardly likely to be accepted if our society continues to move in an increasingly egalitarian direction. In any case, I do not see the current drift in our gene pool as a critical problem, for its effects are slow compared with the rate at which other crises are emerging, and reproductive patterns fluctuate from time to time.

It seems to me that another eugenic approach, essentially ignored in the past, may be more likely to prove acceptable: one with the humanitarian goal of increasing human satisfaction, and decreasing misery, by minimizing the production of individuals whose genetic endowment would seriously limit their capacity to find a sense of usefulness and fulfillment in a complex world. In this approach an improved endowment would not be an alternative to an improved environment, but the two would be complementary approaches to the solution of persistent social problems.

For a number of reasons, which I shall now summarize, I think it may be only a few decades before we will be facing the question of whether or not to institute a eugenic program, most likely of this kind.

Trends favoring the development of a eugenic program

a. *Stabilization of population size.* The inescapable need to limit the size of our population will surely force us quite soon to accept restrictions on our freedom to procreate. Once this step has been taken, it may not seem a large further step to make these restrictions selective: i.e., to license some families to have more children and others to have fewer or none. For just as the shift from an unlimited to a tight budget promotes more careful and selective use of any other resource, it is likely to influence our attitude toward the future gene pool.

b. *Progress in genetics.* Our present knowledge of human genetics, and especially of psychogenetics, does not provide a nearly adequate base for a eugenic program; and as I have noted above, this very important area of scientific investigation is not thriving today. Yet since scientific knowledge is cumulative and verifiable, its advance is inevitable, even though the rate is not predictable. Hence genetics will surely become an increasing part of the study of psychology, psychiatry, sociology, and education. This development, along with improvements in psychological testing, and the use of computers in the statistical analysis of large numbers of variables, will provide a much firmer scientific basis than we now have for measuring genetic potentials.

c. *Progress in general education in biology.* Though there are still many schools in this country where biology is taught without mention of its most fundamental principle — evolution by natural selection — this know-nothing attitude cannot persist much longer. For the spectacular advances in molecular genetics, and the resultant fear of genetic engineering, seem bound to encourage public interest in the principles of human genetics and evolution. Will we not then see increasing acceptance of the notion that we should use this knowledge to promote peace, happiness, and self-fulfillment for future generations?

d. *Progress toward equality of opportunity.* Twin studies, and other studies of the correlation of intelligence test scores with degree of genetic relationship, have provided evidence that the differences presently measured by these tests are as much as 80% genetic in origin, when the measurements are made among people with similar socio-economic and cultural backgrounds. However, where there are large differences in background, and where racial prejudice or other obstacles have interfered with social mobility, the heritability of the test scores drops so much that the tests cannot be used as an index of genetic potential. Hence the significance and the reliability of such tests can be expected to increase as our growing concern with social injustice and racial discrimination promotes a closer approach to environmental parity.

Suppose we then find that performance in intelligence tests, and in future tests of other behavioral traits, shows a high, reliable coefficient of heritability. And suppose, in addition, that a low performance is strongly correlated with social maladaptation — whether judged in terms of coventional success, useful contributions to society, happiness, or criminal behavior. Will not people then ask whether it is kind or cruel to allow those to be born who will predictably have more than their fair share of difficulty in coping with their complex world? Moreover, in our growing concern for the quality of life, will we not have to take into account the potentialities of the individual, as well as the quality of his environment? To put it another way, will not the physicians to our society, given enough understanding of its diseases, recommend preventive as well as curative measures?

e. *Pressure to use technology.* Since we are beginning to question, as a society, whether we have to build everything — including supersonic transports and biological weapons — for which we have the technological capacity, a eugenic program, however feasible, might well remain rejected. However, this response would probably require continued widespread conviction that such a program would do our society more harm than good; and I do not think this conviction can indefinitely survive the trends listed above. Moreover, it is unfortunately all too easy to predict our response to news of the eugenic equivalent of a Sputnik. Hence it seems to me that before too long we will be asking not whether to have a eugenic program, but whether it will be a humanitarian force or a weapon in nationalistic competition.

Comments on a eugenic program

   The eugenic movement was founded by Darwin's nephew, Francis Galton, at a time when the science of genetics, and even the concepts of genes and mutations, did not exist, though the principle of natural selection had become the subject of enormous discussion. Unfortunately, Galton's motivation included scientifically naive, snobbish notions about the hereditary superiority of the British upper classes. Moreover, eugenics later suffered even greater distortion into the obscene racism of the Nazis, and of our own white supremacists. Small wonder that this field, despite the altruism of Muller and other recent supporters, has long had a bad name among those committed to promoting human freedom and dignity. Nevertheless, for the reasons that I have summarized above I do not think we can afford to simply dismiss eugenics on the basis of its sad history. For eugenics was born prematurely: in the future it will have a much broader and firmer scientific base, while the world will be much more crowded and will surely have a very different social structure. Let me therefore note a few considerations that may bear on these future developments.

   a. *Race prejudice.* Any rational eugenic program would be concerned with evaluating the genetic potential of individuals, and not of ethnic or social groups. And since the accuracy of this evaluation will surely increase, as I have noted above, with advances in genetics and greater uniformity in the environment, the resulting knowledge should be able to displace the ignorance and the prejudices that underlie the racist judgment of an individual in terms of his membership in a group. Nevertheless, the danger of going off the road here is real, which is one of the reasons for my stressing our present unreadiness. Clearly, an essential prerequisite for a humanitarian eugenic program is that it not be based on race prejudice.

   b. *Adaptability for the future.* Since the survival of a species requires adaptability to future changes in the environment, and since we cannot accurately predict man's future environment, it could be argued that we might do long-term harm by tampering with his evolution. However, I think we can safely predict one feature of our future environment: in the absence of a cataclysm it is bound to grow in technological complexity. Hence individuals will face even greater demands on their capacity for carrying out the operations, and with-standing the stresses, imposed by a complex environment. There will be less and less need and opportunity for the man with the hoe. Hence our present, unplanned tampering with evolution will probably do increasing harm if continued in the future. For though environmental change is usually the main source of challenge to natural selection, man has paradoxically inverted the evolutionary process: we have simultaneously maximized the rate of change of our environment and minimized the pressures of natural selection on our species. From a strictly evolutionary point of view, then, our species could clearly benefit from a strengthened selection for adaptation to its radically altered world.

c. *Aggression and cooperation.* While intelligence is presently the most easily measured of the characteristics that seem important for adaptation to a complex civilization, cooperativity may be even more significant for the survival of our species in the atomic age. For human evolution in the past has selected for both aggression and cooperation — indeed, this mixture is what makes our ethical problems so ob-durate. And though we cannot readily measure the hereditary com-ponent of aggression, its importance is affirmed by the recent dis-covery that the presence of an extra male (Y) chromosome is frequently correlated with criminal behavior. However, there are no present grounds for distinguishing genes promoting antisocial aggres-sion from those promoting desirable forceful qualites, such as leader-ship and independence of judgment; we still do not know how to follow Socrates' advice that we select for virtue. This area is clearly a very important one for research, since intelligence is only one of the behavioral traits that should ideally be taken into account in a eugenic program.

d. *Evolutionary perspective.* Perhaps it is premature to be discuss-ing a more or less distant eugenic program at a time when guilt over our sins, both against people and against our planet, has precipitated an acute concern with the environment. But if we build on unsound preconceptions, and deny genetic reality, we will only face later dis-illusion. Nature always has the last word, and I hope it will not be a mocking one.

We must therefore focus on the promise as well as on the threat inherent in eugenics. For as Dobzhansky[6] has pointed out, man crossed one Rubicon when his cultural evolution permitted him to begin to control his environment; and having very recently begun to understand evolution and genetics, he is almost ready (on an evolu-tionary time scale) to cross another. "Evolution need no longer be a destiny imposed from without; it may conceivably be controlled by man, in accordance with his wisdom and his values." Surely such a prospect offers students of ethics an enormous challenge.

In summary, I doubt that advances in molecular genetics will have any impact, in the foreseeable future, on intelligence and personality in man, since these traits are highly polygenic. A more realistic technical possibility is the production of precise genetic copies of individuals, which would have real value in agriculture but would raise serious moral issues if extended to man. However, it would be irrational and destructive to cut down basic genetic research at this time in order to avoid possible remote future social problems created by developments in genetic engineering. For one thing, since we cannot separate research that might contribute to these developments from research much closer to controlling cancer and various genetic disorders, social controls should be applied at levels close to visible fruits, and not at the roots. Moreover, a tyrant wishing to use biological means to promote enslavement could already find at hand powerful psychological, pharmacological, and nutritional tools, and we must learn to protect ourselves from their misuse long before similar dangers might arise in applied genetics.

The earliest type of genetic intervention is likely to be a eugenic program, not dependent on any new laboratory techniques. At present we lack an adequate scientific basis, as well as a suitable social structure and intellectual climate, for such a program. Nevertheless, we may have to face the problem within a few decades, when we are forced to stabilize our population size. Most eugenic proposals have involved positive selection; but our increasingly humanitarian and egalitarian trend may lead to a broad program of negative eugenics, aimed at preventing the birth of persons whose inadequate genetic endowment would condemn them to lives of misery. I would advocate serious consideration of the issue by social planners, and increased research in psychogenetics, in the hope of guiding a future program along lines that would increase the humanity and the dignity of man.

Acknowledgment: I am grateful to Leon Eisenberg and Rollin Hotchkiss for helpful comments.

Notes

1. Medawar, P. B., *The Future of Man*, Basic Books, New York, 1960; Symposium on "Evolution and Man's Progress," *Daedalus*, Summer 1961; Wolstenholme, G., ed., *Man and His Future*, Little, Brown & Co., Boston, 1963; Lederberg, J., "Molecular biology, eugenics and euphemics," *Nature 198*, 428 (1963) Sonneborn, T. M., ed., *The Control of Human Heredity and Evolution*, Macmillan, New York, 1965; Roslansky, J. D., ed., *Genetics and the Future of Man*, Appleton-Century-Crofts, New York, 1966; Huxley, J. S., *Essays of a Humanist*, Harper and Row, New York, 1964.

2. Medvedez, Z. A., *The Rise and Fall of T. L. Lysenko*, Columbia Univ. Press, New York, 1969.

3. Etzioni, A., "Sex control, science, and society," *Science 161*, 1107 (1963).

4. Muller, H. J., "Human evolution by voluntary choice of germ plasm," *Science 134*, 643 (1960).

5. Sonneborn, T. M., "H. J. Muller, crusader for human betterment," *Science 162*, 772 (1968).

6. Dobzhansky, T., *Mankind Evolving*, Yale Univ. Press, 1962.

Organ Transplants as Related to Fully Human Living and Dying

There is not time to spell out the full ethical basis presupposed by my treatment of the subject in hand. However, there are two closely related working principles most relevant to this study. The first is that one should always act so as to promote the greatest possible harmonious system of value in the human community. The other is that all one's choices should be guided by respect for every man's dignity as children of God and by intentions of loving kindness toward all persons affected by those choices. As far as Christian people are concerned, these intentions are governed by loyalty to the spirit of Jesus Christ.

Ethical questions of any profession must be seen in relation to the function of that profession in society. The profession of medicine, in the broad sense, seeks to contribute to the health of human beings. Corollary to this purpose is the effort to save people from death, for it is obvious that if a patient is abandoned to death he cannot be restored to health.

1. The Hippocratic Oath

It is important to see these matters in proper perspective. It sometimes appears that the all-controlling purpose of the physician is to defend the patient against death. Indeed, the Hippocratic Oath is often understood to require this. Actually, however, the relevant sentences of the Oath read as follows:

> The regimen I adopt shall be for the benefit of my patients according to my ability and judgment, and not for their hurt or for any wrong. I will give no deadly drug to any, though it be asked of men, nor will I counsel such.[1]

If we accept this statement, then the supreme concern of the physician must be the "benefit" of his patients. This may not always be the same as the postponement of death, even though deliberate euthanasia is forbidden, I think rightly. These thoughts will be in the background as we address the problems in hand.

2. Who Will Be Chosen to Live?

Now we must ask which patients are to be given the benefit, if there is to be benefit, of organ transplants. When the shortage of donors, of equipment and of the needed expert personnel means that only a fraction of the patients who would be suitable recipients can be served, who will be chosen? According to an editorial in the *Journal of the American Medical Association* in June, 1968, for example, about 50,000 patients die of uremia each year. Of these about 7,000 would be well suited for hemodialysis or for kidney transplants, but only about 1,000 can be accommodated, or one out of seven. Which will be enabled to live? What six will be left to die?

We may support the plea that more resources and personnel be prepared so that surgeons will not have to make such choices. But the surgeons are not afforded the luxury of playing ethical games about a future improved situation. They must decide today who will be chosen and who must be left to die.

Both professional training of the physician and the background of a Judeo-Christian culture make the very question distasteful. Every person is of worth beyond calculation. God cares for the least, as well as for the greatest. Nevertheless, the choice must be made.

I see no way to avoid a calculus in which account is taken of many factors. First must come the medical considerations. Considering only the renal transplants, which patient has the best chance of survival with the transplant — assuming that all have been found unable to survive without it? Which has the most suitable donor? Assuming that the issue has not yet been settled, some non-medical considerations must now be faced. Whose life — under the somewhat impaired health predictable — will be most valuable to other people? Here must be confronted the questions of dependents — economic or personal — and of broader social usefulness. Who might be expected to have the most years of useful life ahead if seen through this present crisis successfully? None of these questions can be answered with certainty. With available data the surgeon or team of surgeons, with any other consultant they choose to invite, must do the best possible to decide aright, with humble dependence upon God for purification of motives, guidance of thought, and forgiveness of mistakes which may yet be made. By whatever method or criteria, the problem is agonizingly complex. Whoever must make the decisions is worthy of utmost understanding. He can be assured of divine forgiveness if he makes mistakes, as any such person is sure to do, even with the best of human wisdom and good will.

3. *When Are Heart Transplants Justified?*

Cardiac transplantation is an especially heroic procedure. It is unusual in its demand for a donor who has just died with heart unimpaired, in the extraordinary requirements of extensive teamwork by rare specialists, in small proportion of recipients who survive for significant periods, and in the unusual psychological effects which often occur in the recipient and in others.

The Board of Medicine of the American National Academy of Sciences issued a public statement proposing guidelines on the undertaking of heart transplants. Pointing out some troublesome features inherent in this particular type of transplant, the Report continued, "Thus the procedure cannot as yet be regarded as an accepted form of therapy, even an heroic one."[2] Hence it is believed that the doing of a heart transplant can be justified only under highly restricted conditions. It must not only be judged to offer the only hope for the recipient, but there must be resources present for gaining maximum scientific value for the future of medical service. Exacting requirements should, therefore, be made of the institution where the operation is to be performed.

In the report to which reference has been made there is a proposed requirement that a donor be selected only with unanimous written agreement by a "group of experts, mature physicians — none of whom is directly engaged in the transplantation effort." This opinion must be based on "evidence of crucial and irreversible bodily damage and imminent death." [3]

Does this mean that the heart may be taken from such a person before he has actually died? Apparently so. It is specified that death must be "imminent," not that it has occurred. This would appear to imply a plain case of medical killing even though the purpose is not to kill this patient but to save another. The medical profession generally would reject the rightness of this provision. So I think would most moralists.

Much more authoritative in American practice is the Report of the American Medical Association Judicial Council, approved by vote of the House of Delegates in June, 1968. It specifies rigorous requirements regarding the physicians, the medical institution, and the selection of both recipient and donor. Regarding the latter, it states,

When a vital, single organ is to be transplanted, the death of the donor shall have been determined by at least one physician other than the recipient's physician. Death shall be determined by the clinical judgment of the physician. In making this determination, the ethical physician will use all available, currently accepted scientic tests.[4]

The Report specifies that before death the donor must be provided with all the care which would be given to any other patient in his condition, and lays down other conditions to protect his rights and those of his relatives.

But when is a human being actually dead? This used to be a matter of holding a cold dry mirror to the lips, the feeling of the pulse or the attempt to produce a reflex in the eye of the patient. But now it is not so simple. In these days both breathing and heart action may stop and yet the patient may be restored to life and recover.

Some neurologists have advocated using electroencephalography to determine when activity of the cerebral cortex comes to an end. However, at the twenty-first annual meeting of the American Academy of Neurology in Washington, this procedure was a subject of some controversy. A committee reported sending questionnaires about it to "2600 neurologists and experts in electroencephalography." The physicians questioned reported 23 "survivals" chiefly attributed to drug overdoses. But many of the specialists doubted the adequacy of the measurements in those instances.[5] In any case, we can readily see the wisdom of the AMA position insisting that several criteria be employed and not one alone.

4. Psychiatric Complications

Any change in the body as radical as the transplanting from another of an important organ may produce psychiatric complications. These usually result mainly from change in self-image or side effects of drugs used to prevent rejection. Transplantation of the heart brings several other potential trouble-making factors into play. In literature and common usage the heart is the symbol for emotion or for the depth of personal identity or, as in ancient biblical literature, for the intellect. To have a new heart, then, may lead the patient to expect a new life, new loves and new abilities. The knowledge that one's new heart is that of a dead person may lead to depressing thoughts. The fact that the heart is an organ of such obvious and constant activity, of which a heart patient is especially likely to be frequently and keenly aware, adds to the danger of unhealthy emotional effects.

That the danger of psychiatric complications is serious is well attested by Donald T. Lunde, experienced psychiatric consultant to a cardiac transplant team at Stanford University.[6] Dr. Lunde tells of psychoses induced by transplants and also of undesirable effects upon members of a donor's family who felt that their own loved one had not completely died so long as his heart was beating in the chest of another. As a result they followed the recipient's fortunes with abnormal anxiety and suffered a new trauma of grief when he finally died. I have been told of a similar instance near Washington.

Such complications give further reason for conservative policy regarding cardiac transplantation. They also indicate the need for taking pains to instruct the recipient and his family and also the family of the donor to allay the effects of traditional mythology about the heart.

5. Can a Medically Under-Staffed Nation Afford Such Heroic Transplants?

For people who can pay for it, medical care in the United States is very good indeed. This is also so for many other persons who are fortunate enough to receive generous charitable care. But for the population as a whole, it is far from being the best among the nations. The rapidly increasing shortage of hospital space, physicians, nurses, and members of other health professions, together with the escalating costs, are principal causes of our national shortcomings in this respect. The United States has fallen behind fourteen other countries in the rate of infant mortality and behind seventeen other countries in life expectancy.[7] The number of people who are unable to receive hospital care or medical service in our national capital, even when they are in critical need, has become an open scandal. It is probably even worse in many rural areas and other less publicized places.

Physicians as individuals seem to me to be usually generous and kind beyond praise. But sadly their one powerful political arm, the American Medical Association, effectively obstructs realistic measures to correct this condition.

The question whether this or that medical team or hospital should prepare for heart transplantation must be seen against this background. Time and money devoted to preparing equipment and personnel for this heroic procedure and then to performing the operations and caring for the patients cannot be used to protect the health of mothers and infants or to restore sick and poor young people to health. The time devoted to the possible extension of one life by a heart transplant might bring many years of good health to many persons needing only ordinary preventive or curative medical service.

Probably it is right that a very few of the teams in the nation now doing heart transplants should continue with care, for the sake of future breakthroughs to more satisfactory procedures. But until we establish a far better ratio of health equipment and personnel to population and distribute these resources far better, we cannot afford to spend so extravagantly of the inadequate resources available.

6. Prolonging Dying.

a. *"Not Allowed to Die."* A letter to the *British Medical Journal* tells of a venerable and able physician who was incurably ill and suffered cardiac failure. By heroic measures he was resuscitated and lived on in great pain, with further deterioration of his hopeless condition. He gave explicit instructions, orally and in writing, that if he were to undergo another cardiac failure, he was to be allowed to die with no further effort to resuscitate him. Yet when there was another such episode the attending physician again took heroic measures and was again "successful." [8] Has a patient no right at all to say when or whether he wishes to undergo a procedure at the hands of his physician? It often seems that no such right is recognized.

Every experienced pastor and innumerable other people have observed extreme measures used by physicians in hospitals to extend the half life of people reduced to a level of existence worse than death. These measures must often be paid for by survivors who have not ordered them and cannot afford them. The dying man may have provided carefully to arrange for a decent income to support his widow when he was gone. Yet now the base of that income and of means for support for her meaningful life is used up in the heaping of indignities and pain upon him only for the unwanted prolonging of his dying. It is widely delivered that human principles and professional ethics require such postponement of death.

b. *Maintaining Half Life.* It is possible now to maintain some biological processes for months, sometimes for years, after all recognizable human personhood is gone. Artificial lungs, hemodialysis, transfusions, drainage through tubes in stomach and bladder, and other artificial devices can often keep blood flowing and lungs inhaling and exhaling for a long time after life has ceased to have positive meaning or value for the victim.

I am not here speaking of euthanasia, the deliberate taking of a person's life at his request or the request from next of kin when he is incapacitated for decision. This I oppose. Life is too sacred and the confidence of every patient in the medical profession too sensitive and important to permit medical doctors to serve at times as agents of death, however benevolent their motivation. The live ethical questions are at different points.

c. *The Right of a Patient to Decide.* One is the question whether a patient who engages the services of a physician and enters a hospital under his care loses thereafter the right to say whether he chooses to receive or not to receive specified further treatments which the doctor proposes. No sound ethical principle would support a doctor or hospital in assuming such loss of basic right. Primary responsibility for care of my body is my own.

It is true that I do not have the individual right to harbor a contagious disease without medical treatment, because in this instance my rejection of treatment subjects the community around me to the dangers of infection. If I have become mentally incapable of judging responsibly, my next of kin and the doctor may decide what is best for my interest. In the case of a treatment which offers some hope of curing my ailment or even without cure restoring me to such meaningful life as I could rationally choose to have, they ought to employ that treatment. If the treatment promises, at most, to prolong some of my vital processes without hope of my returning to meaningful, conscious life, or to restore consciousness but only for a period of great pain and continued deterioration until early death, then they are obligated to decide the issue negatively on the basis of concern for my own best interests.

d. *Bodily Life Not the Highest Good.* The American Medical Association deferred some questions about treatment of terminally ill patients to Brian Whitlow, Dean of Christ Church Cathedral, Victoria, British Columbia, and to Fred Rosner, M.D., Division of Hematology, Maimonides Hospital, Brooklyn, New York. Dean Whitlow, in his thoughtful response, writes,

> The notion in much contemporary thought, that life as such (the vital or biological principle) is the highest good, is an error. It is far removed from the Christian view that there are many things more important than mere existence.[9]

I suppose that most people whether Christians or not would agree that there are causes worth the cost of dying. We do honor martyrs of the state, of science, and of faith. This fact shows there is in principle a wide agreement that there are more important values than the continued biological existence of a human body.

It must be noted that in martyrdom the price is paid for the sake of values (such as freedom, truth, sanctity) to be experienced by other persons. There is nothing of value apart from actual or potential experience of a person — human, divine, or other if there be other. But a radical distinction must be made between the biological existence of a human body or its organs and the life of a person. A kidney, stomach, or heart kept biologically alive in a nutritive solution is obviously not a person. Neither is a larger part of the human body nor a whole body, in which various biological processes are occurring, to be equated with a living person. Such a body may exist without any sign that it embodies a person capable of desiring, suffering, appreciating, loving, or enjoying, or capable of setting a value or disvalue on anything at all.

On the other hand, a body may be so far deteriorated in vital functions that it is irreversibly moving to death. It now becomes possible for the physician to intervene and retard the process. Meanwhile, when the patient is conscious he may be plainly living a nightmare existence, with anguished pain, with the sacrifice of personal dignity to helpless dependence on mechanical equipment and on other persons for care of his ordinary bodily functions, and with sustained processes of thought and communication impossible. The sheer maintenance of life in such a body is not necessarily a service of love to the patient or to his family.

e. *Initial Presumption: the Duty to Extend Life.* Whenever a physician or anyone else faces a question of what to do about an injured or ill individual, the initial presumption must be to try to sustain life and to do all that is possible to restore it to health. The burden of proof is on the patient or doctor, next of kin or friend who is making the decision, to show cause why such life-sustaining efforts should not be made. But there are many circumstances in which the necessary countermanding evidence is at hand.

When the patient himself is making or participating in the decision, his primary concerns must be for faithful stewardship of his earthly life and for love of others whom his life affects. He has not the right to despise and destroy the life which God has given. Even if life has become a burden to him, so long as he is still capable of receiving and communicating love and faith in relations with others who love him, in a way to be of positive value to them, he is morally bound to choose continued life. He may, however, decide, while he can rationally choose and clearly communicate his decision, that under certain predictably probable conditions the efforts to prolong his bodily life are to be discontinued. If he senses that death is near and he believes it is God's will that he now enter it, he may ask that no one interfere. If his choice has been rationally made, it should be respected. Indeed, if the ailment is believed by the doctor to be incurable, the physician has no right to force on the patient, under such circumstances, treatment which the patient has chosen to reject.

f. *Ordinary and Extraordinary Treatment.* Whitlow and many other churchmen have maintained a distinction between ordinary treatment and extraordinary or heroic treatment, the former being always obligatory, the latter optional under rare circumstances. Extraordinary treatment is understood to be "very costly, or very painful, or very difficult, or very dangerous." Certainly the differences must be taken into account. The pain or danger attending a proposed treatment will certainly be of concern to the patient and must be weighed in the balance against the possible hours or months of extended life the treatment might bring. So will the cost if financial means are not unlimited and survivors will genuinely need the money. Since these matters would be of concern to the patient, they also must be to others who may be compelled to decide in view of his incapacity to do so. Of course in the latter case, both the physician and the family must take heed to keep their own motives pure.

While the distinction is relevant and may be decisive in some cases, it is not conclusive in itself and in principle. Stewardship of life and love for others concerned must be primary concerns. In relation to them empirical facts of the individual case must be decisive.

g. *Restoring the Living, but "Only Caring for the Dying."* As Paul Ramsey insists, we must never cease "caring for the dying"; but we are not always called upon to interfere with the process of dying. Indeed, love may dictate that we are not to interfere.[10]

Similarly, despite earlier stress on the distinction between ordinary and extraordinary treatment, Whitlow seems to imply a position similar to Ramsey's when he says,

> In my view, essential medical or nursing care must always be given: food, warmth, washing, and easing of bodily position. But beyond that, decision must be left to the physician.[11]

So long as there is ground for hope of recovery to life of positive meaning and value, certainly the decision maker(s) ought to choose the hopeful treatment. On the other hand, as Whitlow says,

> If the Christian physician concludes that death, not recovery, is God's will for the patient, he will believe himself morally justified in ceasing to obstruct the process of dying and in beginning instead to cooperate with it.[12]

Without the theological language, Rosner adopts a similar position in his own report to the AMA. He says,

> Most people would probably agree that withholding of treatment or discontinuation of instrumentation and machinery in an incurably ill patient would be permitted if one were certain that in doing so, he is shortening the act of dying and not interrupting life.[13]

The distinction made by Rosner, Whitlow, and Ramsey between shortening life and interfering with dying is helpful. But it seems to me not adequate by itself. Every human being alive is inexorably set on the course to death. Most of us do not know what will finally deliver the decisive blow, but we are all on the way to it and no medical science can prevent it. All that medicine can do about the death of anyone is to delay it and perhaps ease the dying when it comes. Many people, especially older people, are thoroughly aware of the advancing ailments in their bodies which are incurable and will finally kill them if nothing else overtakes them on the way. But in most instances such inexorable coming on of death provides no reason for refusing treatment to slow the process and delay death.

It will be protested that there is a great difference in time here. Very well, then. How much time must there be of life in prospect before death, in order to permit the discontinuance of treatment to extend it? And by how much time must the treatment offer hope of extending it to make it ethically mandatory?

h. *The Decisive Consideration.* A little thought will quickly show that time is not the decisive factor, though it is highly relevant when taken with other considerations. The decisive question must be: What quality of life is there hope of extending? If it is only biological existence of some vital processes in the body with no hope of renewing life of value to the possessor or to those who love him, then there is no obligation to extend that. Indeed, there may be emphatic obligation *not* to employ the procedures which would extend it — at the expense of both the emotions and the limited financial means of the family, for example.

But can the doctor be sure that while extending bodily processes a little, he or someone else may not find a further way of renewing meaning and valued life once again? When there is reasonable doubt, certainly the initial presumption must hold. Treatment must be given. Reasonable doubt, however, does not include the theoretical possibility unsupported by any facts, that an absolutely unexpected miracle might occur. No rational ethical decision on any consequential question can be based on such a consideration. At best, the choices are painfully difficult, yet we have to judge as reasonably as we can, on the basis of all available evidence, always giving life the benefit of the doubt.

i. *True Obligation to the Dying Person.* To decide not to use treatment of an incurably ill person only for the hope of extending a life that is either meaningless or overwhelmingly negative in meaning to him and his loved ones must not lead to his abandonment. The obligation to love and care for the dying is as deep and is even more poignant and the time to show concern for him is short.

Indeed, to love and care for the patient who is dying is the one all-inclusive obligation to him. What love requires must be done.

This last statement brings us back to the question of the *rights* of the patient. A right which is too little observed in these materialistic, body-oriented days, is the right to be respected and so to know the truth about oneself, and when the time comes, to die with all the dignity and all the communication of love which the condition of the patient will permit.

Here again it must be insisted that the life of the body is not all-important. Because physicians, by the nature of their work, tend to make it so, the hospital room of a dying man is often more like a biology laboratory than the chamber of a child of God. Wife or husband and family may even be sent out so that they will not be in the way of all the apparatus. Certainly when the incurably ill patient is in intense pain and wants relief, relief should be administered, even if it puts him to sleep and so cuts off communication. But while he is conscious, it is far more important that such a patient be in fellowship with his loved ones than that technical means be employed in hope of postponing a little further the processes now pushing him irreversibly away from even partial recovery. Love is for the loving, aspiring person, not for a mere body.

j. *The Right to the Truth.* The affirmation that a patient has the right to know the truth about himself does require some qualification. The initial presumption should certainly favor the doctor's telling the truth to him — directly or through a chosen mediary. Indeed, if one had to choose one way or the other, it would be better for all physicians always to tell patients the truth, with care and concern, yes, but the truth, rather than to have the predominant evasion and withholding of truth which now prevail. There are, it is conceded, irrational or seriously neurotic patients, who might speedily become much worse or even die of heart failure if told the truth. But such cases should be regarded as the exception. Most people have remarkable reserve capacity to meet a crisis of life and death when they know the facts about their situation.

For the serious Christian the knowledge that soon death will probably or surely come provides opportunity for some of the most effective testimonies of faith. The Christian has a right to use them. When once it is granted that the life of the body is not the ultimate good, then it should be apparent that the living, aware person who relates in love or anger, hope or despair to other persons and to God has claim to the truth which usually supercedes any real or presumed danger the truth might offer to the body. This is especially so in the very cases in which the truth is most often withheld, namely when the illness is incurable and death is not far in the future, whatever may be done.

The withholding of truth not only keeps from the patient what is due to him as a person, but also prevents his making decisions and performing acts in full view of reality. It also isolates him psychologically from everyone around him at the very time when he needs them most. In the misguided effort to shield him, doctor and family and friends spread around him a curtain of evasion. Again and again, first as son of a father who slowly died at fifty-one, and later as a pastor and friend, I have been told by dying people that they felt this isolation and the need for someone who would talk with them openly. In many instances, probably most, a person fully conscious when coming near death, knows it or at least deeply suspects it. Other people try to hide the truth from him. He thinks they do not want to face it and so he joins in the evasion. Thus they put on masks of pretense and play games with each other instead of meeting in the full light of truth and seeking each other's love and God's grace together in conquest of death.[14]

k. *The Test of Faith.* The way in which doctor, patient and loved ones deal with dying expresses as clearly as any decision we ever make our understanding of life and our ultimate faith. If the life of the body is ultimate, if as people often say, "the main thing is to keep your health," then death is simply defeat. In that case we are all doomed to defeat. One can understand why a person who believes that might sacrifice truth, dignity, fellowship with family and friends, and funds long saved for a loved one's support, to fend off the enemy until the last possible minute. Yet even then it would seem more worthy of a man or woman to accept that final defeat for what it is believed to be rather than to evade or pretend that life would still be going on as long as some machinery could keep blood flowing and cells alive in a miserable remnant of the body.

But if one is a Christian, or anyone who believes that bodily life is not ultimate and that death has not the last word nor the power to cancel the meaning of life, then radical revision is needed in our common present attitudes toward death and many current decisions about care for the dying.

Notes

1. *Encyclopaedia Britannica,* Fourteenth Edition, Vol. 15 (New York: Encyclopaedia Britannica, Inc., 1929), p. 198, "Medicine, History of: The Hippocratic Oath."

2. *British Medical Journal,* 23 March, 1968, p. 762.

3. *Ibid.*

4. The Report may be secured by request sent to the AMA Judicial Council, 535 N. Dearborn St., Chicago, Ill., 60610.

5. *The Washington Post,* May 18, 1969, p. A28.

6. See his "Psychiatric Complications of Heart Transplants," *American Journal of Psychiatry,* Vol. 126; No. 3 (Sept., 1969), pp. 369-373.

7. See "TRB from Washington," *The New Republic,* July 12, 1969, p. 8.

8. "Not Allowed to Die," *British Medical Journal,* 17 Feb., 1968, p. 442.

9. *Journal of the American Medical Association,* Oct. 23, 1967 (Vol. 202, No. 4), pp. 226-228.

10. Lecture on "Only Caring for the Dying," at Wesley Theological Seminary, May 14, 1969.

11. *Journal of the American Medical Association,* Oct. 23, 1967, pp. 226-228.

12. *Ibid.*

13. *Ibid.*

14. For an interesting and useful, though very uneven symposium on telling the truth to the patient, see Samuel Standard, M.D., and Helmuth Nathan, M.D., editors, *Should the Patient Know the Truth?* (New York: Springer Publishing Co., 1955).

Genetic Engineering and the
Normative View of the Human

The growing capacities for intervention in the course of development of human life raise in an exacerbated form one of the oldest of philosophical and theological questions, namely what is the *normatively human*. By normatively human I mean to indicate an evaluative concern. Are there some things we value about man that set limits on what we are morally permitted to do in our biological interventions? Are there some things we value about man that indicate the sorts of qualities of human life that ought to be kept in view in the controlled genetic development of man? The difficulties in coming to a consensus on the normatively human are almost insuperable, yet it is my deepening conviction that some efforts must be made to overcome them.

The development of this thesis requires two distinct stages, namely making a careful case for the importance of the question, and making substantial proposals about how it can be answered. The latter is the most difficult, and to be pursued properly it requires more extensive discussion than is possible in one paper, or even in one book. Indeed, it requires ongoing discourse between persons representing various points of view and interests, scientists, literary artists and other humanists, religious thinkers, and others. Thus, here I shall primarily attend to the first stage, namely that of marshalling support for the proposal that the question of what constitutes the normatively human is the most important issue that lurks in all the more specific and concrete problems we face when ethical issues are raised about developments in the field of genetics.

As a procedure I shall move from some specific possibilities for intervention, to some ways in which arguments can be made about their moral permissibility or non-permissibility, and attempt to show that at crucial points, the decisions one would make depend upon some assumptions about what is valued about human life, that is, what constitutes the normatively human.[1]

I. *The contemporary emergence of the question of normative humanity*

Any number of actual or future possibilities of significant interventions into the biological processes can function as the back-drop for reflection. Genetics is not the only field that raises the question. The attention of the public has been called to such possibilities through various television shows, a number of articles in popular journals, and through such books as Gordon Rattray Taylor's *The Biological Time Bomb*.[2] Dr. Bernard D. Davis's article in this symposium provides the reader with a careful assessment of what the major possibilities for genetic engineering or manipulation are. The sort of possibilities that Dr. Davis develops have engendered both anxieties and hopes in many persons. Some of them, as he aptly indicates in his article, raise moral questions of varying degrees of seriousness and difficulty. Perhaps the most dramatic one that has fascinated the reading public is that of cloning human beings. I shall proceed to formulate and discuss four different possible responses to the actual and potential scientific capabilities that Or. Davis describes and discusses.

1. A scientist has the moral right to do anything he has the technical capacity to do in research, such as the procedures suggested in Dr. Davis's article.

Various reasons might be given in suport of this proposition, though they would not all be equally cogent. a: New knowledge is intrinsically valuable, and therefore it is worth getting regardless of the means that are required. b: The "right to know" is a basic human liberty, and any restraint upon it is an infringement of the freedom of the scientist. c: Intellectual curiosity and growth are two of the most distinctive characteristics of the human species, and thus the fulfillment of these capacities is in accord with what it means to be human. d: It must be assumed that man has the right to know anything he has the capacity to find out; if it is not, fears and suspicions will lead to restrictions of inquiry as they have in the past, and many important and socially useful consequences would not occur. e: Men will do anything they have the capacity to do anyway; so it might as well be assumed that the right to do something arises from the capacity to do it. (This latter reason probably would lead to negative responses by almost everyone if it were universalized in an unqualified way. The technical capacity to develop the means of germ warfare does not entail the moral right to develop them, and certainly not to use them.)

2. A scientist has no right to intervene in the natural processes of human life, because it is sacred.

This position would not be advanced by any serious intelligent person in the modern world. Obviously men have intervened in the natural processes from the earliest time of human development in order to make human life more comfortable, healthier, and more rewarding. Thus, once the right to intervene is taken for granted, the lines of discussion can no longer be held to this proposition, but it does provide the antithesis to the first, and therefore is useful to introduce for our purposes in this paper.

3. A scientist has no right to intervene in the natural processes in such a way that he might alter what men believe to be, and value as, the most distinctively human characteristics.

Various reasons might be given in support of this third proposition. a: A qualitative difference in the meaning of human life would occur if the effects of research were to radically alter life as we now know and value it. The risk is too great to give up the degree of certitude we have about life's meaning and values for the uncertainty of qualities and meanings that might emerge. b: A qualitative difference in the powers to control human destiny would occur, and if these powers fall into the hands of those who do not share the same values most men share, they could lead to tyranny, and worse. It is, after all, not "man" in general who will be in a position to determine human destiny, but rather some men who have certain knowledge and power. c: Man is made in the image of God, and to fundamentally alter the image of man is to "play God," which is not only idolatry in a religious context, but is a movement beyond a healthy recognition of human finitude that keeps various forms of evil in check.

4. A scientist has the right to intervene in the course of human development in such a way that the uses of his knowledge foster growth of those distinctive qualities of life that humans value most highly, and remove those qualities that are deleterious to what is valued.

Various reasons might be given in support of this proposition. a: The basic motivating reason for any investigation is to achieve some control over the processes to which human life and development have been subject, over the processes to which men have in the past passively consented. This has been the case with the development of surgery, drug therapy, means of birth control, chemical fertilizers, etc. There is an implicit intention in all research to enlarge the human capacities for self-determination. It has been assumed that these capacities are directed toward the goal of the improvement of the conditions of human life, for examples, relief from suffering, and prolongation of life. b: One of the profoundest and most persistent aspirations of human life is to improve its conditions, and improve human life itself so that persons find it to be more "fulfilling," "rewarding," and "pleasant." Thus any interventions which are in keeping with this profound and persistent aspiration are worthy of moral approval. c: That which is most distinctively human (in comparison with other forms of created life), and thus that which is in the "image of God," is the capacity for self-determination and "self-creation," and thus the pursuit of interventions which might improve the qualities of human life are themselves in accord with one feature of what is descriptively, and thus in the eyes of some persons normatively, most human.[3]

My judgment is that the second proposition would be universally rejected by scientists, theologians, philosophers, and other humanists. Whatever the "sacredness of life" means, its meaning does not entail a moral prohibition against all forms of intervention into the course of its development, either as a single organism, or as an ongoing developmental system. The first proposition might be more controversial, for there might be some scientists who would distinguish the roles of the pure researcher from those of the technologist who determines how the research is to be applied. They might argue that while the researcher has the right to do anything he has the capacity to do, the same would not hold true for the technologist. Behind this distinction would be an assertion that while the pure researcher creates the necessary conditions for certain technological developments, his causal-responsibility for creating these necessary conditions does not entail a moral-responsibility for subsequent developments. Even within this distinction which limits the moral accountability of the pure researcher, however, it is possible for him to raise the moral questions about the right to use information for any purpose man has the capacity to pursue.

Both the third and the fourth propositions raise the questions of what constitutes the distinctively human. It is clear, however, that a simply *descriptive* answer to that question would not be sufficient. The two propositions raise the question of which human characteristics are *valued*, or are to be valued. The third proposition raises this question in terms of the criteria one might set which would limit the sorts of interventions that would be morally permissible or impermissible. The fourth assumes the moral permissibility of interventions, but raises the question of the normatively human with reference to the purposes to which they would be put.

II. *Some efforts to answer the question.*

If the issue were merely what constitutes the *distinctively* human, it might be resolved by empirical comparative research. Distinctively human capacities might be listed, and evidence be adduced for their uniqueness to man, such as his advanced capacity for speech and other forms of communication, for abstract reasoning, for intellectual curiosity and exploration, for a different kind of control over his destiny than other animals have, for a sense of moral responsibility, for love, etc. But such a listing, no matter how thorough and well-supported, would not of itself resolve the normative question about what is to be most valued in human life. This becomes clear simply by recalling that it is a distinctive capacity of human beings to develop technologies that deeply upset the ecological balance in nature, and in turn threaten human existence itself. A capacity or capability is not to be highly valued simply because it exists in human beings.

To develop a list of what persons have valued in human existence is also no simple task. Certainly there is the most primitive valuation of physical existence itself; whether one gives theological or other reasons for this makes little difference to the reality that we have a profound respect for life, particularly human life, and most particularly each for his own physical life. All of the exceptions to this do not add up to a negation of the generalization.

Sages in various traditions have sought to ascertain what end or goal is most valued on the part of human beings. Aristotle thought through this puzzle by looking for that which human beings sought as an end in itself, and not as a means to any other end, and he came up with *eudemonia,* with happiness or a sense of well-being.[4] Hedonistic utilitarians thought through the same puzzle, and came up with a complex notion of pleasure.

Some contemporary Christian thinkers use the language of "wholeness" or "completeness" or "maturity" to suggest what it is that makes human life truly (or normatively) human. Paul Lehmann, who discerns the presence of God's action wherever human life is made and kept truly human, at one point defines this normative wholeness or maturity as "the integrity in and through interrelatedness which makes it possible for each individual member of an organic whole to be himself in togetherness, and in togetherness each to be himself."[5] The analogy, though suggested under Biblical auspices, appears basically to be drawn from biology.

Not only theologians and philosophers have entered into the efforts to define on one basis or another what is valued, or ought to be valued about human beings. Professor Hermann J. Muller, in one of many places where he makes proposals for positive eugenics, generalizes on the valued qualities of life. "Among the qualities of man most generally valued are a genuine warmth of fellow feeling and a cooperative disposition, a depth and breadth of intellectual capacity, moral courage and integrity, an appreciation of nature and of art, and an aptness of expression and of communication." These in turn become "directions" that genetic development ought to take; they become both educational and genetic goals. "We need a strengthening and extension of the tendencies toward kindliness, affection, and fellow feeling in general, especially toward those personally far removed from us. As regard other affective traits, there is much room for broadening and deepening our capacity to appreciate both natural and man-made constructions, to interpret with fuller empathy the expressions of others, to create ever richer combinations of our own impressions, and to communicate them more adequately to others." We also need "advances in those traits of character that lead to independence of judgment and its necessary complement, intellectual honesty," and "also a much greater capacity for analysis, for quantitative procedures, for integrative operations, and for imaginative creation." And Muller does not forget things that imply certain valuations with reference to physical developments of man, "to better the genetic foundations of health, vigor, and longevity; to reduce the need for sleep; to bring the induction of sedation and stimulation under more effective voluntary control; and to develop increasing tolerance and aptitudes in general."[6]

Many other sorts of documents could be brought forth to indicate what people believed to be valuable about human life. America's founding fathers were concerned with "life, liberty, and the pursuit of happiness." The United Nations document on Human Rights could provide another such list. At this juncture I only wish to indicate that all through the history of man persons have developed statements about what the chief end of life is, about the qualities of life that fulfill it, about the ends and rights that define at least in a loose sense what is normatively human. It is clear that there are significant differences of opinion about the normatively human, and that often the isolation of a single end or value draws so much up into itself that even if one might agree, for example, that happiness is what men seek, the complex question of what constitutes happiness quickly comes to the surface.

In the efforts to flesh out propositions three and four of the first part of this paper, however, some recourse is taken, implicitly or explicitly, to judgments about what is to be valued about human life. For example, does an intervention in experimentation violate the person's "right to happiness?" Does it eventually contribute to his "pleasure," or to the "pleasure" of a large number of mankind? Does it keep him from achieving "maturity," or does it contribute to his capacity to "be himself in togetherness, and in togetherness . . . to be himself?" Does the research eventually make a contribution to Muller's goals; toward genuine "fellow feeling" and a "cooperative disposition," toward "depth and breadth of intellectual capacity, moral courage and integrity," etc.? Some conception of the normatively human is involved in the development of propositions three and four. The issue that confronts us is what constitutes normative humanity.

III. *Epistemological problems in answering the question.*

The obstacles to the developing consensus on what constitutes the normatively human appear to be insuperable. And certainly the expectation that all men in all cultures could ever agree upon a list is a utopian one. There certainly is no universally acceptable normative concept of what individual rights are inviolable, and what particular values or qualities are sought in personal and social well-being. Different cultures have different conceptions of human rights and values, and thus the fact of cultural relativism prohibits the achievement of a perfect consensus. Also, at different stages of this development men and cultures have different norms, which are related to the particular difficulties that they are currently experiencing. Physical survival, for example, takes priority over the liberty to be self-determining in certain crises, such as our present ecological one.

In spite of these difficulties, men have in the past aspired to provide some basis for common understanding. To do so has required that the epistemological problem be addressed in one way or another. How are these rights and values to be known? How does one come to know what is normatively human? What warrants can be given for any particular conception of it? Certainly any effort to move toward even a modest consensus must face the epistemological issue.

Some of the ways of knowing that have been claimed in the history of Western thought about man are worthy of noting, if only to suggest the markers on the trail and some of the obstacles to be avoided. One of them has been reflection on human experience, and generalization based upon that reflection. This seems to be basically what Aristotle was engaged in in the writing of his *Nicomachean Ethics.* He discerned that many things men valued and desired were means to other ends. One can imagine his observing and wondering about all sorts of human behavior, and thinking about what ends various values seem to serve. Finally, as I noted above, he appears to have asked what end is sought for its own sake, and not for the sake of any other end, and thus he arrived at the concept of *eudemonia*. The utilitarians appear to have arrived at the concept of pleasure in a roughly similar way. Herman Muller seems to have taken the same path; it appears that he observed not only what he valued, but also what was valued by the particular society of which he was a part, and on the basis of that came up with a list of the preferred qualities of life.

Religious thinkers have claimed revelation as a warrant for their understanding of the normatively human. The notion of revelation refers only to some idea that God in his infinite wisdom and power inscribed ideas on stones or in books. If the so-called second table of the Ten Commandments is taken as an example, it is clear that the ancient Hebrew people gave authorization to certain human rights, obligations, and attitudes on the basis of God's having revealed them to Moses. Murder and bearing false witness are violations of certain God-given rights; the attitude of covetousness is prohibited. In other strands of the development of Jewish religion, justice and mercy are noted as the requirements of God upon man. In Christian theology there developed the notion that the nature of "true manhood" was revealed by God in Jesus Christ. Thus, one looks to the accounts of Jesus' life and teachings for a depiction of what men are meant to be, or at least for certain "prominent lines" of what God wills that human life, both individually and socially, ought to be.

In these religious affirmations of what constitutes normative humanity, other warrants for the particular values and obligations, or for the model of true man, might well be given than a revelation from God. What one has, however, in the religious community, is the affirmation that certain patterns of human life are in accord with what God created man to be, or in accord with the purposes of God for mankind. Walter Rauschenbusch, the social reformer and theologian of the early decades of this century, put it more simply than many other theologians would, but he made a widely affirmed point when he wrote that "the will of God is identical with the good of mankind."[7] In answering what constitutes the "good of mankind" one looks both to the religious tradition and to reflection on human experience.

Christian thinkers did not always seek to define normative humanity exclusively in Biblical language; they joined with other philosophers in seeking the *telos*, the end of man, through the epistemology and the metaphysics that characterized the classic natural law position. The assumption here has been that there is a moral order to the universe, which includes an inherent tendency in individual men and in their togetherness to be inclined toward that which is good. This moral order could be apprehended by rational persons; human reason has the capacity to define the first principles of the natural moral law. And human reason has the capacity to apply these principles through secondary principles to the particular historical occasions of life. Thus certain moral principles and human values could be stipulated as being grounded in what man is essentially, and therefore what he ought to be normatively. Reasonable men ought to be able to agree, on these assumptions, on what the fundamental goal or end of human existence is, and they ought to be able to deduce from this, or infer from this, what values constitute normative humanity. In turn, they ought to be able to define the fundamental rights of man that cannot be violated, or the fundamental ends of man toward which he and his societies ought to be developing. Though this method of ascertaining the normatively human has been under severe challenge from many quarters for a long time, it remains for some Catholic and secular thinkers the epistemological approach that promises the most fruitful efforts at formulating a public consensus about the values of human life.[8] The fact that it is used to support the official papal position against "artificial" methods of birth control in itself suggests that all rational men do not agree, however, on what either the first, or the derivative principles of natural law ought to be.

There are other procedures that have been attempted to give warrant to certain values as being normatively human. The work of certain cultural anthropologists has suggested that there seem to be certain "moral requisites" not only for the survival of persons and societies, but also for their well-being. Professor David Little has suggested in a recent article that there might well be some basis in the writings of anthropologists Kluckhohn, Linton, Mead and others for inductively formulating a natural law from cross-cultural studies.[9] The epistemological point is that one would not claim the capacity of reason to apprehend the fundamental moral order of the universe, the inherent *telos* in all things, but rather that one could inductively proceed from information about human life in a variety of settings to formulate certain generalizations about what is required for meaningful human life to exist. This in turn might provide at least certain "conditional absolutes" that would give guidance to the development of man.

Also, there are persons who would appear to rely primarily on the sensitive conscience intuitively to perceive what the truly, or norma-

tively human life is. Among theologians, Paul Lehmann seems to be
assuming what the philosopher Maurice Mandelbaum calls a "percep-
tual intuitionism" as the way in which one discerns under particular
circumstances what the normatively human is. Lehmann writes, for
example, about the sensitivity of the conscience to perceive what God
is doing to make and keep human life human.[10] The most obvious
problem with this view is how to settle disputes between persons who
perceive the human thing to do to be very different under the same
circumstances.

Certainly this enumeration of various epistemological stances that
have been used to gain insight into the normatively human suggests
that any proposal for clarification of the problem under the pressure
of developments in genetics is in serious difficulties. The presence of
cultural relativism would appear to provide overwhelming odds
against any successful fruition of the enterprise. The high level of
generalization that is involved in the formation of normatively human
values, no matter what epistemological approach is used, seems to
make the application of these values to particular instances of intervention into biological processes a very difficult task. Also, it soon
becomes clear that the things that men have determined to be needed
for meaningful and fulfilling human life, or all the rights that they
have judged to be sacred, do not fall into a neat pattern which re-
moves the abrasiveness and tensions between them.

I would argue, however, that it is imperative at the present time to
seek to move toward some rational formulation of certain rights,
principles and values to provide at least certain points of reference, or
principles of consideration and re-consideration, even though such
a formulation would not immediately and absolutely determine what
interventions are morally warranted, or what uses of research are
held to be morally good.

IV.   *A procedural proposal*

How might such a formulation be used with reference to the possibilities of genetic engineering or manipulation? From any formulation
of what the complexities of the normatively human are, even from
one that states that to be human is ultimately a mystery that defies
complete rationalization, two different styles of practical ethics are
possible. The first would impose a rigid and static conception of man,
what his relations to others ought to be, on to any possibilities for
genetic development. This approach would tend to be restrictive in
an *a priori* way about what procedures would be permissible, and
what ends ought to be sought.

If held to consistently, this mode of practical ethics would restrict many of the interventions into nature which we now accept, not merely as having occurred, but as having resulted in new benefits for mankind. It is characteristic of this mode of practical ethical thinking to have its first disposition to be restrictive; transplantations of organs are questioned because they violate the principle of totality, of the function of an organ in its own total organic complex. Other efforts on the part of science and technology also are brought under restrictive questioning immediately upon proposal. Development, potential progress, experimentation are all stifled in important ways. The meaning of becoming human is not something discovered as man develops in the course of his evolution and changes, but it is something known authoritatively, and thus is imposed upon his actions from without. Institutions with the claimed capacity to know what the human is set themselves as the judges and guides of all processes of human development. Morality is defined by an authoritative voice, and this voice seeks to impose morality on others. Such is one way to deal with ethics and genetic experimentation. One would define the licit and illicit kinds of experiments in the light of an *a priori* definition of what man is, and everything done both in learning, and in doing from what has been learned, would have to conform to these determinations.

In contrast to this, let us offer another possibility. It is that man has always been developing new ways to determine his own life and that of the human race. He discovers new procedures for effective education; he finds new modes of relaxation. He has never assumed that he was fated by the natural forces which made him anxious or uncomfortable, but has constantly discovered new ways to fulfill his aspirations and his ends. He has discovered new things about what it is to be human; he has found institutions long accepted by man to be inconsistent with human fulfillment, such as slavery and capital punishment. He has discovered the subtle ways in which he is deprived of certain qualities of life by virtue of social structures and customs; this is the meaning in part of the new black consciousness. He finds thousands of ways to intervene in the natural processes in order to make a better life for the human race. He has improved the qualities of seeds; he has learned to irrigate the barren lands; he has concocted fertilizers and herbicides and pesticides which increase the food production. To be sure, his interventions in natural processes are not unambiguously for the good; he now becomes aware of ways in which the natural balance is adversely affected by his activities, and he discovers that to live he must limit his pollutions of air and streams. But he has assumed and seized the right to intervene in nature, including his own nature.

The priority is on the capacities for intervention, on what Karl Rahner calls "self-creativity." This is the kind of being that man is. He will continue to attempt to do whatever he is able to do, and his ability to do new things will expand with his knowledge of the fundamental processes of life. But he discovers that many things he is capable of doing are not for the well-being of the human community. He discovers this not by imposing upon himself, or having imposed upon himself, some fixed image of what man ought to be in the particularities of his existence as an individual with others. To live in this way would be to live in accordance with ethics which stultify human development. Rather, he discovers the direction in which development ought to go as it is consistent with, or abrasive upon, the moral requisites for human life and community. These requisites, many of which can be delineated and objectified by the human mind, can become the guide marks and the lights of intention which give direction to the course of future human development.

My basic point, then, is that the procedure for thinking ethically about human experimentation ought not to begin with a fixed image of what was, is, and always ought to be, from which are derived authoritative and unalterable rules which govern experimentation. Rather, the weight is on human initiative, human freedom (if you choose) to explore, develop, expand, alter, initiate, intervene in the course of life in the world, including his own life. But this does not mean there are not guidelines and lights of intention which can give direction to the uses of new knowledge. It does not mean that there is nothing to give warnings against certain possibilities, and to give positive support to others, or to set certain limits beyond which man cannot go.

I would close with a very apt sentence written by a sensitive French Jesuit that states both the beginning and the end of the moral seriousness of the human situation in which the possibilities of genetic engineering and other technical capacities places the human race. "We have become aware that, in the great game that is being played, we are the players as well as being the cards and the stakes."[11]

Footnotes

1. In this section of the paper I am using and expanding part of my unpublished paper, "Basic Ethical Issues in the Biomedical Field," which is more comprehensive in scope that the present article. I have deliberately not opened in this paper the question of the locus of moral accountability, whether it is in the researcher or in the technologist who applies the research.

2. Gordon Rattray Taylor, *The Biological Time Bomb*, New York: World Publishing Company, 1968.

3. Karl Rahner, S.J., comes close to this position in his paper, "Experiment: Man," *Theology Digest*, Sesquicentennial Issue, Feb., 1968, pp. 57-69.

4. Aristotle, *Nichomachean Ethics*, Book II.

5. Paul Lehmann, *Ethics in a Christian Context*, New York: Harper and Row, 1963, p. 55.

6. H. J. Miller, "Should We Weaken or Strengthen our Genetic Heritage," *Daedalus*, Vol. 90 (Summer, 1961), quotations from pp. 445, 446, and 447.

7. Walter Rauschenbusch, *The Social Principles of Jesus*, New York: Association Press, p. 128.

8. For example, see the statements by John Courtney Murray, S.J., in *We Hold These Truths*, New York: Sheed and Ward, 1960, pp. 109 ff., pp. 295-336.

9. David Little, "Calvin and the Prospects for a Christian Theory of Natural Law," in Gene Outka and Paul Ramsey, eds, *Norm and Context in Christian Ethics*, New York: Scribners, 1969, pp. 186 ff.

10. Lehmann, *op. cit.*, see pp. 116-17, pp. 358-59. Mandelbaum's argument for intuitionism is built from the work of several Oxford philosophers of a previous generation, and is found in his *Phenomenology of Moral Experience*, Glencoe, Illinois: The Free Press, 1955, Chapter 2.

11. Pierre Teilhard de Chardin, S.J., *The Phenomenon of Man*, New York: Harper Torchbooks, 1961, p. 229.

Social Investment and Patient Welfare in Organ Transplantation

A society accustomed to the effectiveness and bounty of complex modern medicine but uneasy over its expense and maldistribution has found in organ transplantation a procedure that symbolizes the very prototype of complex hospital care devoted to the treatment of individual patients. The public now asks, "Is it worth it?"

Attention has been drawn to transplantation as a symbol of so-called luxury medicine by three factors:

1. The increasing success-rate in kidney transplantation, which has made it a world-wide procedure now numbering almost 3,000 cases. It is no longer an isolated medical curiosity.

2. The ethical challenges of choice between real injury to a living person (a living donor) and the use of a recently deceased cadaver (involving a new definition of death; there is no simple unitary solution to the donor problem).

3. The sudden advent of heart transplantation, a little bit "too much and too soon," exposed suddenly to the public view as a weanling when it should have been kept in the nursery. Excessive publicity has made this the very image of "human experimentation" overextending itself, and with miserable results.

These three factors have joined to make transplantation a target or whipping boy, if you will, for those who would have medicine constrict its efforts to assist the sick if it is either too expensive, too complicated, or too strange to a conservative mind. There is a contrast between the hospital performance of such operations and the inadequacies of American care for the underprivileged, a seeming distraction of personnel who are looking after a patient with a new kidney when they should be out on a public health mission or in some form of community care. This has worried some, and it has given rise to such rhetoric as "consider a society able to provide luxury operations that cannot deal with daily care of children in the ghetto."

I believe we are entitled to enquire whether or not hospital medicine, even if it is expensive and complicated, is truly in competition with improved medical care delivery-systems or whether it is just a part of them. But our main mission today is to examine the social investment in transplantation (people, beds, facilities, costs), in the light of its dividend, the welfare of the patient, to see if it is an acceptable investment, and a viable social undertaking.

When we speak of transplantation, we are speaking of kidney transplantation and that should be quite clear. There have only been 150 heart transplants done with a handful of survivors. There is really no use getting into long-term problems with that. There have been 83 liver transplants done with about 4 survivors over 6 months. Organ transplantation today is kidney transplantation.

First of all, we must dispose of this word-picture of a luxury operation. This calls to mind a fancy operation for a rare disease in a wealthy patient. The complexity of disease and its treatment is no respecter of position or social status. People of high social position have very humble diseases and very humble people can have very complicated diseases. A mother of four, struggling in an underprivileged area to raise her family can have renal failure. In fact, glomerulo-nephritis, the commonest source of disease for which transplantation is used, is generally a disease of the poor rather than the rich. Its background of poor hygiene, streptococcal infection, and rheumatic disease is not something confined to the upper classes.

What about the cost of this? A dollar figure for a transplantation today ranges from a low of about $8,000 to a high of about $80,000 to $100,000. The lowest figure is for a patient with a well-matched sibling donor who comes in, who is dialyzed and transplanted and leaves the hospital in about two weeks to go back to work or to go home. The higher figure is for those patients who have had complications or difficulties or who have other coincident diseases, particularly disease of the heart or the great vessels. In terms of bed occupancy, if a living donor is used, two beds are obviously required, one for the donor and one for the recipient. The donor usually stays in the hospital about ten days because very careful study of the donor's kidneys is important. The recipient will stay in from fourteen to one hundred days, depending upon how the operation goes. Cost also includes operation, operating room, anesthesia, x-rays, all sorts of medical procedures, and it requires the devotion of a lot of people. Transplantation takes a big team. It is hazardous to the patient if we try to cut this team down. Bringing biological science to the bedside of the sick is no game for a lone wolf or a singleton. It is a team effort, and there is probably no field in which biological science is brought so rapidly to the bed-side as in transplantation, and this can never be done by just one person. The cost of prolonged dialysis is somewhat less than this in a month or a few months, but it is still a considerable expense running from $5,000 to $12,000 per year.

Who bears this cost? The best answer is society. The patient rarely pays for this out of his own pocket. One of my jobs is to conduct the financial affairs of a surgical department. We have paid for most of our kidney transplants from a number of sources. I know of no person who has paid these bills completely from his own pocket. One or two rather well-to-do patients have either paid for much of their procedure or given handsome donations to the research group. But on the whole they are paid for by insurance companies, and one can say that this raises the premium. They are also paid by hospital en-dowment funds, and we should not lose sight of that; also by char-itable foundations. But the principal payor has been the Government because, up until this year, it has been possible to put direct patient cost into research grants. The reason for that was that the National Institute of Health study-sections realized that you could not study this new way of treating people without treating people. Now that is changing. This type of cost will not appear in research budgets. We are, therefore, in a financial squeeze. Patients are in need of this treat-ment, and it is hard to know how we are going to pay for it. I should say also that the doctors help pay for it because the transplant opera-tion is only rarely covered by a professional fee to the surgeon or physician.

How does this cost compare with other medical procedures? Are transplants unique? Of course not. If you have a coronary occlusion and are admitted to a coronary care unit, you may have some arrhyth-mias which may take your life at any moment. If they are diagnosed and corrected, you may have a happy and useful life for many years. That is what a coronary care unit is all about. But it is terribly ex-pensive, around $250 a day. The treatment of cancer by complex sur-gical methods is also very expensive. Cardiac surgery is expensive, as are burns. We have a small burn unit. A person came into our hospital the other day burned from the midthorax up, and if he survives, he will be a perfectly useful citizen. But right now he is being kept alive by a machine. If he does "make it," it will cost somebody around $75,000. Transplantation is not unique in this regard. True, it consists of lavishing much care on a few. That is what medicine is. The few is one, the one is the patient, and the name of the game is the care of the patient. Transplantation is no different from other complex measures.

Is this cost truly in competition with community medicine for the underprivileged? Only in the broadest sense of expenditures of social resources. A new community must have a market plaza, garages, individual dwellings, and a school, as well as low rent multiple housing units. The carping critic can say that the school or garage is in competition with building the multiple housing unit. You need them all in order to build the community, and in medicine you need all modalities. You need the community physician, the primary doctor. You also need the complex hospital that can deliver care when the illness is complex. The personnel involved in transplantation are not trained to move out into the ghetto. They are trained to treat illness, often the illness of the poor, and this they do. Community medicine must involve prevention, case finding and treatment. Transplantation is one aspect of treatment.

Another concern often expressed is that the procedure is just keeping hopelessly sick people alive against their will. Nothing could be farther from the case. A patient coming in for transplant today usually walks into the hospital, frequently with his wife or her husband. He has been on dialysis. He is not an end-stage bit of human wreckage being reassembled for a few precarious moments. He is about to be released from the fetters of three-times-a-week dialysis by being given a kidney which will return him to society. We should compare this to surgery in late cancer. In dealing with cancer of the breast, it is important to operate on patients with a hopeless prognosis. Once metastases are present, they all die. But with adrenalectomy frequently 18 to 36 months of good living with their family is given, and we should do so. Very few people have looked at the late course of cardiac surgery. How do the patients do? They have many problems. Very few of them live out a normal life expectancy. By contrast, some of the late results from kidney transplantation are quite hopeful. This is not in any sense a question of keeping hopelessly ill people alive.

Have we in this country reached the phase where we are ready to face what you might call civilian triage? Can we turn our backs on certain of the sick because their treatment is expensive, complicated, or new in order to take care of more patients who have simpler illnesses to treat?

This certainly is a distasteful idea, and I believe that we have not reached that stage. When salvage is possible, we should treat the sick.

For Doctor DeWolf, I would like to call attention to the fact that in terminal illness (whether vascular disease of the central nervous system or cancer) much more restraint is exercised in our hospitals than is generally realized. I do not think that it is a thing that prospers on public discussion, but there are patients where the most merciful thing is the withholding of therapy. We have a tradition in this country of being able to do that. In some countries in Europe it is a legal requirement of the practice of medicine that as long as there is respiration and heart beat, all effort must be expended to keep the individual alive. That is not the situation in this country, and this makes it possible for hospitals to exhibit restraint.

The question of identity loss has been brought up as a price to be paid. Many people receive blood transfusions that are so numerous that their own blood is many times replaced. Have they lost some identity or dignity? Is this the origin of the psychiatric problem in transplants? I do not think so. There have been some excellent studies of transplant phychiatry. These patients have severe psychiatric problems, but they are not those of loss of dignity or identity. They are instead the problem of a person who was sure he was going to die and whose family was sure he was going to die, coming back to life. Those are serious and very disturbing problems. Recently transplantation has developed an unexpected problem which nobody saw in it at the start, namely, the growth of tumors in patients who have had transplants and been on immuno-suppression for a long time.

The title of this symposium is the prolongation of life. I think we should make it clear that tissue transplants as we know them now have no impact whatsoever on the populational prolongation of life in the sense that life expectancy of large populations can be increased as it is by public health or preventive medicine. Transplants are an episodic treatment for individual sick patients. A transplant saves a life, it extends a life, but there is no likelihood now or in the future that enough people will be transplanted for populational life-extension to be a result. It is not a public health topic in that sense.

The social returns of this huge investment can only be counted in turns of individual patient welfare. It can only be measured by the fundamental biblical ethic that underlies all of medicine; help to the suffering. If there is some other object or some other valid purpose of medicine, which would exclude helping the patient with renal failure, I have not heard of it. How about the yield in those terms? Well, in the early days survival was poor. Now the patient can expect from 50 per cent to 85 per cent likelihood of good kidney function for five years or more depending largely on the relationship and matching of the donor. This survival period is basic to his welfare, but it is not the only element.

What else constitutes welfare? Is it hope? Do we believe it is beneficial for a person who thinks he is going to die to be given some hope? Is it assistance to his family? Families, especially those in modest circumstances, who have very sick members, have a very severe problem. When a doctor takes charge and helps that family, he exhibits the fundamental act of medical care which is the assumption of responsibility. The family is grateful. How about survival? Well, it has to be for a length of time, and the quality of life must be satisfactory.

We thus have four things we can look at in patient welfare:

1. Hope, or other emotional factors in the individual.
2. Assistance to the family or other factors in the family.
3. Duration of survival.
4. The quality of life.

In kidney transplants today we are scoring quite well on all four of those things. Patients who have had other treatments and then receive a transplant report an entirely new outlook on life because it seems to embody more hope for the future. The family is often involved as donor; their medical burden is lightened. Survival has already been mentioned. If all goes well, the quality of life is almost normal; but if there are severe complications, rejection or infection, then the quality of life is poor. Transplant research today is devoted to a reduction in those complications by the development of better methods of immunologic management. This research is essential for future improvement in clinical methods and in the quality of life with a transplant.

In summary then, I welcome this chance to have a dialogue with theologians about transplants. But we are a little bit worried. We are worried that the dialogue is on the wrong topic. Is it really tissue transplants that are worrying the clergy so much? Well, maybe it is, but possibly that is all over with. They should have done that worrying in the middle 50's when all of us were having a really tough struggle, a very high mortality rate. I might also say in summary that in our lifetimes we have seen a truly remarkable new form of treatment arise, largely devoted to the treatment of chronic renal disease, and it uses a kidney from another person. That is a unique and wonderful thing.

Transplantation is being absorbed into the regular fabric of surgical care. I would like to close with a quotation from Sir Peter Medawar who said, "The transplantation of organs will be received into the ordinary repertoire of surgical practice. This is going to happen and much faster than anyone would have thought possible, even five years ago. You do not have to think up deep philosophical reasons why this should be so. It is going to happen because people are so constituted that they would rather be alive than dead."

Biological Considerations of Aggression, Violence and Crowding

William James once remarked that "man is the most formidable beast of prey and indeed the only one that preys systematically on its own species." If war is defined as lethal fights between groups of animals of the same species, it appears according to this definition that only men, rats, and some species of ants wage war. War is thus rare among animals. The British psychiatrist Anthony Storr has written in his book, *Human Aggression*, "the somber fact is that we are the cruelest and most ruthless species that has ever walked the earth."

We Americans are especially violent. Our homicide rate is 8 times that of England and 4 times that of Japan, Australia and Canada. One-third of all Americans report that they are afraid to walk alone at night in their own neighborhoods. In 1967, 21,500 deaths were caused by use of firearms in this country; of these 7700 were murders, 11,000 were suicides and 2800 accidental deaths. In addition there were 55,000 cases of aggravated assault by gun and 77,000 cases of armed robbery by gun. There were over 100,000 non-fatal injuries caused by firearms in 1966, and in 1967 some 4,585,000 firearms were sold in the United States.

Our children are fed violence continually by the mass media. One study shows that the average American child from three to sixteen years spends more hours watching television than in attending school. A study reported that sixth graders spend 80% of their waking time watching television, and a report of the president of the National Association for Better Radio and Television, given before a senatorial investigating committee, stated that for one week in November 1960, television displayed 144 murders, 143 attempted murders, 52 justified killings, 14 cases of drugging, 12 jailbreaks, 36 robberies, 13 kidnappings, 12 thefts and burglaries, 7 cases of torture, various cases of extortion and blackmail, 4 attempted lynchings and one massacre scene in which hundreds were killed.

For 600 years the citizens of ancient Rome watched with pleasure circuses in which men killed each other or were killed by wild animals. Hundreds of thousands of gladiators thus perished in municipal arenas to the delight of the public. Today we get vicarious thrills out of seeing actors die violent deaths nightly on television in our livingrooms, and this, I suppose, represents progress over the intervening two thousand years.

While the violence of warfare and crime in the streets is deplorable, there is no doubt that aggression and competition among animals, including our ancestors, has had real biological survival value in the course of evolution. Indeed, aggression is adaptive, making for the support of social organizations (flocks, packs, herds, prides, etc.) and stabilizing them by spacing animals in feeding and hunting ranges and by the selection of the dominant and most vigorous males to father the next generation.

Konrad Lorenz, and other ethologists, have pointed out that animals well armed by nature in competing with each other for social status in the herd, pack or flock, or in competition for mates and territory, seldom do each other much damage. Their fights are formalized duels in which threats play a major role. On the other hand, naturally unarmed animals such as doves and rabbits, if confined together in a limited space, may fight to the death. They have never had to evolve surrender signals, as have the well-armed carnivores, horned ungulates and hawks. Man is also biologically an unarmed animal, lacking fighting teeth, claws or horns, and, according to Lorenz, his behavior has the unrestrained property in combat of the rabbits and doves in contrast to such animals as wolves, lions and hawks. In this connection I would like to point out that chickens are armed with beaks and claws that are relatively ineffective for fighting, and their short spurs are dull affairs. The flock pecking order is established usually without lethal combat, by threats and relatively innocuous pecking, but, under some conditions of confinement, chickens like doves, may peck each other to death. But, if two roosters, particularly of certain breeds, are equipped with steel spurs and confined in an enclosed area they will fight to the death. Galinaceous birds, including fighting cocks, like ourselves come from species relatively unarmed by nature that has not needed to develop surrender signals, but give us lethal weapons, spurs or guns, and we can be killers. Hawks, well-armed by nature, would not behave in this way. Predatory animals such as wolves, large and small cats, birds of prey and horned ungulates are well-armed. They indulge in ritualized combat to establish status since were they to use their lethal weapons on each other, the best of them would die and the aggression therefore would be biologically non-adaptive. Aggressive gestures, i.e., bluffs and formalized duels are adaptive and stabilize social organizations in which each animal knows its place with respect to those lower or higher in the dominance hierarchy.

This type of organization is characteristic of nearly all vertebrate animals including, of course, man. While we are unarmed by nature, our great cerebral cortex has made possible weapons today that can extinguish us as a species. These monstrous weapons would be suicidal if used because of the retaliation they would bring about. The time may come when history may record, if there should be any history after World War III, that man perished from the earth because his great cerebral cortex — his most characteristic and humanizing feature — had turned out to have been a phylogenetic tumor leading to his extinction.

Territoriality is characteristic of most social animals. Man has his own definitions of territory and every competitive animal is very much aware of social hierarchies in which he finds he must fit. Thus a man is prepared to defend not only his home and country but his ideology — his politics, religion and philosophy — as part of his territorial identification. Status in our social hierarchies is of great importance to us and is determined for many by possessions — by keeping up with, and surpassing, the Joneses — and the positions we achieve in business and the professions. We exert aggression in obtaining position on the ladders of rank and we exert aggression, and sometimes violence, to hold such positions. Thus there is marked competition to attain a rank of professor, colonel or general, director or president, bishop or cardinal, or gangster leader. Man finds himself in many roles and usually aggressive competition is involved in attaining and maintaining the roles of his choice. The parallels between the social behavior of many animal species and that of *homo sapiens* shows many points of resemblance, as one might expect, since aggressive behavior in general is adaptive, although it may become non-adaptive in going too far and resorting to violence. Thus Hitler's aggressions were non-adaptive both for him and for Germany and a nuclear war would be non-adaptive for the human species as well as for many plant and animal species that would be destroyed along with us, especially in the northern hemisphere.

There is a close relation between violent behavior and crowding, and the threat of nuclear war will increase with population growth. Many studies of animals prove that crowding beyond specific limits, either in nature or captivity, results in fighting, collapse of social hierarchies, cannibalism, particularly of the young, and failure of various aspects of reproduction processes. In this way animal societies ranging up from lower invertebrates reduce their populations when they exceed a critical number. Thus animal populations tend to grow and decline in regular cycles. War, famine and disease — the Malthusian factors — cause similar fluctuations in primitive human societies: These cyclic fluctuations of populations with crowding have been demonstrated with rats, mice, hares, monkeys, lemmings, deer and many other species, including a host of insect species. Among mammals, the dying off with crowding is characterized by overactivity of the adrenal cortex called upon via the hypothalamic pituitary axis to meet competitive stresses. This stress response mechanism ultimately breaks down if the stresses of crowding are sufficiently prolonged and severe. The overstressed adrenocortical system may produce atherosclerosis, hypertension, enhanced susceptibility to all infectious agents and a variety of other endocrine and metabolic disorders resulting ultimately in increased death rates, thus reducing the animal population.

Time does not permit us to discuss the many fascinating experiments and observations both in the laboratory and in the field that prove these methods of population control of animal societies. In man we know that crowding in concentration camps produced overactivity of the adrenal and probably deaths from the stress syndrome, even when the prisoners were well fed and housed. As with other animals, organized social relations among prisoners collapse above certain levels of crowding. We suspect, but it has not been studied adequately, that in slums and ghettos, crowding may account in part for crime, delinquency and rioting. Schizophrenia is much more prevalent in crowded urban areas than elsewhere. People with low flash points of violence, of whom there are estimated to be several million, are likely to be triggered off when crowded.

The world population average growth rate of 2% will double the population in thirty-five years. Growth is faster in the poorer countries and in some of the poorest countries the population is doubling in 18 or 20 years. Under these stressful conditions, the probability of wars and revolutions is increased. Indeed, there is striking correlation between poverty, population densities and occurrance of revolutions and wars. Thus the hazard of international violence and nuclear war is enhanced by competition for space, food, dwindling supplies of metals and fossil fuels and other stresses resulting from burgeoning populations.

The "Pill," the most effective and still most widely used oral contraceptive, was discovered by the late Dr. Gregory Pincus and Dr. M. C. Chang at the Worcester Foundation for Experimental Biology in collaboration with Dr. John Rock and Dr. Celso Garcia. About 15 million women are estimated to be taking the pill, and new and improved fertility controlling agents are on the way, but even the most perfect contraceptive methods are worthless if not used. Population control, or its lack, depends primarily on social and psychological factors and is rooted in the cultures and prejudices of political and religious groups. While voluntary family planning has been accepted in some of the developing countries, it often results in quite inadequate reduction in birth rates. For example, a family, which in the recent past might have 8 children, 4 of whom would die, now plans to have 6, 5 of whom live, so that the net effect of such an example as this is to increase the population. It is rapidly becoming apparent that much more positive steps must be taken by governments if the world is not to be swamped and polluted beyond endurance by too many people.

I would now like to consider physiological bases of aggressive behavior and violence. There have been intense controversies over the years as to the significance of instinctive behavior at various levels of evolutionary development. Programmed into the nervous systems of animals by their genes are rich varieties of elaborate behavior patterns that may be triggered into action by stimuli from the environment. Among invertebrate animals it is generally assumed that most of their behavior is of this kind; spiders are not taught by their parents to build webs. They are programmed to do it by their genes. Steps in the production of an embryo, human or otherwise, are programmed into the developing embryo and its mother without conscious action on the part of either of them. Intake and utilization of food and water and elimination processes are clearly programmed into us by our genes.

In the developing bird and mammal, Lorenz and others have shown that the tendency to follow a moving object, called imprinting, comes about at an early age and cannot be elicited beyond a certain period in the animal's development. Imprinting assures that the young will follow the mother in its first adventures beyond the nest. Elaborate mating rituals of birds and of fish and their migrations over great distances are certainly not learned but programmed into their genes and stimulated by environmental factors and internally secreted hormones that trigger the patterned mating rituals.

We are familiar with squirrels that bury nuts in the ground in caches for the future. But we may not be aware that the same squirrel, if given a nut in a room with a concrete floor, will go through all the motions of burying it, since this process is instinctive and unlearned.

Neurophysiologists have learned much about the mammalian brain in relation to functions of tracts of nerve fibers and cell centers laid down by the genes that mediate the behavior characteristic of hunger and thirst and about tracts and centers concerned with expressions of rage and fear — tracts triggered into action by appropriate stimuli. Indeed advances in neurophysiology, brought about by surgical ablation of specific anatomical regions and tracts, by electrical recording of the impulses from nerve tracts and cells and electrical stimulation of specific areas and by the injection of minute amounts of chemical agents into localized regions of brain, have markedly expanded our knowledge of brain and behavior in recent years.

Localized electrical stimulation of brains of cats is illustrative. Cats which normally do not attack rats will do so during stimulation of specific regions of the hypothalamus. If the lateral hypothalamus is stimulated, a cat, that has never attacked a mouse or rat, quietly and efficiently stalks and kills an experimental rat, biting it in a characteristic way. Non-killer rats have also been stimulated in exactly this same way and turned into killers of mice. Animals, when so stimulated, if no object is available, will explore in a restless manner, searching for a victim. The cat stimulated in the lateral hypothalamus shows unlearned preferences in the type of stimulus objects it will attack. An anesthetized rat will be attacked more quickly and persistently than a stuffed rat, but there is little tendency to attack a rubber block the size and shape of a rat. Stimulation of the medial hypothalamus produces a different kind of aggression. The cat then attacks with a scream, tearing at the stimulus object with unsheathed claws. In this case the object may very well be the experimenter. The limbic brain includes the amygdala and hypocampus, the phylogenetically ancient cerebral cortex, and these regions have rich connections to lower-brain structures such as the septum and hypothalamus which are definitely affected by localized electrical or chemical stimuli. Focal stimulation or ablation of regions of the limbic brain produce emotionally charged responses of one kind or another, depending on the region, with fear and rage as extreme examples. Thus bilateral amygdalectomy will change a savage wild animal into a gentle, friendly one. This has been demonstrated for the usually untamable lynx and also for savage and dangerous macaque monkeys and other fierce animals. Following such an operation one may put one's hand in the mouth of an animal, which normally would have bitten it off, and which post-operatively shows no aggression in response to handling. There are few animals more savage than wild Norway rats. Following bilateral amygdalectomy they can be handled as pets and put on one's shoulder or in one's pocket. Delgado, of Yale, and his colleagues, have implanted electrodes in the limbic brain of monkeys and, by telemetry, have been able to turn on and off aggressive behavior by electrical stimulation from a distance. The small stimulating wires are connected to a miniaturized stimulator buried under the skin, or attached externally, which picks up electrical signals from a distance. Under these circumstances the dominant, alpha monkey of the group has been reduced to the bottom of the social hierarchy by limbic stimulation each time he showed threatening behavior to other group members. Immediately following such stimulation he would retreat from his threatening posture and soon was reduced to the bottom of the hierarchy. Indeed the stimulus key was left in the cage with the monkeys and a submissive, but obviously bright, monkey discovered when he was threatened by the boss that all he had to do was to push the key to remove the threat and in this way he could control the situation — one way, I supose, for "the meek to inherit the earth."

There is also Delgado's famous experiment in which a Spanish fighting bull with implanted brain electrodes charges at a man in the arena armed only with a telemetry stimulating box. Pushing one button stops the bull in full charge and pushing another turns it to trot amicably away.

The human brain contains similar structures to that of other mammals and man's ancient limbic brain involved in mediating emotional behavior is most similar. A number of experiments with human subjects have been carried out, especially in relation to treatment of epileptics and brain trauma patients. Thus a mild-mannered woman became violently aggressive and hostile when electrically stimulated in a region of the amygdala. When the current was turned off, she instantly reverted to her mild-mannered and apologetic self. Investigators have discovered in brain systems suppressor circuits which are antagonistic to the aggression circuits. Interruption of these suppressor circuits can turn peaceful, gentle animals into killers. We can also, by cutting circuits mediating aggressive behavior, dramatically reduce it. This was demonstrated in the lynx that I have mentioned which, by amygalectomy, was turned into a friendly creature.

It has been shown by a number of investigators that spontaneous firing of the aggressor circuits in man, as detected by recorded electrical activity, may make these people a constant danger to those around them and to themselves. A few courageous surgeons have operated on these people with success by producing lesions in the posterior hypothalamus. Lebeau in France recommends singulectomy on intractable cases of anger, violence and permanent agitation. The patient's hostile feelings are thus brought under control. Indeed a patient of Dr. Sano, after temporal lobe incision, reported that he couldn't get angry if he wanted to. Robert Heath in New Orleans has reported implanting permanent electrodes in the septal region of violent psychotics. A raving, violent paranoid patient, when stimulated by these electrodes, became relaxed, his hostility dissipated, he smiled and was at peace with the world. Such a condition may last hours following a thirty-second period of stimulation. Moyer, and also Ervin, have pointed out that it is a short step from this to giving the patient his own transistorized power pack with an anti-hostility button which he can press himself whenever he feels intolerable hostility coming on.

To me the most interesting work being done along these lines is that of Frank Ervin, William Sweet and their collaborators at the Massachusetts General Hospital. There are three major types of epilepsy — major convulsive seizures known as grand mal, transient lapses of consciousness or petit mal, and temporal lobe epilepsy, which has been called psychomotor epilepsy. This last type of epilepsy is characterized by periodic distortion of perception, hallucinations, psychotic behavior involving the limbic brain systems. The temporal lobe epileptic can get in much difficulty socially, and alcohol can easily trigger off violence. While 85% of other epileptics can be controlled by drugs, 80% of temporal lobe epileptics are refractory to them. Surgery has been the only genuinely effective therapeutic procedure for temporal lobe epilepsy. The brain surgeon is aided in detecting focal epilepsy by the use of the electroencephalogram, although recording through skull and scalp is highly limited and not of much use in localizing deep lesions or those in amygdala or hypocampus. To improve on these procedures, the group at M.G.H., in collaboration with Delgado of Yale, have designed and constructed a remarkable, light-weight telemetry apparatus. A stylet is inserted deep into the brain, containing at intervals along its length 15 small contact electrodes that can either pick up the local electrical activity of the brain or deliver electrical stimuli. The stylet is held by a plug-in box connected with the surface of the skull into which may be plugged leads to a small stimulator box attached to the subject, or to a broadcasting device which picks up the brain waves and feeds them by telemetry to a distant EEG recording machine and computor. The stimulator can pick up electrical pulses generated at a distance and activate one of the 15 brain leads to deliver highly localized currents.

The electrodes are located at various places in the limbic brain so that stimulation and recording can test multitudinous tracts involved in emotional behavior. With this equipment patients are free to move about unrestrained. They may be stimulated by an experimenter, unbeknownst to them, who presses a key as much as a hundred feet away and in another room, and the brain waves also can be picked up from one or more of the 15 leads, recorded and correlated with the overt behavior of the patient. With this device it is possible to locate the source of abnormal brain waves and direct the surgeon to the proper place for treatment, such as tract cutting or tissue removal in the case of tumors or other types of brain damage. This device is also used for treating intractable pain by stimulation of the lateral amygdala where a stimulus delivered for roughly thirty seconds twice a day will relieve intractable pain for eight to twelve hours.

Some studied cases of violent behavior are illustrative: A twenty-two year old daughter of a physician had an irresistible urge to take long walks or runs at any hour of the day or night and she also had at times gross illusions about the appearance of her face. During these seizures she might dangerously attack persons. On one occasion she plunged a blade of scissors into her nurse, who had failed to take prompt interest in her statement that she felt a running urge coming on. She stabbed another woman in the heart when the lady inadvertently brushed against her. Electrodes were implanted in the hope of localizing a hypocampal lesion and she was stimulated, without being told, by telemetry while she was chatting amicably with her psychiatrist. Before and after the stimulation her EEG was recorded and corresponded to the behavioral changes. She promptly lost interest in her conversation and suddenly directed an attack against the wall with pounding fists. This coincided with high voltage spike-like deflections in the right amygdala and hypocampus. A similar attack occurred the next day in which, following similar stimulation, she swung her guitar past the head of her surprised psychiatrist, smashing the instrument against the wall. In each it took about two minutes following the brief stimulus to build up the electrical seizure, followed by the furious outburst.

Another patient was a baby-sitter who killed her crying charge by smothering it in a plastic bag. Later she confessed she had also destroyed another crying baby in a similar way, although at the time the cause of death had not been known. She also had occasional outbursts of violent destruction of things in her room. At nearly all other times she was pleasant and balanced. All her neurological tests were normal, as was her EEG, and spinal fluid tests, but a pneumoencephalogram suggested a lesion in the tip of the left temporal horn. In attempting to locate this more precisely for surgery, chronic localized electrode implacement was used. With the electrodes in place, an experiment was carried out in which a phonograph record of a crying baby was played to the patient. This immediately produced a seizure pattern in the limbic brain and a violent response, which was of great interest in view of her murders of two crying children. When the crying baby record was turned off, the electrical seizure pattern stopped and so did her tantrum.

A clinic at the Massachusetts General Hospital has been studying the episodic loss of control involving some 200 patients, 135 of whom have been worked up in detail. Sixty percent of the group have been arrested for violent crimes and eight are murderers. Many have used an automobile for assault. It is of interest in relation to the 55,000 people killed by automobiles annually in this country and the million persons suffering injury, that about 50% of these deaths have involved the use of alcohol and that young people with criminal records have been responsible for a very large fraction of these accidents. Violence incidentally is the major cause of death in the United States of people between the ages of sixteen and twenty-four years. In the M.G.H. group of 200 patients, a quarter of them showed temporal lobe EEG electrical discharges of six and fourteen per second, characteristic of psychomotor epilepsy. In childhood most of them showed either late enuresis, cruelty to animals, fire setting and a recurrent history after puberty of violence to persons. Stimulation of certain areas in the limbic brain or the cutting of fiber tracts may relieve these attacks. Indeed a properly placed electrical stimulus, lasting only a minute, may cancel out aggressiveness for periods up to twenty hours daily so that self-shocking with suitably implanted electrodes may well result in self-control of these dangerous people, many of whom come to the clinic voluntarily because they fear that violence they have displayed in the past may be repeated.

These neurological approaches to violence are new — so new in fact that they have not as yet found application beyond hospital walls, but their potential for diagnosing violence and for correcting it are promising. It is believed that there are about a half-million temporal lobe epileptics, many of whom are dangerous. Post-mortem examination showed that Charles Whitman, who deliberately shot and killed so many people from a clock tower at a Texas university had a small, slow-growing temporal lobe tumor.

Prisoners arrested for violence, including the so-called psychopathic personalities, many of whom may be suffering from temporal lobe epilepsy, are seldom studied by psychiatrists and given any form of therapy. It is especially significant that those arrested for violence show a 50% rate of recidivism. There is little information about the number of people with low flash points for setting off the brain mechanisms mediating violence. Genetic factors play a role here. Thus two Y chromosomes (the male sex carrying chromosomes) are found quite often among prisoners serving terms for crimes of violence. It has been known from time immemorial that certain chemical factors enhance violent tendencies and male sex hormones play very significant roles. This is clear from results of castration, turning bulls into gentle oxen, roosters into capons, fierce stallions into geldings, tom-cats into house pets and men into eunuchs. Moreover, the administration of the male hormone, testosterone, restores aggressiveness in all these cases. In one study of female prisoners, 62% of the cases of violence occurred in the prementrual week and only 2% occurred in the post-menstrual week.

Of all the drugs to which men are attracted, only alcohol seems to be agreed upon as an agent promoting violence when imbibed in sufficient amounts by susceptible persons. It seems likely, however, that there may be developed in the future specific chemical agents to activate special brain centers that may serve to block violent aggression. The present pharmacological tranquilizers do shift mood and damp down emotions to some degree, but they are relatively nonspecific.

Neurophysiologists working in cooperation with biochemists, psychologists and psychiatrists offer hope of diagnosing and perhaps ultimately bringing under better control violent behavior.

A topic we might consider is the place of religion in the control of aggression, and I would like to conclude with a few remarks on this aspect of the topic that seem relevant to me.

In 1942 I discussed religion from the point of view of a biologist interested in the brain.* I pointed out that the brain is an organ of great survival value, enabling animals better to adapt to their environments. The brain developed to enable animals to make configurations of their environments to which they could react effectively. Such configurations are necessary for motile animals to enable them to find food, mates and escape from predators, etc. In the course of evolution, brains have become enlarged. (I was taught that there are over 10 billion neurones in the human cerebral cortex. I understand now that this figure is nearer 100 billion.) The increased numbers of circuits and increased capacity to synthesize sensory data into meaningful

* H. Hoagland, "Some Comments on Science and Faith," Chapter 3, Conference on Science, Philosophy and Religion, New York, 1942.

configurations to which the organism can respond efficiently renders it better able to survive by natural selection. I then argued, and still believe, that man's concern with making sense of his universe is a direct product of the integrative properties of his brain. Science, theology, philosophy and art are aspects of behavior that bring significant portions of our world into relationships that we believe to be meaningful and therefore emotionally satisfying. The exercise of curiosity and imagination is a reflection of this basic property of the brain to form meaningful configurations — we also see this in animal behavior from simple vertebrates on up the evolutionary scale. Primitive man endeavored to bring order out of the chaos of his universe by animism, magic, symbolism and myth. Sophisticated men have developed all-embracing ideologies, theologies and monistic philosophies and science to interpret the universe, hopefully to control it, and enable them to adapt to it. Thus, for me, religion in all its forms is a reflection of this process of adaptation in which man has attempted to bring sense and meaning to life and death and his own destiny in relation to the world, real or imagined, he finds about him — his "ultimate concern," as Tillich has used that term. I also argued then that the all-embracing ideologies of communism and fascism were examples of synthesizing social concepts that brought the same type of satisfaction to its adherents as one found in religions and that thus psychologically nazis and devout communists had much in common with devout religious persons.

Inevitably the profound conviction of being right about an all-embracing theology or ideology results in intolerance towards others of different views. Thus most of the organized violence in the world has been caused by the rigid religions and ideologies and superpatriotisms controlled by authoritarian faiths. Such faiths, held by large numbers of people, give opportunities for power-hungry leaders — priests and kings and dictators — to exploit the ambitions of their followers and utilize their latent biological patterns of aggression for their own purposes. I believe more blood has been shed in the name of religion, thus broadly defined, than for any other reason, and religion, as I understand it, cannot be very helpful in the control of international aggression and war. By its very nature, it promotes them.

The ethics of Judeo-Christian religion, and many of the other great religions, are based upon teachings of gentleness and the golden rule, and it is true that religions, including some primitive religions, have defused individual aggression and widened brotherhood to adjust personal conflicts among those of the in-group, but on a larger scale one thinks of the cruelty of the Crusades and the vicious Catholic-

Protestant wars of the 16th and 17th centuries and of today in Ireland, the Mohammedan-Hindu wars and our 20th century ideological wars involving fascism, nazism, communism, militarisms and superpatriotisms.

The role of the supernatural in religion, has to my mind, more often than not enhanced intolerance — after all, when authority for one's belief is revelation from God, there is little room for dissent. Warring nations have always claimed that God, or the gods, were on their side. In 1914 belt buckles of the German soldiers were stamped with the legend, "Gott mit uns."

I believe that as a byproduct of advances in science the supernatural has played, and will continue to play, a decreasing role. I am aware of the recent upsurge in interest in witchcraft and fortune tellers and understand that there are about 10,000 astrologers in the United States and only about 1000 astronomers, but I believe that this sort of thing is ephemeral and will pass. I hope that a humanistic religion can be found in which man, as a species, will acquire the loyalty now spread over quarreling national sovereignties and competing ideologies. Such an approach to human relations could mean profound improvements in our ways of living together, but so far I have seen little sign of its emergence. Indeed our era has shown enhanced fragmentation into hostile nation states.

Perhaps the time may come when nations can agree that the main aim of all their foreign policies is to live in a world with enforceable laws to prevent war. There would also have to be an educational system to teach the young that one has to be a human being before one can be American, Russian, Chinese, white or black, communist or capitalist, and that basic human values worthy of loyalty and respect are independent of racial, national, political or ideological boundaries. While all this may seem too Utopian, it is nevertheless to be hoped that some of the rebellious students around the world may become leaders in developing such an educational system to advance world peace through world law.

ROGER L. SHINN

Population and the
Dignity of Man

At this stage of human history and knowledge, I need not waste time arguing that population is a threat to mankind. Human life is a glorious gift, but there can be too many lives for the good of man. The population explosion is the name we give to the multiplication of people at a rate that doubles the earth's population in approximately 35 years. We are familiar with the projections: if the present rate should continue, earth's 3.6 billion people in 1970 will be 7.2 billion by about 2,005, 14.4 billion by about 2,040, 28.2 billion by about 2,075, and so on. We have heard that 600 years of such increase will mean a person for every square yard of earth (including arctic tundras, deserts, and mountain tops), after that a little longer there will be a person for every square foot, that some day man will outweigh the earth, then the solar system, and even the universe. Obviously all this cannot happen, but nobody knows what cost of starvation, pestilence, or carnage will stop it. Humane methods of meeting the threat are possible, but nobody yet knows whether they are probable.

The problem arises because man is a unique being within nature, a creature who in some ways transcends nature and exercises a measure of control over nature. The powers in which he has often exulted now threaten him. He wonders whether he will outlive the rats and roaches, or whether the abilities that have enabled him in some ways to outwit nature now doom him. Loren Eisely has said it with characteristic eloquence:

> It is with the coming of man that a vast hole seems to open in nature, a vast black whirlpool spinning faster and faster, consuming flesh, stones, soil, minerals, sucking down the lightning, wrenching power from the atom, until the ancient sounds of nature are drowned in the cacophony of something which is no longer nature, something instead which is loose and knocking at the world's heart, something demonic and no longer planned —

escaped, it may be — spewed out of nature, contending in a final giant's game against its master.[1]

Thus an anthropologist puts in contemporary language an ancient biblical theme — that man's creativity is intimately related to his destructiveness. In the language of theological tradition, mankind, although not conspicuously obedient to most of the divine commands, has prodigiously carried out the first of them: "Be fruitful and multiply, and fill the earth and subdue it" (Genesis 1:28). If Immanuel Kant, bachelor and moral philosopher, were present, he would immediately point out that even if man in this case did what was commanded, he did not do so *because* it was commanded. He had his own reasons, and he was the victim of unreckoned facts and unreasoned desires. Granted. But the consequences of radical conformance to this one command or invitation and neglect of others is the population crisis.

The population explosion is a moral problem. Like most moral problems in modern civilization, it has important scientific and technological aspects. But it is a moral issue because it involves questions of the good of man, of values and conflicts of values, of man's self-esteem in relation to the rest of creation, of relations between personal, tribal, or national purposes and the welfare of the human race.

Hence we may wonder why theology and the church have not spoken and acted more emphatically on this issue. There has been no lack of bold statements on other intense controversies of our time. I do not argue that the church at large is an immensely radical force in the contemporary world. But its centers of leadership and intellectual energy have not hesitated to affront the public mood with strong stands on questions of race, economic justice, and revolution. They have been more timid, even inhibited on the question of population.

In 1960 Richard M. Fagley of the Commission of the Churches on International Affairs (an organ of the World Council of Churches) produced a good book, *The Population Explosion.*[2] The Geneva Conference on Church and Society, convened by the World Council of Churches in 1966, said some sensible things about the necessity for restraining population growth,[3] as did the Fourth Assembly of the World Council of Churches at Uppsala in 1968.[4] But the debates and the findings were marked by a caution uncharacteristic of those bodies on some other controversial issues. The Board of Christian Social Concerns of the United Methodist Church is exceptional in urging recognition "that families with more than two children contribute to the population explosion."[5]

There are reasons for the reluctance of the church to mount crusades on this issue. To determine whether the reasons are valid requires an analysis in some detail.

I. Caught by Surprise

One reason for the perplexity of the modern church and of modern man over population problems is the way in which the human race has been caught by surprise. Population pressures on a world scale are recent. Regionally they are an old problem, often met in the past by exposure of infants, abandonment of the aged, and conquest of the lands of others — all methods that raise severe ethical questions. But the question of an over-populated *world* is not one on which traditional wisdom has spent much energy.

Prophecy is not the same as prediction, and the prophets of Christianity and the world religions did not predict the present situation. The demographers were not much better. The records of the 1930's abound in dire predictions of depopulation due to the reluctance of many families to reproduce their own numbers.

In one sense the population explosion came with incredible speed. It took all of human history until 1850 — some say a million years, others say far longer — for earth's population to rise to a billion persons; now we add a billion in less than 15 years. This is not simply acceleration; it is transformation. It requires major reconsideration of ethical traditions, prestige symbols, political practices, family *mores*.

But in another sense the change slipped up on us. It was not marked by any instantaneous event — like the destruction of Hiroshima or the 1969 Hurricane Camille — that alerted governments to instantaneous action. In a way everything happened gradually. There was a lag between certain acts and their consequences: at a minimum the familiar nine-month lag, on the big scale a lag between many personal acts and their momentous social consequences. Because immense change was never immediately discernible, men always found more urgent problems to work on. People might get concerned about projections of future crisis, but there was no shortage of immediate crises demanding response; so the population problem was filed in the back of many minds as an issue to get around to some day.

But all the time the future emergency was becoming visible in present emergencies, and rather suddenly in the last decade a large part of the world realized that disaster is imminent. Anthony Lewis recently has reported in the *New York Times* the fairly widespread view among scientists that the human race has 35-100 years of life on earth, with population the biggest single element in the threatening syndrome.[6] Scientist John Platt writes about "a shorter life expectancy than people have ever had in the world before," and he estimates, "We may have even less than a 50-50 chance of living until 1980."[7] If nuclear weapons pose the most immediate threat, in his judgment, population is not far behind. Paul Ehrlich predicts that even the most effective crash programs can no longer prevent starvation of hundreds of millions of people in the 1970's.[8] If the agricultural revolution refutes his predictions,[9] the fact remains that it only delays the disaster unless mankind does something to limit its numbers. Meanwhile, if the world should manage to feed people more successfully than it is now doing, its educational, social, and political institutions seem unable to cope with exploding populations.

Such a situation calls for revision of inherited values and ethical criteria. Part of the work of ethics is always shaking loose from old ethical modes. Ethics is the worst enemy of ethics — traditional ethics or innovating ethics. Yet an innovative ethic can rarely simply scorn and destroy the ethic it would replace, because the tradition may have something precious in it. The traditional ethic embodied a concern for human life — including helpless life of infants, life still in the womb, event potential human life. That ethic may make us wince when we hear callous talk of surplus people, as though every person were not valuable. We cannot demolish that ethic without destroying something of our humanity. The question is how the concern for life that created the ethic may today require its revision. Such decisions are made, not by a few professional intellectuals, but by the intricate processes and symbol-systems of whole societies. Modern man and the modern church, caught by surprise, are engaged in that process of revision. It takes time — but not much time is available.

II. *Doctrinal Inhibitions*

Ethical transformation, which is always precarious, becomes particularly difficult in this case because it is compounded by some specific religious and doctrinal inhibitions that have influenced men's perception of the problem. The Christianity that has contributed to the concern for persons in our ethical heritage has also frequently harbored within itself docetic and Manichean heresies that demeaned the flesh. One expression of this mood has been the exaltation of celibacy, which if it were persuasive to enough people might solve the population problem. More common has been a grudging acceptance of sexual activity as a necessary part of procreation and as ethically justifiable only when procreation was intended. The result is the anti-contraceptive mentality that persists in some Christian thinking to this day.

I describe this attitude as heretical, because it is contrary to the joyful biblical celebration of the flesh, marked by the words of Genesis that are later quoted by Jesus: "Therefore a man leaves his father and his mother and cleaves to his wife, and they become one flesh" (Genesis 2:24, Mark 10:7). The issue here is a subtle one. There are forms of heroic service, involving renunciation of many of life's delights, that are in no sense heretical. But the docetic contempt for the flesh, frequently renounced as heretical, kept creeping back into Christianity and sometimes permeated its cultural expressions.

Today Christianity is working its way out of that bind. The issue is one of several in which the pressures of the secular world are helping the church to rediscover its own biblical heritage. But the process moves at an uneven pace. Within Roman Catholicism most theologians of the United States and northern Europe are ready to advocate contraceptives, both because of the demographic problem and because of the meaning of the sexual relationship within marriage.[10] They regret that the papacy, counteracting a 70-14 vote of the Papal Commission on Birth Control, remains on record as opposed to contraception.[11] Catholic laymen in many areas have resolved the problem with their own consciences, often with outspoken support from priests.[12] In any event considerable evidence shows that Catholic families, on a world-wide basis, are not distinguished by large size.[13]

Eastern Orthodoxy has no centralized teaching authority comparable to the papacy, and it looks for guidance less to dogma than to a mystical sense of tradition, which is not precisely formulated and which is subject to development. Thus far the tradition is largely anti-contraceptive. Although there are elements of the tradition that make change on this issue foreseeable, the Eastern Orthodox churches are largely silent on the question of population.

Protestantism, by and large, has accepted contraceptives and the importance of limiting family size, whether out of authentic theological insight (as I would like to believe) or out of easy adaptation to the spirit of the times (as some critics would charge). All the major Protestant denominations in the United States and the predominantly Protestant National Council of Churches have adopted statements endorsing family planning.[14]

The caution of the World Council of Churches (mentioned above) is not due to a lingering docetic heresy. It can be attributed to a reluctance of Protestant leaders to offend groups (the Eastern Orthodox within the Council and Roman Catholics outside it) with whom they are just beginning to learn to live in peace.

III. *An Ideological Struggle*

In most international discussions of population and economic development, an ideological argument frequently skews the considerations. The advocacy of population control is taken to be the ideology of affluent whites, and it may be rejected by spokesmen of Asia, Latin America, and Africa. Likewise within the United States there is increasing resentment in the black ghettoes toward organizations, usually white dominated, that advocate family planning. The economically deprived, who are often also the dark-skinned, resent the exhortations (as they hear them) of affluent whites advising them to limit their population. They may respond by rhetorical resistance to ethnic suicide or genocide.

They have a point. That is, impoverished peoples have a right to resist the advice of wealthy peoples, who use the population problem as an evasion of their moral responsibility to the poor whom they have exploited. Racial and economic exploitation are conspicuous facts in our world. And there is plenty of evidence that programs of economic aid to under-developed nations and groups are (1) pitifully inadequate in scope and (2) often cunningly contrived to help donors more than recipients. When affluent societies then righteously complain of their sacrifices and blame the poor for breeding habits that keep them poor, anger is an appropriate response.

This ideological issue is another reason why the World Council of Churches has been cautious on the population problem. Within its discussions the issue is usually raised by white Westerners within the context of discussions about economic development. The answer usually comes from Asians or Latin Americans who tell the spokesmen from more industrialized societies that they cannot use this device to evade their responsibilities.

Archbishop Helder Camara, a courageous champion of the poor in Brazil, has made the point well in objecting to the "smokescreens" that have obscured international economic problems. "One such smokescreen is the insistence that the Third World's problems would be eased if a massive birth control program — that modern cure-all — were to be imposed on that world."[15] Let us clearly grant three valid points in that sentence: (1) birth control is no cure-all; (2) it will not resolve the economic problems of Latin America or any other area; and (3) it cannot be "imposed" on any society without destructive consequences.

The other side of the story is that no other solutions will do much for Latin America, Africa, or Asia unless these societies check their eruption in population. To this extent Malthus remains unanswered and unanswerable: no social devices, however ingenious, can counter the inexorable logic of the geometric progression. Interestingly, Marxism has recognized the issue. Marxists at times have indulged in gibberish to the effect that population was a bogey of capitalist societies with their deliberate restraint of production; but lately most Marxist societies have seen the importance of policies to restrain population expansion.

One important fact remains to de-ideologize the discussion. The limitation of population is as urgent a demand upon the wealthiest societies today as upon the poorest. The affluent have no right to ask the poor to adopt a discipline that their condescending advisers reject. If starvation is a more urgent problem for India than for the United States, the ecological destruction wrought by an expanding high-consuming United States is greater than that inflicted by the "teeming populations" of Asia.

The United States, whose 6 per cent of the world's population consumes something like 40 per cent of the world's production, manages to despoil its own home and exploit the homelands of others. Its combination of rising population and rising standard of living congest its national parks and produce emergencies of waste disposal in most of its cities. John Platt writes in Science that "many scientists fear the destruction of our whole biological and ecological balance" within the next 20 years.[16]

Man knows too little of ecology to reckon accurately the risks he is taking. But an example or two are clues to the danger. Industrial man fills the air with carbon dioxide from combustion, while he reduces oxygen-producing plants and forests. He does not know at what point the upset of atmospheric balance may create disaster, perhaps raising the earth's temperature, melting polar icecaps, and inundating coastal cities and plains. Again, the increased use of chemical fertilizers pours phosphates and nitrates into streams and lakes, spurring the growth of algae, while the discharge of sewage magnifies the same effects, thus fouling clear waterways and destroying fresh water fish.

Over Kennedy airport alone airliners in a year discharge 10,000 tons of carbon monoxide, 3,000 tons of hydrocarbons, 330 tons of nitrogen oxides, and 100 tons of particulates, largely carbons.[17] I am ready to guess that the scientists coming to the annual meeting of the American Association for the Advancement of Science pour more poisons into the atmosphere by this one trip than they would emit in a lifetime if they were desperately poor villagers in India. And probably they consume more paper in these few days than they would in a peasant lifetime in India.

The answer is not solely population control. What is needed is a technology directed more toward a profit-and-loss statement for the total society and its environment, less to the balance sheets of competing corporations. Even so, the overwhelming probability is that this world cannot endure simultaneously rising numbers of people and standards of living. Population is not the problem solely of the poorer classes and societies; it is even more urgently the problem of the affluent.

IV. *The Predatory Legacy of Western Christianity*

The issues of ecology require an inquiry into the cultural and theological history of those civilizations that have done most to plunder the earth. François Mergen, dean of Yale's School of Forestry, has said, "Sometimes I think the students who earn degrees in ecology should be ordained — they're so serious." Beyond his witticism can be discovered a curious relationship between theology and ecological dilemmas.

Cultural historians have frequently pointed to a relationship between biblical faith and technological progress. Perhaps it is not sheer accident that technology has developed in civilizations influenced by the Hebrew-Christian scriptures. The Bible in its radical monotheism desacralizes nature. Sun, moon, and stars are no longer divine and they may not be worshipped. Brooks and trees are no longer inhabited by spirits. There is one God; the world is his creation. Man, given dominion, may investigate and appropriate the objects of nature. No tabus, no forbidding mysteries, no divinities block enterprising man. In recent years theologians like Harvey Cox[18] and Arend van Leeuwen[19] have taken up this theme in hymns of praise to urban, technological civilization.

But historian Lynn White has investigated this same theme with a chastened conscience. In his 1966 address to the Washington meeting of the American Association for the Advancement of Science, he told Christians, in effect: repent, don't boast over this technological prowess. Within three years the ripple effect of this address has reached far into literature and journalism about technology and ecology.

In White's words, "The victory of Christianity over paganism was the greatest psychic revolution in the history of our culture," and its effects persist in this era often called a post-Christian age. "Especially

in its Western form," says White, "Christianity is the most anthro-
pocentric religion the world has seen. . . . By destroying pagan animism, Christianity made it possible to exploit nature in a mood of
indifference to the feelings of natural objects."[20] Tracing the story of
the union, little more than a century ago, of the previously diverse
histories of science and of technology, he finds that they "joined to
give mankind powers which, to judge by many of the ecologic effects,
are out of control." And for this history, he maintains, "Christianity
bears a huge burden of guilt."[21]

Other scholars from other disciplines have been making comparable inquiries. Economists Barbara Ward and Kenneth Boulding have
made familiar the symbol of the earth as a spaceship. This planet
earth, says Barbara Ward, "has acquired the intimacy, the fellowship,
and the vulnerability of a spaceship."[22] As Boulding puts it,

> We have to visualize the earth as a small, rather crowded space-
> ship, destination unknown, in which man has to find a slender
> thread of a way of life in the midst of a continually repeatable
> cycle of material transformations. In a spaceship, there can be
> no inputs or outputs. The water must circulate through the kid-
> neys and the algae, the food likewise, the air likewise. . . . Up to
> now the human population has been small enough so that we
> have not had to regard the earth as a spaceship. We have been
> able to regard the atmosphere and the oceans and even the soil
> as an inexhaustible reservoir, from which we can draw at will
> and which we can pollute at will. There is writing on the wall,
> however. . . . As the spaceship society approaches, therefore,
> we must move towards an extremely conservationist point of
> view, in which every scrap of material substratum of human en-
> vironment and culture is carefully scrutinized, identified, and
> followed through a cycle which is capable of being sustained in-
> definitely.[23]

Boulding is a Quaker Christian, and he thinks the new society may
call for a closer adherence to the ethic of Jesus than the ethic of
recent centuries. But he finds profoundly inadequate the inherited
form of the Christian ethic and suggests that in an ecumenical age we
may need to learn from the ethic of the East. "The East has never had
any illusions about being able to conquer nature, and has always regarded man as living in a somewhat precarious position, as a guest
of doubtful welcome, shall we say, in the great household of the natural world."[24]

Lynn White, also a Christian, sees a wisdom in Zen Buddhism that is appropriate to our needs. But he proposes also that the radical Christianity of St. Francis of Assisi may inform us that we men live in this world with birds and wolves, with Brother Ant and Sister Fire, who praise "the Creator in their own ways as Brother Man does in his."[25]

We often hear that the technology that has, in a sense, made our ecological problems is the power that can answer them. But if this technology is basically predatory in spirit and is allied with a predatory religious spirit, the fact may be that some reformation of technological and religious spirit is required in our time. Such is the judgment of William Pollard, Oak Ridge nuclear physicist and theologian:

> One hears much these days, and gratefully so, about conservation of natural resources, environmental health, pollution control, beautification programs, wilderness and wildlife preservation. This is of course all very necessary. But almost completely lacking from all such discussion is a sense of the sacredness and holiness of the earth, or of the awful dimension of the sacrilege which man has wrought in spoiling it. What is needed at this juncture more than anything else is a theology of nature.[26]

> White's conclusion is similar: "Both our present science and our present technology are so tinctured with orthodox Christian arrogance toward nature that no solution for our ecologic crisis can be expected from them alone. Since the roots of our trouble are so largely religious, the remedy must also be essentially religious, whether we call it that or not. We must rethink and refeel our nature and destiny."[27]

If there is any truth in the observations of Boulding, Pollard, and White — as I believe there is — man cannot meet his population problem solely by more effective contraceptive technology and by marshaling the technology of persuasion to convince masses of people to abide by the ethic of the new high priests of demography and ecology. Modern man must revise his sense of his own relationship to nature and to his fellowmen.

V. *Freedom, Coercion, and Social Responsibility*

Man's relation to nature and to his fellowmen bear upon the most difficult ethical problem connected with population: the problem of human freedom. To what extent is society justified in limiting the right of persons to procreate? This right is usually considered a basic personal right; yet society suffers when persons exercise the right irresponsibly.

One conference called by the World Council of Churches walked directly into the dilemma without finding the way out. At the Geneva Conference on Church and Society, Section IV on Man and Community in Changing Societies came to these two different findings:

> Responsible parenthood is not just a matter of individual family concern: it must be accepted as an integral part of the social ethic of the day. (Par. 60.)
> Every couple has a right to make its own responsible decisions on the planning of its own family in accord with its moral and religious convictions. (Par. 105.)[28]

The earlier paragraph points out that procreation is a social issue requiring an ethic that reaches beyond individual families; the latter paragraph reverts to the more traditional location of the issue within the family. Anyone familiar with the drafting methods of assemblies seeking consensus can guess that the two paragraphs came from two subcommittees with diverging opinions and that the larger group never succeeded in reconciling the differences.

The United Nations often struggles with similar dilemmas. The Universal Declaration of Human Rights, adopted by the General Assembly on December 1, 1948, declared:

> Men and women of full age, without any limitation due to race, nationality or religion, have the right to marry and to found a family. (Article 16.)

By December of 1966 the General Assembly, while still giving "due regard to the principle that the size of the family should be the free choice of each individual family," expressed clearly its concern for the "economic, social, cultural, psychological and health factors" in demography. And U Thant, the Secretary-General, said: "Economic development at the level necessary to improve the quality of individual life demands also that the scale of human reproduction be moderated according to each family's deliberate desires, its religious convictions and its ability to provide."[29]

In the nature of the case the General Assembly and the Secretary-General must do all they can to minimize any possible conflict between the emphasis on freedom of the family and the social perils that may result from that freedom. Others are not so constrained. A long-nascent conflict of values among those concerned about population is suddenly erupting as an obvious controversy. The past emphasis has been upon freedom of the family to determine its own size, independent from external controls, ecclesiastical or political. The newly-voiced emphasis is upon the necessity of measures to require families to limit reproduction.

The conflict was vividly illustrated in two successive issues of the *New York Times*. On September 21, 1969 a dispatch by Harold M. Schmeck, Jr. was headlined: "Family Planning: New Focus in U.S." It reported that the federal administration was giving high priority to "the related issues of population and family planning," with reliance upon the desire of many people to space their children if only they had access to information and methods. On September 22 the headline of a dispatch filed by Gladwin Hill read: "Scientists tell Nixon Adviser Voluntary Birth Control Is 'Insanity.'" The text told of a meeting in Aspen, Colorado, where Garrett Hardin, spokesman for a group of specialists, said to Presidential Counsel John Erlichman: "In the long run, voluntarism is insanity. The result will be continued uncontrolled population growth."[30]

At this stage in human history there is considerable agreement among those most knowledgeable and most concerned about population that a zero growth rate for the human race has become desirable.[31] There is equal agreement that purely voluntary methods, even assuming vastly increased education and distribution of contraceptives, will not quickly bring the zero rate. Hence it is not surprising that some persons, deeply concerned about the issue, are raising questions about the necessity for compulsion. Paul Ehrlich wonders why society readily practices the coercion of war, yet shudders at coercion in constraint of reproduction.[32] Kenneth Boulding, a social scientist as sensitive to human values as any, has proposed an ingenious plan for combining government regulation and personal freedom to achieve the zero growth rate.[33] Bernard Berelson, president of the Population Council, has catalogued an immense variety of plans for limitation, ranging from coercive to voluntary.[34]

Conflicts of values, usually painful conflicts, are part of almost all serious ethical decision. So it is with population policy. A desperate world may use coercion to limit population, as single societies have sometimes done in the past. But the dilemma is a bitter one. We started with a concern for the dignity of man. Human dignity demands limitation of population. But some methods of limitation destroy dignity. Infanticide, for example, is as bad as any problem it is designed to solve. It may remind us of the army officer who explained that he had to destroy a village in Vietnam in order to save it. Compulsory abortion or sterilization are a shade less brutal, but they so violate the consciences of many men as to be destructive of dignity.

In any crisis society qualifies personal rights, but part of ethical wisdom is to avoid crises that permit only destructive choices, and another part of wisdom is to maintain a maximum of human integrity even in crisis. Certainly any humane population policy will seek a maximum of free decision, a minimum of coercion. Hence it is encouraging to find Philip Hauser, director of the University of Chicago Population Research and Training Center, saying: "The fact is that decreases in fertility in what are now the economically advanced nations were achieved completely on a voluntary basis." [35] It is encouraging to see Roger Revelle, director of the Harvard Center for Population Studies, call it an emphasis on "the drama of living human beings" rather than on quantitative calculations alone. Revelle points out that a social security system reduces the motivation for large families in those societies where parents must rely for old-age security on their sons, that a reduction in child mortality (while temporarily increasing population) reduces the incentive of parents to conceive many children.[36] Such attention to wider cultural and ethical considerations relieves the starkness of the dilemma of destructive freedom and destructive coercion.

Yet mankind can never expect to evade the dilemma. Life permits no total freedom or total coercion. Society, if it is to survive, will probably learn to limit population by persuasion and pressure that fall somewhere between uninhibited freedom and overt coercion. Many methods of persuasion and pressure are possible. Prestige systems, economic pressures, taxation, housing policies, and skillfully contrived propaganda are a few of the devices by which societies are likely to move increasingly as they see the necessity of limiting reproduction. It is not wrong for society to use such pressures. Society itself is under immense pressure; there is no reason why the families within it should evade the pressures.

Yet there is danger in the propensity of society to manipulate its members for their own good. Donald Michael has pointed to one of the basic conflicts of our time: man increasingly sees himself as a manipulable and manipulated object among other objects in social and physical systems; yet he increasingly rebels with humanistic passion against this premise that he is a manipulable object.[37] In the few years since Donald Michael published those reflections (in 1965) a generation of college students has made its protests so loud that society cannot block out the noise. Participatory democracy is rarely tidy and is not always wise; yet it has *elan*. Population policies that emerge from participatory democracy, informed by accurate knowledge, can accomplish some results unattainable by methods that impose elitist solutions on unwilling people.

Yet there is much that is still unknown about the ways of relating personal freedom and social responsibility in this technological age. Any theological and humanistic ethic must ponder such questions deeply. Their answer will have much to say for our beliefs concerning the identity and dignity of man.

Notes

1. Loren Eiseley, *The Firmament of Time* (New York: Atheneum, 1962), p. 123.

2. Richard M. Fagley, *The Population Explosion* (New York: Oxford University Press, 1960).

3. *World Conference on Church and Society: Official Report* (Geneva: World Council of Chrches, 1967). The findings of Section I, Economic Development in a World Perspective, point to a need for reduction of population pressures in some areas and regret that "specialized agencies of the United Nations do not speak and act more openly" on population problems. But even while it claims that the World Council of Churches can speak with a freedom unavailable to politicians in some countries, it indicates its own constraints in deference to disagreements within its membership. (See pp. 72-73.) The Report of Section IV, Man and Community in Changing Societies, asks the churches to support research on contraception "with a view to providing methods that are inexpensive, effective, and acceptable on medical, moral and religious grounds." (See p. 178; cf. pp. 167-169, 177-178.)

4. *The Uppsula Report 1968: Official Report of the Fourth Assembly of the World Council of Churches* (Geneva: World Council of Churches, 1968). See reports of Section III, World Economic and Social Development, p. 50; Section IV, Towards Justice and Peace in International Affairs, p. 68; Section VI, Towards New Styles of Living, p. 92. See also Recommendations of the Committee on Church and Society for Post-Assembly Programme, p. 244.

5. Statement on Responsible Parenthood of the Board of Christian Social Concerns of the United Methodist Church, October 8, 1969.

6. Anthony Lewis, "Not with a Bang but a Gasp," *New York Times*, December 15, 1969, editorial page.

7. John Platt, "What We Must Do," *Science*, Vol. 166 (November 28, 1969), p. 1116.

8. Paul R. Ehrlich, *The Population Bomb* (New York: Ballantine Books, 1968), Prologue.

9. Jean Mayer, one of the world's foremost authorities on nutrition and organizer of the 1969 White House Conference on Food, Nutrition, and Health, thinks that the world can overcome its food deficit in the next 20 or 30 years, but he sees other urgent reasons for limiting population.

10. Cf. Gregory Baum, "Ecclesiological Commentary on 'Humane Vitae.'"

The Ecumenist, September-October, 1968, pp. 180-185. Cf. *Contraception and Holiness,* a symposium with introduction by Archbishop Thomas D. Roberts, S.J. (New York: Herder and Herder, 1964).

11. The papal encyclical, *Humanae Vitae,* July 29, 1968, condemned all "artificial" methods of contraception. The vote of the Commission is reported by the Rev. John A. O'Brien in "Birth Control and the Catholic Conscience," *The Reader's Digest,* January, 1969, pp. 2-6.

12. John A. O'Brien, *Family Planning in an Exploding Population* (New York: Hawthorne Books, Inc., 1968). Cf. John A. O'Brien, " 'The Vatican Speaks Out,' " *The Christian Century,* Vol. LXXXVI (December 10, 1969), pp. 1580-1582.

13. France and Ireland led the movement to declining family size in Europe. Today in Europe the birth-rates in predominantly Catholic countries are not noticeably different from those elsewhere. See *Population Profile* (Washington: Population Reference Bureau, Inc.), July, 1969, pp. 4-5. Latin America remains a different situation, but there are signs of change there.

14. John A. O'Brien, *Family Planning in an Exploding Population,* Ch. 13, "Churches Speak Up."

15. Helder Camara, "From Dichotomy to Integration," *The Christian Century,* Vol. LXXXVI (December 10, 1969), p. 1575.

16. John Platt, "What We Must Do," *Science,* Vol. 166 (November 28, 1969), p. 1116.

17. Bayard Webster, reporting a study by the Department of Health, Education and Welfare, *New York Times,* December 21, 1969, p. 66.

18. Harvey Cox, *The Secular City* (New York: The Macmillan Co., 1965).

19. Arend Theodoor van Leeuwen, *Christianity in World History* (New York: Charles Scribner's Sons, 1964).

20. Lynn White, "The Historical Roots of Our Ecological Crisis," *Science,* Vol. 155 (March 10, 1967), p. 1205.

21. *Ibid.,* p. 1206.

22. Barbara Ward, *Spaceship Earth* (New York: Columbia University Press, 1966), p. v.

23. Kenneth Boulding, "The Wisdom of Man and the Wisdom of God," in *Human Values on Spaceship Earth* (New York: National Council of the Churches of Christ in the U.S.A., 1966), pp. 6, 8.

24. *Ibid.,* p. 14.

25. Lynn White, *op. cit.,* p. 1206.

26. William G. Pollard, "Toward a Theology of Nature," unpublished paper prepared for the Joint Commission on the Church in Human Affairs, August, 1968, p. 9.

27. Lynn White, *op. cit.,* p. 1207.

28. *World Conference on Church and Society: Official Report* (Geneva: World Council of Churches, 1967), pp. 167, 178. It should be noted that this conference was not an Assembly of the World Council of Churches and did not speak for the Council.

29. "Special Statement for the Victor Fund Report by the Secretary-

General of the United Nations" (New York: The Victor Fund for the International Planned Parenthood Federation, No. 8, Spring, 1968), p. 6. The same publication carries the Resolution of the General Assembly, December, 1968, just quoted above.

30. Garrett Hardin's views were already on record in "The Tragedy of the Commons," *Science*, Vol. 152 (December 13, 1968), pp. 1243-1248.

31. See the address by William H. Draper, Jr., retiring chairman of the Population Crisis Committee, "Is Zero Population Growth the Answer?" December 2, 1969, distributed by the Population Crisis Committee, Washington, D.C.

32. Paul Ehrlich, *The Population Bomb* (New York: Ballantine Books, 1968), p. 166.

33. Kenneth Boulding, *The Meaning of the Twentieth Century* (New York: Harper & Row, 1964), Ch. 6, "The Population Trap."

34. Bernard Berelson, "Beyond Family Planning," *Science*, Vol. 163 (February 7, 1969), pp. 533-543.

35. Philip Hauser, *Population Crisis*, Part 2, 1967-68. Hearings before the Subcommittee on Foreign Aid Expenditures of the Committee on Government Operations, United States Senate, on S. 1676 (Washington: U.S. Government Printing Office, 1968), p. 492.

36. Roger Ravelle, "Can Man Domesticate Himself?" *Population Crisis*, Part 5-B, 1966, reprinted from the *Bulletin of the Atomic Scientists*, Vol. XXII, No. 2, February, 1966 (Washington: U.S. Government Printing Office, 1967), pp. 1532-1539.

37. Donald N. Michael, *The Next Generation* (New York: Vintage Books, 1965), pp. 163-165.

Panels

Problems with Genetic Manipulation

Preston N. Williams: Our dialogue is not simply one between scientists and theologians, but also with humanists. We haven't made much mention of that fact because scientists and theologians consider themselves to be humanists. We have as our chairman of the panel today, however, a great humanist, Dr. Hans Jonas.

Hans Jonas: To my left is Dr. Isaac Asimov, Professor of Biochemistry at Boston University, and to my right is Dr. John R. Platt, Associate Director of Mental Health Research of the Mental Health Research Institute at the University of Michigan in Ann Arbor. I will adopt the accident of alphabetical order and call on Dr. Asimov to present his comments on this morning's sessions and on the topic in general with which we are dealing.

Isaac Asimov: Although alphabetical order is accidental, it has been with me all my life. So that I am always called on first and never have a chance to listen to what the others have to say and so gage my own responses.

I happen to be, alas, a pessimist. I am not sure that genetic manipulation is a real topic for concern. I fear somehow that it is entirely theoretical, entirely scholastic. By the time genetic manipulation has really advanced to the point where we must make decisions, the ultimate decision will be upon us. Enough years will have passed, enough population will have come, enough pollution will have intensified, enough resources will have diminished, so that the only decision left for us to make is the exact method of our dying. Nevertheless, since it isn't comfortable to take this attitude, one must — no matter how pessimistic one feels — argue as though the end were not upon us.

Consider what decisions we will have to make for genetic manipulation if we are ever in the position to make them. Obviously, we want to improve the condition of man. There are people here who can argue exactly how we ought to go about this. I will leave that to them.

We can improve that condition, by the way, by ceasing those lines of behavior which damage mankind, for instance the damage to unborn children of smoking, of noise pollution, and of overcrowding. If somehow we could end these deleterius effects, that in itself would improve the quality of the human race. I am in favor of this, but what can we do beyond that?

I would like to make a far-out suggestion. People know me as a science fiction writer. When I look toward the future, the sort of thing I look at — not because I think it is likely to happen considering the situation on earth, but merely because I like to look at it — is a colony on the moon. By the year 2000 I want to see an "in-being" colony on the moon which is, if possible, ecologically independent of the earth. I argue — at times perhaps with more enthusiasm than realism — that this is possible by cycling all resources very carefully and adding to them from the material to be found in the moon's crust. Hopefully there is water there somewhere. And if so, what need be done to make such a colony viable? There is only one thing we cannot create on the moon so as to imitate earth's environment completely. If we make sufficiently optimistic guesses as to the nature of the moon's sub-soil, we can argue ourselves around every possible contingency but this one. We can create an earthlike environment in a cavern under the moon's surface all except for the force of gravity. Gravitational attraction on the surface of the moon is one-sixth that of the earth. There is no known way in science today that this can be altered. The best we can do is to have centrifuges running on the moon so that people can get into the centrifuge for a half an hour a day — or whatever it takes — and subject themselves to normal gravity so that their muscle tone can be maintained. I look forward to a time when one of the progressive and useful objectives of genetic manipulation will be that of developing strains of mankind which can resist the possible untoward effects of low gravitation, a strain of mankind which is at home under conditions of low gravitation and even under conditions of zero gravity over long periods. As far as I know, nobody today knows anything about what I might call "gravidic medicine." Nobody knows the effects on human beings of extended periods at low gravity. We have had astronauts subjected to it for as long as two weeks at a time; this does not impress me because that is always under conditions under restraint. They are in a capsule and they can't move around. If you keep yourself under restraint for two weeks under normal gravity, you suffer untoward effects. I want to know how a person's physiology is affected by two weeks at moon gravity if he is allowed at all times to engage in exercise and activity. It may be that there will still be bad effects. It may be that an organism which has been designed ever since the conquest of land to resist the constant pull of one G of Gravity cannot but be affected by .16 of gravity.

Now once we can study what gravity does to the body and can correct for it by genetic manipulation, we have a new strain of human beings for the moon and of course immediately one asks of what relevance it is. If we could set up a viable colony on the moon with people adjusted to low gravity before the earth is destroyed, we will still have a group of people left to carry on humanity. These days I am thinking more and more longingly of the possibility of a kind of Noah's Ark on the moon to start all over again.

John R. Platt: I am afraid that your colony would, however, be starting all over again with none of the problems solved, and I suppose that after a billion years or so, or perhaps two or three million years, they might get up to a high density on the moon and on Mars and be faced with exactly the same problems we have today. So to simply multiply ourselves in other environments is no solution to our present problem today; although it may be a solution to a long run problem.

It is worth, perhaps, repeating some remarks made in a recent article of mine in *Science Magazine* called "What We Must Do" which emphasize the uniqueness of our present situation. In the last century we have increased the speed of communications to the speed of light, with radio and television around theworld. It is a factor of 10^7. We have increased the speed of jet planes and maybe supersonic planes to the factor of 10^2. We have increased our energy resources by a factor of 10^3 and if we should get fusion power, it would be more like the factor of 10^6. We have increased our speed of data handling by about 10^6 in the last forty years. We have increased the power of weapons from the twenty-ton block buster of World War II to twenty megatons of hydrogen weapons. It is a factor of 10^6 in thirty years. It is no wonder the younger generation under thirty lives in a world totally different from the older generation. As Margaret Mead has said, it is like immigrants coming to a new country — a country which is more different from the world before 1940 than any difference from one country to another on the earth's surface. And the immigrants "don't spek de new language so goot," and they wear funny clothes and eat the funny food and they smell bad. In this new world, it is the *children* who are the "natives"; and they have different views of the world and different expectations of what is possible and what men should do with their lives, in large part because they are in this new world which is so incredibly different.

I would emphasize that these large factors of change I have mentioned have been given as "powers of ten" because I want to emphasize that they are not merely changes by a few percent nor by a few hundred percent. They are changes by *orders of magnitude*. They are the vastest and most sudden changes that have ever occurred in the world before. There are no human organizations which are prepared to deal with changes of this scale. When we had colonial wars a hundred years ago, the news filtered back over a three month or six month period. Today they are in all our living rooms for dessert that same evening. And this makes the difference in the quality of our response and the quality of our consciences.

Besides these quantitative changes there are enormous qualitative changes in these last few years. We have come to the end of the exploration of the earth. Men now live at the North and South Poles with hot and cold running water and helicopter service when they get sick and nuclear power to run their lights and generators. In the last sixteen years we have gone to the top of the highest mountain and to the bottom of the deepest ocean, and we have stepped out into space. I say *we* have done this, because we have paid the taxes for this at any rate. This is just an example of the greatest change of all, which is the end of evolution. In the last few years and in this generation, we are coming to the end of evolution by *natural* selection — three billion years of it! — because we are at the beginning of evolution by human selection. *Man's* activities all over the world determine the numbers and densities of animals and plants of all kinds. It is *our* predation, *our* pollution, *our* breeding, or *our* protection which puts DDT in the antarctic penguins, and which has reduced the great whales to a number estimated to be less than three thousand. They will only last for another five years or so at the present rate of fishing. The tigers of India are down to less than two thousand. It is *man,* consciously or unconsciously, who will now determine the nature of the bio-sphere on the earth.

The result is that we are at a very sudden watershed of history, or as I said in one of my books, "The present generation is the hinge of history." We may not survive this sudden epoch of change, but if we do, we can only survive by moving to a new kind of life, a new kind of abundance, a new kind of human relations all over the planet, to a view of the world-wide eco-system as man's garden, to a view of *survival* as man's concern and his first concern. This is a step to a new form of hierarchical organization of our social systems, a step as dramatic as the emergence onto land of the land animals; or more dramatic in many ways than the appearance of speech, or the appearance of tools and fire two million years ago, which were in fact the initiating causes of this power over nature that we have now acquired.

Our situation is like the joke about the anthropologist who came back from Africa and announced to the reporters that he had found the "missing link" between ape and man; and the reporters said, "What is it? Show it to us." And he said, "It is us." We are in the midst of a transformation to a new form of human life which is more dramatically different from our present form than any mere change of species would be; because it means new forms of food, of population control, of housing, of energy sources, of predation, etc. This means that we are suddenly emerging from a density which has been determined by force and accident, which has been determined by disease and ignorance and isolation, to a form of life in which we are now responsible for the future of the earth and for our own future.

Harvey Cox, the theologian, has an amusing recent book called, *On Not Leaving it to the Snake.* He says that Adam and Eve were put in the garden of Eden to have dominion over all the animals, all the fish and fowl and beasts of the earth — and then when the crisis came, they let the snake decide. He makes this a plea for our responsibility in human affairs. I would say that if man is made in the image of God, and if God is the creator, then we are now at the beginning of the era of Man, the Creator. Man the Creator taking the responsibility for his creations, taking the responsibility for the care and maintenance and preservation and growth of his garden. The earth is potentially a garden of Eden. This fantastic amount of energy available makes it possible for us to find resources where no resources were, because we can mine low-level rocks. It makes it possible for us to create food out of coal. Ten percent of the coal we use today would be enough to feed the world if it were turned into carbohydrates and proteins. We are not in any danger of running out of food as long as we have energy, and when we have energy, we can create structures, we can move outside the earth's atmosphere, we can create artificial environments as long as we have this fantastic abundance of energy — at least up to the level of the thermal-pollution that will probably limit the amounts of energy we can use.

The result of all this is to say that our first concern today must be *survival*. We must begin to treat the world as a whole ecological system, in which we try to maintain those plants and animals necessary to us and to maintain those parts of wilderness which are necessary to our sanity, to keeping a collection of wild species available so that we don't lose those valuable genes.

At the same time, of course, we must maintain the world so we can feed the human populations. We need to do both things — to feed and clothe and house every human being, and also to find ways of limiting the population pressure that makes this so difficult. The next ten or fifteen years are the period in which we will either learn how to do these things or we will die. The time in which humans need to make new biological manipulations on their own bodies and their own genetics is probably fairly far off, in the next century or so. It is true that there are some things we can do genetically against recognized diseases, against phenylketonuria or maybe schizophrenia. Possibly we can have special diets, or perhaps some day the injection of genes making the proper enyzme for the metabolism of phenylalanine, or to cure diabetes. But these are genetic mechanisms against *recognized* diseases. The time when we will need to use more profound genetic manipulation for the shaping of our own genetics can be put off for a hundred years, or possibly a thousand years if necessary, until we understand very much more about the biological consequences of this kind of manipulation. At the moment — for the next ten years and the next fifty years — we have all we can do to take care of survival, to take care of this eco-system, this garden that we have been put in charge of without getting mixed up in tinkering with our own shapes, figures and forms.

In the long run, of course, if we survive, we will almost certainly begin to enlarge tissues, and begin to change the processes of growth, or begin to multiply the number of arms and legs or sensoriums, because this is the direction in which evolution — evolution which is essentially a process of the universe understanding itself — must almost certainly travel in the long run. This sort of change is very far off, indeed, and we can postpone it without any serious damage for a long time, provided we put efforts *now* into the process of restoring and maintaining our garden.

In fact, this whole discussion of "genetic manipulation" of human beings runs a certain danger of turning biologists away from needed studies in the genetic manipulation of animals. I know several biologists who are refusing to work on problems such as genetic nuclear transplantation or parthenogenesis applied to mammals, simply because they fear that these techniques might someday be used on humans. They say, "We have meddled enough." or "It is immoral to work on techniques which might eventually be used on humans." I would contend rather that it is immoral *not* to work on techniques which might greatly increase the food of the world, as for example genetic copying of champion animals. The genetic copying of the best animals — the champion Kenya cow or the champion sheep of Kazakhstan — might increase our meat production by a factor of two within two or three years.

At the present time we only know how to do genetic copying with frogs and lower animals. A few experiments are being done on mice; but this is a pitiful effort by comparison with the thousands of agricultural experiment stations that are trying very hard to breed animals by the old methods so as to increase meat production and protein production, milk production or egg production. To deny the possibility of genetic copying of animals as a method of achieving these same objectives is to cut ourselves off from an important part of biological potentiality.

Of course, genetic copying is something we have been doing with plants for a long time. A whole orange grove is frequently just a single high-yielding tree which has been copied again and again by being grafted onto stumps of a lower-yielding tree. We have been copying plants for thousands of years. The copying of animals is something that has become possible in the last few years. The morality of the one is not substantially different from the morality of the other. But will such experiments lead to human copying of an immoral type? I claim this is a bogey issue. We do a lot of things with animals that we have never thought seriously in democracies of doing with human beings. We herd animals, we breed them, we slaughter them, we eat them, but we do not do these things to humans. And if we always discussed improved methods of cattle-breeding or improved methods of insemination by bulls, as though they were going to be immediately applied to humans, it would be dragging a red-herring across some important aspects of scientific research which might be of great value to the world. Similarly, to discuss the needed genetic copying of animals as though it were simply a preparation for genetic copying of humans is a red-herring. Unfortunately the AAAS has had a number of meetings now — and several legal and philosophical societies have also had meetings — warning of the dangers of genetic copying of humans. But I have never heard of one of these societies having a meeting on the genetic copying of animals as a needed resource in food production. I would like to see the kind of morality in these discussions in which we use biology to try to see how to feed starving people of the world instead of blocking ourselves by worrying about mythical dangers that will not be important for 100 years or more.

Jonas: I would like to put in a word in order to focus on what to my feeling is the basic and ultimate problem we are faced with. To my regret, I cannot share Dr. Platt's soothing view about the remoteness of genetic manipulation applied to man. Not only is it contradicted by the confident and sometimes brash assertions of young molecular biologists as to feasibility, but the preparation of a public climate for this kind of thing is definitely noticeable in our science-conscious, science-governed and technological society. It so happens that I shortly will be participating in a conference in New York under the title "Freedom and Coercion in Bio-Medicine," and the first of the topics there to be treated is "Freedom, Coercion and Asexual Reproduction." The description of the topic begins with the statement, "Asexual reproduction in man by means of nuclear transplantation probably will become feasible within the next five years." It would make little difference if it said ten years or fifteen years. "This technique," the statement goes on, "will be briefly described and its potential uses on a person or group by producing clones of genetically identical individuals will be discussed," and so on.

Platt: But multiplication by stud bull is possible in mankind right now.

Asimov: Yes, but you have got to remember that the concept "human" is being used in two senses. A very few men, for instance, demand that their wives be impregnated by some stud prize human, but every man will want to submit to cloning if he thinks this will create another one like himself. In the former instance, one dies; in the latter instance, one continues to live. So that the pressure for the one will be much greater than the pressure for the other.

Jonas: I want to spell out what to me is terrifying in that and similar potential projects. I am not completely at ease with Dr. Gustafson's very understandable concern with arriving, by consensus or otherwise, at a normative concept of man. Even if inspired by the highest standards and deepest insights, such a normative concept of man — when normative now means practically governing future selection — presumes a knowledge on our part concerning what is wholesome for man, and what man should be, ought to be and should be made to be by some fixation of genetic patterns, which I think entirely surpasses what we can rightfully claim to know. We have always been conditioning man according to certain normative conceptions. We don't leave it entirely to chance. We have education. We change social conditions. We have influence through ideas, and so on. This is a conditioning of a very different kind from the genetic one because in some sense or other it appeals to freedom. And freedom is freedom for good and evil. You can't have a freedom that is restricted, let us say, to kindheartedness, to an automatically non-aggressive, compliant, helpful, cooperative disposition. At first sight it seems desirable to have a society free from the strains of aggression. So let us remove the genes for aggression. But would we know what we were doing? Perhaps aggression is a very good thing in the proper forms with the proper objects. For instance, Mr. Shapiro, who talked here this morning, had a kind of aggressiveness which I would not have missing in any society. In general, any standardizing or homogenizing of mankind is to be avoided, even it it were in the image of Einstein or Mozart. I am not sure that those cloned from them would turn out to be the same. We don't know what the interplay of the opportunity, the historical moment, the situation with the genetic basis is. With all the stacking of the cards, it will still be a blind gamble, but with fewer cards and thus an impoverishment of potentialities. It may be that we will create persons terribly unhappy and impossible to live with. In any case, we will create monotony and fixations. I share in this respect very much the anxiety which we heard expressed.

James M. Gustafson: I would like to respond to that because I didn't really get on to what I described in the introduction of the papers as the second task, namely to begin to define some of the contents of what we value about human life. I would agree that the capacity of freedom to make mistakes is something I value. I think if you got the idea that I had a single, fixed norm in view, you misunderstood me. I intended to talk about a plurality of values that have to be considered with reference to the sorts of manipulations that would take place. I would be very unhappy if there were one fixed sort of principle, one fixed vision, that was adopted. My problem though, is do we leave these things simply to chance? All I was asking for was a degree of objectivity.

Jonas: I would say yes. Leave them to chance.

Gustafson: But when we are leaving them to chance, we are leaving them to the power of the people who will determine certain things. That is, I am not going to have much opportunity to determine certain things about the future. I don't have the knowledge. I don't have the power. I don't have the institutional base. What I am concerned about is that the people who have power take into consideration some kind of rational conception of what these human values are. Frankly, I don't trust them any more than I trust myself with reference to providing some kind of image of what human life ought to be. I'm not asking for fixed standards, but I don't want to leave it to chance because to leave it to chance is to leave it to these people who have the power to make these determinations. That is why I spoke of principles of consideration.

Asimov: I don't think that Professor Jonas is saying leave it to chance means to leave it to anybody to manipulate who wants to manipulate. He means nobody manipulates. Really leave it to chance. I think that his reasoning is that the processes of chance which have produced us really can't be all bad.

Gustafson: The problem is whether it is socially realistic to say that it can be merely a matter of chance. I'm pretty happy with what I have turned out to be, and I'm very happy for all the chancey things that led to it. Some things that I turned out to be are pretty miserable, too. But is that socially realistic? Is that kind of openness still a possibility, given certain kinds of power and capabilities that exist? It would take a social revolution to introduce that kind of radical element of chance back into the society once again.

Bernard D. Davis: The purpose of this meeting, as I understand it, is for biologists and theologians to try to have some cross-fertilization of ideas in terms of problems that we are likely to face or that our children are likely to face. I'm not particularly interested in the possible distant applications ten thousand years from now. On this closer time scale, whether we like it or not, human beings influence their gene pool and will start having increasing power to start doing so. I am scared of it just as much as Mr. Shapiro, but I still prefer to try to discuss it in terms of what is likely to happen in the next few decades rather than in terms of some impossible return to Arcadia. The kind of society that will then reach the decision to start differentially or selectively influencing family size will have a very different structure from the society that we now have. There may be things we can do right now to help steer it in a more rather than a less desirable direction; but I simply haven't seen how to weave this theme of immediate political choices into the general theme that we are discussing here.

Dr. Gustafson's discussion of defining the normative in man was a little too qualitative and this is because the traditions of discussing human values have always been qualitative. We haven't lived with polygenicgenetics long enough or had enough emphasis on statistics in our education for our society at large to begin to think in statistical terms. We will not face the problem of qualitatively eliminating aggression and therefore creating a dull world. Our problem is rather that there are degrees of aggressiveness, as of any polygenic trait, and I would predict that we will reach the stage of saying that in a tremendous range of human behavior certain extreme degrees of aggressiveness go beyond what our society finds acceptable or desirable. The cutoff will be just as arbitrary as the unpleasant cutoff any professor faces when he finally decides that 69 flunks and 70 passes. But we have to do this all the time in order to insure that we produce competent physicians or engineers or theologians or whatever else rather than having incompetent ones let loose on the world. Obviously there are enormous dangers in this system, but I do think as we learn more about quantitative aspects of human behavior, we may begin developing a social consensus on something that at the moment looks horrifying to all of us, including me.

James Shapiro: Dr. Platt has accused me of being immoral, because I am one of the biologists who refused to work on his new transplantations on animals. Now let me say that at the beginning of his talk, I thought he was saying beautiful things. The earth *is* our garden. We've got to take care of it because we are living here. We are poisoning ourselves right now! We've got to stop that! But let us look at the stewardship of our garden. In this country, the United States, the most productive country on earth — it is a beautiful country! — we pay people not to grow food. There are people starving in this country. There are people starving around the world. Yet we don't grow food that we could grow. That's immorality! The problem is that the people who are in charge of this society, the people who have the stewardship of that garden, have decided not to grow food. Senator Eastland gets paid something like $180,000 a year for not planting on his plantations. Those are the people who have stewardship of the garden now. I'm not saying that we shouldn't increase food production. I'm not saying we should stop science because science is a bad thing. I'm saying we should change the stewardship of that garden. That's the issue! It is a political problem! That and the ethical problems are really what we should be discussing.

Dr. Davis talked about two things that I would like to respond to. First of all, he was talking in terms of realistic possibilities and so am I. Vietnam is a real thing; oppression in the Black ghetto is a real thing; starvation in America is real; the use of surplus food shipped to overseas countries to buy their political allegiance is a real thing. Those are the realistic possibilities that we face in this country unless we make some important and radical changes. The other thing he said was that we are going to have to decide how much aggression is too much or that decision will be arbitrary. Well, it *will* be arbitrary. But it shouldn't be made by the people who have the stewardship of the garden now, because we see what they are doing. They are killing people; they are oppressing people; they are doing bad things. It should be made by us, because we are the ones who need the food. That's the problem. As far as the concern with grades and competent physicians, that's the kind of elitism that I don't feel it is very necessary to respond to. We know now that that is just another form of elitism that leads to racism. It's the whole argument that somehow we at the top know better than other people what is good for them. I think we should ask them what is good for them and what they want. Do the people of this country really want enough food to be grown here, or do they want more food? I think the people who are hungry want food.

Jonas: May I just throw one consideration into this discussion, namely a plea for preserving the openness for surprises. Evolution as a whole has been a very surprising business here on earth. Nothing of it could have been predicted by even the most sophisticated biologist. Not, for instance, the coming of mammals when none were there yet. By any planning it would have been prevented. Similarly, I would counsel some trust in the variety of possibilities that are there without our knowing. We should not restrict the horizon of openness that is intrinsic in the dynamics of life. Let us rather be surprised by the kind of children that are born and the individualities that emerge instead of planning them. This is a plea for something, namely, for keeping open the dimension of surprise. This is connected with a plea against the presumption that from our present knowledge we can determine what the true image of man is. If the phrase "image of God" means anything, then it should mean that here is something upon which we cannot by any blueprinting and any particular conception — be it of utility or manageability or even of desirability by the highest criteria — put the seal of our approval and then, of course, by implication, the seal of exclusion of what else may be in store. So if we speak of the dignity of man, it should be in the sense of warning us about genetic engineering. Whether something analogous might not also apply to animal engineering, I do not at this moment want to touch upon — though even there I have my misgiving about a too utilitarian handling of that area, and my idea of stewardship would include some measure of respect for the manifoldness nature has created. But with regard to men there the matter is of an ultimate metaphysical importance which should not be surrendered, not be delivered into the hands of calculations however pragmatically urgent or persuasive they may be.

Platt: I would like to ask you, Dr. Jonas, about this "determination of the future" which you see. At one stage in your life, I suspect you made a decision to go to college rather than to go to work or to go to sea. I think that some day, possibly in a hundred years, possibly in a thousand or a million years, the human race will be faced with the same kind of decision about its own future. The decision of one generation *always* commits itself for the next few years and commits the next generation to some degree. I hope we will never commit the next generation in an *irreversible* way, that is, in a way which goes past some point of no return; but every action we take or fail to take commits the next generation's resources — the houses it has, the streets it has, the politics it has, the education it has to some degree — and in the same way some day we will have the responsibility for committing the genetic changes of the next generations, and the planning of possible genetic changes for the human race as a whole. I hope that when that time comes this commitment will be *diverse;* but I do not see that there is any change of *moral* question from the decision that *you* make every morning, to go to work or not to go to work, or to get a college education or not to get one.

Asimov: Nobody, with great diplomacy, has mentioned anything about the moon colony except for Dr. Platt who dismissed it. This doesn't bother me, because for thirty years I have been talking about things that sensible people have utterly ignored until they happened.

The moon colony I visualize will not face the same problems we face, but on the contrary won't exist at all unless we can solve those problems to begin with. In other words, our problem is that whereas through all of evolution man lived in an essentially infinite world which he could pollute at will and rape at will with no serious damage because there weren't enough of him, now he lives in a finite world which he can no longer pollute because the pollution can't be cleaned up, which he can no longer populate to a greater extent because that is dangerous.

In establishing a moon colony, we live to begin with in a finite world which is utterly filled. The colony cannot exist unless it effectively cycles its resources and does not pollute. Any pollution will be fatal. We will have the kind of society we must develop on earth soon. We might continue bumbling along in our earth society taking solutions and quarter measures and managing to hang on by the skin of our teeth until a well-functioning moon colony shows us exactly how to do it. That will be our blank sheet of paper on which to work out the solutions. That will be our basic research — if you like to call it that — in society's survival which we can then apply to earth. This is actually the most optimistic view I can possibly take of the future.

Platt: Dr. Asimov, you are speaking as though the only problem we have is the problem of treating the earth as a system, and you say a moon colony, in order to exist, will have to treat itself and its problems as a closed system. That's fine, but it is only one aspect of our central problem today. Our central problem today is a political problem. It is a problem of how do men get along with each other? How do they find ways to agree on goals and to implement them? How do they provide for diversity? How do they provide management structures? And when your moon colonists, with their balanced environment, start fighting each other — either over the one woman that is there, or possibly over who gets to go back to earth on the next ship — when these fights begin, then those political problems will have to be solved there just as they have to be solved here.

Asimov: If the fights begin, the colony will no longer be viable. There will be no room for fights if the colony exists at all.

Platt: The only way in which we can progress is by having creative tensions, by having surprising leaders who develop new ideas which other people disagree with.

Asimov: We can't see what the creative tensions and the surprising ideas will be when we lift ourselves to a new level of society so to speak. It will be the height of surprise to discover new surprises.

Questioner I: Actually I was quite surprised that no one did respond to Dr. Asimov's original comment, because I think in all of these other arguments there is a sort of implicit assumption which is part of the neo-Darwinistic concept that man can control his environment. So I am directing this question to Dr. Asimov. Are you of the belief that at the moment we are now going through a Permian eye and that there is no alternative but Noah's Ark? Is this our Permian period just like the Permian period before the rise of man?

Asimov: I make it my deliberate business to be pessimistic. I preach pessimism and speak pessimism and openly state that I expect that mankind will not exist in recognizable form or any form we would *like* to recognize past 2000. I have nothing to lose if I am correct, for then the more I frighten people, the better. If I am wrong, I am the happiest person in the world.

Questioner II: I am a graduate student of music at Berkeley, California. What disturbs me about the whole thing is that you are attacking by individuality. Who are you going to pick or what kind of people are you going to have clone them? How do you know that this is the most valuable person? I noticed that you left musical abilities out among your qualities for humanity. I don't see who you are going to pick for a composer. Maybe you aren't going to pick any musician at all. I can't see that cloning the people you mentioned, like Einstein and Mozart, is an answer. I don't see how you can tell who is going to be a good musician until years have gone by. I don't think that if you asked Picasso if he wanted to be cloned that he would want it.

Jonas: Part of my plea was for a retreat to the humility of ignorance in these matters, and therefore to let chance take its course with its risks, but also with its promises.

Davis: I would like to ask whether any member of the panel offers the slightest support for the idea that cloning is a good thing.

Gustafson: I'm sure I didn't.

Platt: Cloning of animals is one of the most important things we could develop for human food.

Jonas: No advocacy of human cloning has come from this panel, but we must face the fact that feasibility means almost inevitably, application. At least the lure of this is so strong that we have to guard in time against it if we find that it should be resisted.

Platt: Well, let me advocate that we pass a law forbidding the cloning of human beings for *this* generation; and then when their time comes let Mr. Shapiro's children and grandchildren decide whether they want cloning or not — as they will!

Questioner III: I would think that there are other uses for nuclear transplantation which would be preferable to the cloning of humans. There are useful medical applications of this — such as the creation of isogenetic organs for transplantation and solving the immunology problem. It would also create many more moral problems than destroying the human embryo, but this is an area which no one seems to be talking about. Our concern should not be just cloning people, but cloning embryos for spare parts for yourself.

Davis: I don't think this is technically feasible.

Questioner III: It is no more or no less technically feasible than cloning humans.

Questioner IV: While I can see the advantages of limiting the debate and not wanting to bring in societal values on every level, there is something unrealistic about talking about genetic engineering without placing a great emphasis upon the operating values in the society in which this genetic engineering is going to take place. For example, Dr. Davis made the point at the end of his speech that obviously some people are going to have to have fewer children than others. Now in our society with its obsession on technical efficiency and economic productivity, its adulation and worship of the Gross National Product, very clearly I know what that means. It means there are going to be more children for poor people. Ecologically speaking that is very sound, because rich people pollute the environment much more. But I am not too sure that it is going to remain on that basis. I am wondering if we do not have to deal with genetic engineering on the very fundamental basis of the operating values in the kind of society that we have. If it seems that we don't have the way to cope responsibly with human values and what we would like to see come out of genetic engineering, then this ought to determine whether we should do it or not.

Questioner V: We are supposed to have a panel on genetics and planning what science is going to do with genetics. Each one of you has a specialty — Dr. Asimov's science fiction, somebody else talked about the Garden of Eden — but in the next few years it will look as though we have failed our mission here because the government isn't going to organize to clone human beings; somebody in a laboratory somewhere is going to do it. And we are offering no concrete suggestions as to whether there should be government control of it, whether there should be control by the population outside of the government scientific advisory panel.

Davis: As soon as an experimental mammal is successfully cloned, politicians and people-at-large will get very much interested, and it won't take long before there will be a law against cloning human beings. It isn't necessary for us at this time to press for legislation forbidding something that may occur five, ten, or a hundred years from now. We don't really know.

Questioner VI: My question may sound naive. Could somebody please tell me what the value would be to a government to clone human beings? Now surely it is not the obvious one of turning out foot soldiers. Just why would a government want to clone humans?

Asimov: Well, for one thing perhaps if it is a Republican government, to clone Republicans.

Platt: Yes, but they all have revolutionary children.

Questioner VII: I'd like to take exception to something Dr. Davis said. He said as soon as somebody clones a mammal that we will have a lot of legislators very interested in the problem. I would call to your attention that one of the old genetic manipulations which was performed by man was the hybridization of animals. Everybody knows that you can hybridize many species, and in recent times one has to hybridize many more species than one can even contemplate could have been hybridized. I've made a thorough search of the literature and some other investigations to find out if, when, why and why not, no one has come up with a human-subhuman primate hybrid. There is no reasonable reason why it wouldn't work in a genetic sense. Has it been tried and suppressed? Has it not been tried out of fear? There are no laws to my knowledge against such things except local ones and these can be circumvented and often are for all kinds of research. I don't think that governments respond with any kind of urgency to the kinds of problems that are being brought forth now. After all, hybridization has been going on for two thousand years and governments have yet to make any meaningful legislation or show any interest in the problem except for army mules.

Asimov: That's because there is no great demand for hybridization. There aren't any women demanding gorillas. Whereas, even if you passed government laws against cloning, I predict that some rich man would try to find a doctor who would be willing to clone him for a certain amount of money.

Questioner VIII: I am a professor of law. Concerning the law Dr. Davis predicts will be enacted to prevent cloning of humans once we establish cloning other mammals and fetuses, does anyone doubt that even if such a law were enacted, that as soon as we heard that the Soviet Union was cloning its great athletes so that they would be able to win the Olympics, this law would be amended to permit us to clone humans for the same purposes? We would have to close the clone gap.

Population and Behavior[1]

Walter G. Muelder: We have asked Father Charles E. Curran, Professor of Theology at Catholic University of America in Washington, D.C., to be the chairman of the panel this afternoon on Population and Behavior.

Charles E. Curran: I come from a theological tradition that has emphasized order over freedom, and I represent an ascetical background (celibacy) that has tried to do something about the population problem, perhaps not too successfully.

It is my pleasure to introduce to you the panelists here: Dr. Hudson Hoagland and Professor Shinn; Professor Ernst Mayr, the Director of the Museum of Comparative Zoology at Harvard University in Cambridge; Dr. Frank R. Ervin of the Stanley Cobb Laboratory of Neuropsychiatry at Massachusetts General Hospital; and Dr. G. Evelyn Hutchinson, Professor of Zoology, Yale University. Our procedure will be to ask the panelists to give their comments and critical appraisals on the two papers delivered this morning. We will see if this then engenders any kind of discussion, giving the speakers themselves an opportunity to respond and also to question one another, then to continue the discussion among the panelists, finally opening it to the floor for comments and questions. However, I would remind you kindly once we do open it to the floor that we would hope to keep the questions very succinct and the comments even more succinct. So with that then, we would ask the panelists who did not speak to comment on the talks this morning. Dr. Mayr is the first one listed on the program.

Ernst Mayr: My own comments will follow up Dr. Shinn's discussion. My primary question is what can we do about the population explosion and what ethical questions does this problem raise. My own thinking goes along very similar lines to those of Dr. Shinn, and what I present here is primarily a reinforcement of what he has already said. We all have lived through many decades during which we have become used to saying, "Let the scientist or engineer solve our problems." We placed our entire faith in technology, and as far as the average man was concerned, science and technology were one and the same thing. Not surprisingly, the same average man now is peculiarly bewildered when the scientist tells him that technology is not going to get us out of our troubles. It comes as a shock to most of our contemporaries that neither money nor technology is going to solve our problems. The only thing that can save us and better our situation is a change in our own attitudes, a change in our thinking, and, most importantly, in our value systems.

To make that point, let me tell you some of the values that are being attacked in this current intellectual revolution, particularly the revolution of our youth. By citing three examples you will see the seriousness of the situation. Honesty compels us to face the truth that the values of *revealed religion* are questioned by an increasing number of Americans. *Patriotism,* for so long considered one of the outstanding American virtues, often is regarded merely a euphemism for war mongering. Finally, the third one! Politicians have always said if you could not talk about anything else, there was always one safe subject, and that was to praise *motherhood.* Now this ideal is being questioned. To have a family of three, four or five children was, for generations, the ideal of the responsible citizen and happy family man. Now we are told that any number of children beyond two is sinful, a sign of irresponsibility, and a crime against society.

Dr. Shinn pointed out most perceptively that our ethical values are changing. And we are beginning to understand the reasons why they are changing. One of them is the following: we have spent most of our lives in an era dedicated to extreme individualism. This individualism was supported by many largely independent movements, such as existentialism, Freudianism, the environmentalism of much of sociology and psychology, and by the individualistic ethics of Christianity. A manifestation of this individualism was the exclusive stress on rights and freedoms. I am not going to suggest that we cut off this leg on which we have been standing so long, but I do suggest that we will be standing more securely and have a better balance if we take advantage of a second leg, a concern for the community, and add this to our ethical systems. As an evolutionist, I must stress that we are not disconnected individuals, nay, we are members of groups, the largest of which is the human species. As strange as this thought may be to many people, we have an obligation to this species. There are many biologists and even humanists who feel that all of nature — a part of which we are — should be included in this ethical obligation. Dr. Shinn has mentioned Lynn White's discussion on this subject, which I entirely endorse. A careful consideration of these arguments would almost certainly result in a change of our ethical values. Surely nobody questions certain ethical principles, like the axiom "love thy neighbor." The ethical superiority of integrity, generosity, tolerance, over the opposites of these virtues is self-evident, but other ethical values are culture-bound.

Human history is the history of clashes between value systems. At first between hunters and agriculturists, later between peasants and city people, but now we are discovering still another dimension of relativity. We are beginning to realize that many ethical values are "density dependent," as ecologists and evolutionists call it. Many of our so-called freedoms are subject to this density dependence. When population density is low, there is nothing to question "the freedom of unlimited reproduction," but when population density is high, suddenly it becomes unethical to have more than two children. The same principle applies to "the freedom of movement." As long as an area is underpopulated, freedom to move into that area should be defended. However, after an urban area has become over-populated, any further population influx would harm the resident population and such a movement, therefore, would be in conflict with an ethical system that includes a regard for others.

Now Dr. Shinn pointed out correctly that we have been postponing coming to grips with the population problem. We would rather deal with acute current problems than with those coming to head in the future. If we do this, we overlook the fact that many of our current problems are merely second effects of the population problem itself. We must realize that there are proximate and ultimate causes. When a person has a fever, this is always a secondary manifestation of a more deep-seated cause. Giving this person some reducing drugs may eliminate the symptoms of fever, but it will require additional treatment with plasmodium-killing drugs in the case of malaria, or antibiotics in the case of bacterial infection, to cure the actual cause of the fever. Most of the measures for the curing of social ills proposed by sociologists, engineers, and politicians, deal with the amelioration of symptoms, that is, with proximate causes, but not with the elimination of the ultimate causes. Poverty, environmental deterioration, and anti-social behavior in urban slums are, to a very large extent, ultimately caused by excessive human reproduction. Until we tackle this core problem, we are doing no better than the person who treats malaria with aspirin.

What practical measures can we recommend in order to solve the population problem? Money will not be the solution. The food problem is only one of many aspects of over-population. A better pill will not cure the situation either. To save ourselves we must have a change in attitudes. The attitude toward family size, particularly in the underdeveloped countries, at the present time is the greatest threat to mankind. We have passed the stage where we can appeal to the good will of the citizens to do what is best for the community. Unfortunately there are just too many people who lack foresight, common sense, discipline, and a spirit of responsibility. Like it or not, voluntary birth control is not enough. On the other hand, prohibition or coercion by governments is not likely to succeed either, so we are forced to ask whether there is an alternative. Both Dr. Hoagland, and particularly Dr. Shinn, have pointed out this alternative. To adopt a set of incentives, and to build these incentives into our tax structure, into our pension system, and into our entire welfare system. Proposals for such incentives have been presented by various recent authors. They are explained in considerable detail in the hearing of the Reuss committee before Congress, a committee which published its report under the title, *Effects of Population Growth on Natural Resources and the Environment:* negative exemptions from the third child on, a special system of rewards in old age if you have had two or fewer children because you are not relying on many children to carry your old age, and all this sort of thing. There are many such suggestions, and they are quite practicable when they are built into our whole tax and welfare system.

Let me summarize. No one, in the long run, gains from an increasing population. Population growth will have to be stopped sooner or later, and all of us would benefit if it could be stopped now. Secondly, technology and gimmickry will not accomplish this, as Garrett Hardin and others have pointed out. We need a fundamental change in attitude. We need a new density dependent ethic which has equal concern for the rights of the individual and for the well being of the community and of our globe. And third, in order to reinforce the adoption of the new attitude — in order to help along the new ethics that we hope for — it is important that appropriate incentives be built into our tax structure, welfare system and old age pension. There is every reason to hope that eventually this will accomplish what is an absolute necessity for the human species: zero population growth.

Frank Ervin: I will address myself to aspects of Dr. Hoagland's paper which have to do with the issue of aggression and violence. He alluded this morning to the fact that we have been working for the last two or three years on the problem of the biological mechanisms in violence. I want not to elaborate on the points he made, but to abstract what I think is a particularly important piece of that information for me. That is, contrary to many readings of human behavior and much evidence that can be casually cited, it does, in fact, seem to be the case that man in his normal state rarely as an individual attacks another individual with intent to injure. His behavior in groups is something else. But man as an individual is not more innately aggressive nor destructive nor evil than his other mammalian and, indeed, vertebrate kin. In one to one confrontation with another member of his species, he is led to attack, only in two circumstances: when he perceives a threat to himself — which he may perceive erroneously by outside judgment — or when there is any deterrent of the capacity of the cerebral manual to control the very ancient and primitive heritage he carries with him of responding to angry feeling with attack behavior. Let me say that in another way. There does exist within man's brain — as indeed in that of all his kinfolk up the philogenetic tree — a set of very efficient machinery which when called into action leads to effective, purposeful, destructive attack behavior. This can be called into action "consciously by will" in an attempt to defend himself or it can be — as Dr. Hoagland described it this morning — triggered by epileptic discharge, by the scientist exploring electrodes, by peculiar pharmacologic states; but normally it is not brought into play without being turned off, except in the injured brain in the individual.

Now, I emphasize that point because there has been such wringing of hands in the quasi-biological literature of the past decade about this evil quality of man that makes him so aggressive and so self-destructive. I am submitting essentially, that he is not so. It is interesting this theme should come up, and I submit that it has theological rather than biological roots of origin. It goes back precisely to an important point Dr. Shinn made this morning about the creeping into theological doctrine and ethical doctrine of the heresies that revile the flesh essentially. Those heresies have not only given biology a black aura of evil, but also stated that is the biological, animal roots of man which lead to all of his sinful sexual and aggressive behavior. These have ancient philosophical origins. I am suggesting man is not inherently evil, and that indeed it is probably a meaningless question. We neglect to take into account in man the constraints of his genetics, bio-genetic history, his biological limits and capabilities because he is a biological organism, and while he may transcend that on occasion, biology sets the constraints on what he can and will do.

It is an implicit assumption in much of our philosophizing that man is inherently evil and it is his animal nature that gets him into trouble. Much of the formalism of ethics and certainly much of the formalism of law, addresses itself to forbidding, suppressing, repressing man's assumed biological drives. There are many "thou shall nots" that are explicit or implicit through the social structure in which we live. If we are to think of evolving a new ethic, and think about it in a formal way — whether it would be encouraging people to show restraint in reproduction or to show restraint in their other aggressive interpersonal activities — the biological constraint should be taken into consideration; the incentives or the discouragements must be in some reasonable accord with the biological necessity for the organism and the biological limitations of the organisms. I would suggest another quotation to add to the one Dr. Shinn brought up this morning. I belive Engels in *Anti-Duehring* suggested that freedom is the understanding of necessity. The biological organism in the wild knows that meaning of freedom, and man in his social relations should learn it as well.

G. Evelyn Hutchinson: I agree with practically everything in all of the presentations so far. I would, however, like to emphasize what we have heard about the apparent inherent evil in the nature of man, or what theologians would call original sin. There have been two mutually antagonistic types of development in man's behavior and both of them were necessary. We have to take a rather dialectical view of our evolution and remember that all this business of territoriality and aggressive behavior which has been put so very much before the public — partly by people who don't fully understand it — is balanced by something else in human evolution: this is what we might most simply call love.

There is an exceedingly interesting study by Dr. Alison Jolly (Lemur Social Behavior and Primate Intelligence, *Science,* 153: 501 506, 1966; see also *Lemur Behavior,* The University of Chicago Press, 187pp., 1966) on the evolution of manipulative movements in prosimians. She makes a good case for believing that our social life developed largely before our intellectual life, and that manual manipulation in interpersonal relationships, such as mutual grooming, precedes manual manipulation of inanimate objects, which hardly interests the lower primates when unrestrained in nature. Moreover, the social type of manipulative activity is clearly derived from parental behavior and is shown by both sexes. At least in lemurs, social relationships are largely antithetic to sexual activity; the brief breeding season is the occasion for fighting and social disruption. In man, sexual behavior has, to a varying degree become socialized, but it would seem reasonably certain that love is a generalization of the parent-offspring relationship, and is moreover the phylogenetic basis of most of what we regard as ethically valuable. It has continually come up against the territorial aggressive types of behavior and interplaying with it has doubtless been of tremendous importance in making us what we are. Different species of primates show enormous differences in the way this interplay takes place.

At the moment the affectionate parent-offspring relationship is being asked to evolve in a new direction. One of the difficulties inherent is that people just want to have children. This is an unanalyzed statement though certainly a true one. Begetting children is an extremely pleasant activity, but people still do it where effective birth control is available, so that the sexual pleasure involved in procreation cannot be the fundamental reason for a family. We hear about societies in which it is necessary to have children to support parents in old age, but adequate pension schemes do not automatically lead to a declining population. People may want a family to continue their surnames, though in our society this does little for women, and in other cultures parents take names from their children. People also want children to fulfill their unsatisfied aspirations, though they seldom do so. At a very fundamental level, the main reason for having children is the pleasure of having them around. This is entirely reasonable if the parent-offspring bond is a basic component of our social behavior. We like to have a lot of young members of our species that can be picked up and played with. People, in fact, go to great financial and other kinds of sacrifice to achieve this satisfaction, though they usually rationalize these aspects of their behavior in terms of social ethics. One of the most important problems of the future is to find out how, in a society with zero population growth, adequate amounts of this sort of satisfaction can be obtained.

In a more general context, it is worthwhile to point out, after what we have been hearing about Christianity this morning, that the fundamental ethical statements in the New Testament, at least to most people who appear to know what Christianity is about, are the two commandments, derived from different parts of the Old Testament and juxtaposed in more than one context in the New: to love God with all one's heart, soul, strength, and mind, and to love one's neighbor as oneself. It is interesting to realize that at the time of Christ, it was the second of these that required explication; the meaning of one's neighbor being defined in the parable of the Good Samaritan. Nowadays it would probably be the meaning of God in the first commandment that would need examination. I do not want to go further with this theme except to point out that there is a fundamenal problem that may lie behind all we have been discussing. From one point of view, whether we accept what Christ says or alternatively follow the Marquis de Sade in considering murder and wanton destruction to the greatest of pleasures, is a matter of taste, but it is a matter of cosmic taste that goes to the heart of everything, as it involves to which strand of our evolutionary history we want to give precedence. I assume that most of you are on the Christian side in this matter even if you do not acknowledge this explicitly. If I again may quote scripture on a Sunday, given the commandments to love, all the details — the law and the prophets — must be worked out empirically. One of the great difficulties that arises today is not the ends justifying the means, but the means justifying the ends. We get a nice little ethical system that under certain circumstances produces the desirable end of loving one's neighbor. Then conditions change and the system fails to produce the desired end, but we tend to stick to the ethical system as the right thing even if its results are manifestly bad. This type of behavior has been obvious in much conservative theological argument about population problems.

I would finally like to call attention to possible further avenues of research. In the thirties there were a number of statements made and books published with titles like *The Twilight of Parenthood*. That particular title was due to Enid Charles, a highly competent mathematical statistician and a lady of great charm, with, I believe, five children. She seemed seriously worried about the impending extinction of the human race, but not in the casual terms we have come to associate with that unhappy but popular subject. The depression certainly led to a considerable reduction in population growth in the United States. In France where for a time the birth rate approached a replacement value, there was much concern that the German population was increasing more rapidly. Nowadays in European Russia there seems to be a trend towards zero population growth, while in Ireland everything is terrible because the Irish are disappearing, being replaced by German and Italian immigrants. Though the magnitudes of some of these changes often are exaggerated, there are real aspects to them which need study. Part of the variation can be traced to economics, but much must be of more obscure cultural origin. A real understanding of all the economic, psychological and cultural causes regulating population, in the face of birth control or of its prohibition, might be of enormous theoretical and practical importance. I, therefore, commend such problems to the one or two of you in the audience who might develop an interest in them, hoping that you will be capable of far more constructive thoughts on the matter than I am.

Curran: I agree with Dr. Hoagland's point in terms of the problems arising from overcrowding, problems of territoriality, but from a Christian perspective, I find the problem of aggression something deeper. There are possibilities in man for both good and evil which the Christian understanding of love and human sinfulness finds not only, and not primarily, in terms of territoriality, but finds in the very heart of man himself. I think the proper Christian perspective toward anything of creation shows both its limitations, its sinfulness, and its possibilities for good, and I wonder if this might not be true of our own territoriality. Think, for example, of the good results that occur sometimes when twenty people are around an airport at night waiting for a taxi. It was brought out to me last night in this experience, both the good and bad aspects of humanity as it comes to grips with the problem that the back seat will only take three people in the cab, and there were twenty to get in. I saw both good and bad in these circumstances.

Perhaps on the population level, crowding can be an occasion for an incentive to overcome the problem or an incentive for some type of collaboration. There is a great ambivalence about most of these things — the ambivalence of all human creation and technology that man himself can use for good or for ill.

My comment to Dr. Shinn is to underline a number of points he made, especially the realization in theological ethics that freedom cannot be an absolute value, and we have to realize there are other values that must be considered and brought into the discussion along with freedom. The whole communitarian and social aspect definitely has to be called into consideration. And taking a line from Professor Shinn's paper, I wonder if some of the "old theology" might not give us a handle. In Roman Catholic ethics of marriage, we stress the aspect of the good of the species being present in the whole concept of marriage itself, but definitely in the changing environment today, the ethical demands of the species are much different from what they might have been in a different type of population environment.

Roger L. Shinn: This has been a very friendly panel and rather than respond, I might toss a question or two at Hudson Hoagland. He ended by expressing some hopes, and he didn't make them a prediction, he made them hopes. I believe he was wise there. Let me ask in the light of his own paper, inasmuch as we Americans are especially violent and we have produced this kind of civilization, what reason do we have for these hopes at the end? As a subquestion, let me ask, why do you think the vogue of astrology is ephemeral? You called it resurgent. Prior to this resurgance, we might have said that astrology is a cultural lag and that we are working our way out of it. But now if it is resurgent, is there something about this technologically efficient society that generates this kind of counter reaction? So, maybe on the path we are going, it is not just ephemeral.

A second question surely is related to these, and this is a fundamental philosophical question, to which I do not know the answer. I want to know the relation between two lines of thought you developed, both of which have some validity. One is that we see hope of controlling human aggression by electrodes and chemicals and so on, so that the meek may inherit the earth, and — if I may feed you another Biblical line — we can with the help of Delgado make the lion lie down with the lamb. This is one way of doing things. Now the other way is your concluding hope for a humanistic religion in which in an appeal to something non-electronic, non-chemical you are hoping to get an appreciation of basic human values and move toward world peace through law. I don't want to refute either of these, but do you have a way of putting the two together?

Hudson Hoagland: Roger, your questions are indeed challenging. It seems to me that there are currently strong negative reactions, swingbacks against science and technology, on the part of a large number of people. Many young people think that science is both irrelevant and evil because it has been accompanied by technological developments that are threatening and dangerous. On the other hand, I know of no method of getting at what I would call truth except by the methods of scientific inquiry. The system of science assumes that objective truth exists and that there are rules for discovering it and that these methods of discovery must be independent of authoritarianism and of appeals to authority. One's findings must be tested and confirmed by one's peers. This procedure has worked so well in the last three centuries that I cannot think it can long be superceded by revived beliefs in such things as astrology and witchcraft, so contrary to all man has learned in the last three hundred years about himself and the universe he inhabits. Civilization cannot survive unless we have respect for objective truth arrived at through scientific observation and experiment, and that is why I think that these reversions to wishful and primitive thinking are ephemeral. Spiritualism and most of so-called psychic research is another example of an upsurge of nonsense like astrology that occurred after World War I. I have compared these phenomena to those of flying saucers (UFO) that engaged us after World War II. Spiritualism with its ectoplasm is gone now and UFO's are also pretty dead issues.

Your second question was about mechanisms for controlling aggression. The material I talked about this morning is illustrative and certainly remote from widespread application at present. I selected the brilliant work that is going on at Massachusetts General Hospital by Ervin, Sweet, and their collaborators to discuss a form of abnormal brain function. This is not to imply that one can now cure people's meanness and cussedness in general by procedures of this kind, but we do have an orderly way of tapping in on brain centers and fiber tracts controlling aggression. We are able to get information about the brain which, if and when it is increased, may enable us, by localized chemical or electrical stimuli to directly modify even the subtleties of behavior. This, of course, is fraught with dangers of misuse and control of persons in the hands of the unscrupulous, there's no question about it.

Changing people's beliefs and values is still our only practical way of improving things and bringing to reality the hope that we may have a world run by world law instead of via the chaotic hates and fears of nation states with uncontrolled sovereignties. I don't think electrophysiology and drugs are going to have much to do with major social issues such as that. Ernst Mayr emphasized how we should make loyalty to our species important. We can no longer devote our loyalties to the special groups into which we have accidentally been born at the expense of concern for the larger groups of which we are a part. Today in the nuclear age, the unit of survival is indeed the human race. I feel encouraged that the young people are objecting to some of these very things that have made for parochialism in relation to our society and it is my hope for this generation that we may see the development of an educational system that will teach us that we have to be human beings before we are Americans, Russians, black or white, communist or capitalist.

I have deep concern about aggressiveness of people in groups, especially national and political groups, even while agreeing with Ervin that human beings are pretty decent as individuals. Man is an animal and a very special kind of animal; nonetheless he is a product of evolution by natural selection. If we recognize our basic biology as to the nature of man, we will be better off than if we put ourselves on pedestals and talk about our immortal souls. We are, of course, imaginative animals, and when we are cruel, we are cruel in a thoroughly imaginative way. You cannot find any animal that could produce the genocide of six million Jews the way Hitler's Nazis did. This was a human performance. You do not find concentration camps developed by any animals other than man. And I think these are signs of great evil. Genocide is characteristic of the human animal, and so is war. We have been able to invent frightful weapons and methods of destroying each other, and this is unique to man. For that reason I am not as optimistic as Frank Ervin is about us. We treat each other quite well as individuals, but in our national and international relations, we do very badly. As I pointed out twenty-five years ago, our recently evolved neocortex may turn out to be a phylogenetic tumor capable of inventing incredibly destructive weapons, but incapable of controlling the hates of our ancient limbic brain. After all, thousands of species have become extinct for each one that survives. All organisms must adapt to their environments or perish and we drastically changed ours by the invention of nuclear weapons. So far we have shown little inclination to adapt national policies to their existence.

Curran: Somebody should quote the lovely statement that Homo sapiens is the missing link between the primates and human beings. Perhaps now we could open to the floor for a few minutes. I will take the prerogative of asking the people who will be in the participating seminar later to hold either their wisdom or aggressivity until that time, so that other people who will not be there may now make a comment or pose a question to any of the panel.

Questioner I: I direct my question to Dr. Mayr, or any of the members of the panel who wish to answer. With all the problems we face, and if you believe some of these pessimists that we have something like thirty to forty years left, what is the quickest way to translate a lot of the panel talk we have heard into action? What are the steps that have to be taken?

Mayr: This is the $64 question. In this society of ours, it is Congress that makes the laws. It is gratifying how quickly Congress has learned about the population problem, even though we wished Congress would learn even more quickly. Just think of the hearings before a Congressional Committee that I have referred to. Of course, these are outsiders reporting to Congress, but unquestionably this is a tremendous step ahead. Quite obviously, the immediate step is education. Only a few years ago, virtually nobody talked about the population problem. Until last year, the students in our universities did not care about ecology. This year, within twelve months, they have suddenly realized the importance of ecology. I think this is the immediate step to be taken, the vast education of all decision-making people, so that then they try to translate the wisdom of people who have a true understanding of these subjects into an appropriate public policy. There are many steps to be taken. For instance, scientists must give seminars and other courses in government departments. It has to be a getting-together of people with different backgrounds, just like here we have a getting together of theologians and biological scientists. We must have far more gettings-together between biological scientists and educators, and biological scientists and public policy makers, come what may.

Extension of Life[1]

George Fulton: The session will be conducted by our chairman, Dr. Paul Ramsey, Paine Professor of Religion, Princeton University.

Paul Ramsey: Among the panelists are Dr. Moore and Dr. DeWolf, who are known to you. The other two panelists are Dr. Robert S. Schwartz, Chief of Clinical Immunology Service at the New England Medical Center Hospital and Dr. Henry Beecher, who is Research Professor in Anesthesiology at Massachusetts General Hospital.

Henry K. Beecher: I would like to take a modest kind of exception to Professor DeWolf. It seemed to me that, in one aspect, a difficult situation is made more complex than it needs to be. For example, he spoke of these thousands of individual flat electroencephalograms, mentioned the fact that there had been twenty-three recoveries. He did say drugs were involved. But I would like to point out, having checked that situation quite recently, that in more than three thousand consecutive individuals who have flat electroencephalograms there wasn't a single recovery, if you exclude, as we always do, those individuals who are (a) under central nervous system depressants and (b) under hypothermy, that is individuals who are cold. So one must give considerable preeminence to the flat electroencephalograms, much more than we did. Professor Potter and others may be here who worked together with me on the definition of irreversible colon. We said the flat electroencephalogram gives valuable confirmatory evidence, but the neurologists in producing these three thousand consecutive cases with no recoveries, if you exclude those two groups, have made a major step forward. We will have to pay more attention to this than we have in the past.

I am utterly convinced that brain death will eventually be construed as death indeed. This is not going to happen right away, perhaps not next year, perhaps not for twenty years. But eventually this will transpire. Now when that happens, or before it happens, we should be giving very serious thought as to what this redefinition of death will mean in terms of changes in medical principle, of changes in medical practices. It seems very sad to me that in the transplant situation there has been such a tendency to describe these activities as experimentation. That was a mistake. One can validate the fact that it was a mistake by looking back through the history of transplantation. It would be far better to have said that transplantations represent desperate efforts to save desperate situations, such as we carry out all the time in medicine. At the same time, one must recognize that there is an element of experimentation present, but so is there always experimentation in any major therapy. It would have been far better if transplantation had not been tarred with the brush which is so offensive to many laymen, experimentation.

Robert S. Schwartz: This question of unwanted prolongation of life is not the topic of this panel, as I understand it. Transplantation, particularly of the kidney, does not fit that phrase, and therefore most of the discussion of Professor DeWolf is beside the point. He mentioned that our resources are inadequate for transplantation work. I disagree on this point. The resources of this country are quite adequate for this, and it would be a pity to abandon the leading edge of medicine in favor of programs of so-called delivery of health care. The two have to go hand in hand. One is part of the other. They are not mutually exclusive operations. If we did abandon the frontier of medicine, we would learn about it to our dismay within five years. As Professor Michael Woodruff of Edinburgh has pointed out very clearly, nobody in the transplantation field or, in fact, in any other field of medicine is attempting to give patients immortality. It would be a mistake to believe that is the role of a doctor. With regard to the Hippocratic Oath and the use of dangerous drugs, which are certainly used in transplantation work, I remind the panel that all drugs are dangerous. The bottle of aspirin in your medicine cabinet is a lethal weapon. Doctors are faced every day with the decision to use dangerous drugs. Well established, well known drugs — digitalis, penicillin, morphine — every standard therapeutic agent at the doctor's disposal is dangerous. That's what being a doctor is all about. So the fact that dangerous drugs are being used has nothing to do with the Hippocratic Oath.

Transplantation is only a very small portion of a vast field of research in immunology that is going to benefit very large numbers of patients. The numbers of patients that can be directly benefited by transplantation, even assuming the most ideal conditions, is relatively small. Most patients who arrive at the point where kidney transplant is necessary are medical failures because we do not have measures adequate to treat the renal failure. Therefore, the physician has to resort to a device such as dialysis or to transplantation. The genuine advances are in the development of methods of disease detection and disease treatment *before* the stage of organ death has been reached. This may be the major advance that will come about in the field of therapeutic immunology. We have learned much about the treatment of immunological damage from studies of the transplantation of organs. This treatment is now being applied to patients before their kidneys are destroyed by an immunological reaction. It therefore seems extremely shortsighted to suppose that we know everything about human illness and conclude that further research on how to relieve and prevent disease is unwarranted.

Ramsey: My first comment is directed negatively against one point Dr. DeWolf made in his very excellent paper. He said that in medical practice with sparse resources there is a necessity for "civilian triage," in a sense that medical teams should choose who will live and who shall die by a calculus of many factors, including, I presume, social worthiness. Ethically that is a very questionable proposition. The most well-publicized case of this is the anonymous public committee set up by Dr. Scribner in Seattle, Washington, which as reported in various popular journals takes social needs and worth decisively into account. This committee promptly got into such problems as deciding that the husband of a young woman with one or two children should be allowed to die while the husband of an older woman with four children should be chosen to live because there was, on the basis of the calculation, greater probability that the younger woman could get remarried! The *Life* magazine article concluded with the statement that if one was a resident of Washington state and thought he might have total renal failure, the best thing he could do was to get married quickly, have a lot of children, work at least enough to show virtue and character, but throw all his money away. There is a computerized study presently being made of the practices of 212 dialysis centers in the country where the medical staff makes the decision, but this study will show at 42% of the centers (a) explicit social worthiness considerations being used by a staff and (b) such criteria are often used implicitly under the guise of medical criteria.

Without arguing the point I will simply state the alternative ethical judgment to which I would adhere in matters of life and death in the use of sparce medical resources. Maritime law and the ethics of the over-loaded lifeboat situation should prevail; that is lottery. A policy of first come, first served is in effect an on-going lottery. If we don't do that the medical team ought to have public committees to assist them. This is because social worthiness judgments filtered through public committees and not simply made by medical people are apt to bring a broader range of value judgments to bear upon that question. I agree we should have been debating the ethics of kidney transplants in the 1950's, not now. But the experimental nature of heart transplants and their very limited therapeutic value are current questions. On this, the sound, quiet and balanced statements made by Dr. Moore this morning about heart transplants are one thing. But the way these operations are reported in the press is apt to raise false hopes. For example, the year end report that in 1968 of ninety-nine heart transplants that had been done, fifty-nine had died while *forty were still alive.* That means if you keep on doing heart transplants rapidly enough you can maintain what looks like a good figure. Forty out of ninety-nine looks like good therapy. The stark fact was, however, that except for Thomas in Dallas, who was working in the bank at that point, only nine had as yet lived more than three months. Now the kidney transplant people have another way of reporting their successes and failures that communicates a true situation better to donors or recipients alike. They say, for example, that they have obtained 50% four-year survival rate from parental or sibling donors, or from 15% to 20% four-year survival rate from cadaver donors, and that at Denver a far more favorable figure had been achieved — 95% one year survival. Now these figures show human life between one's first dying and one's second dying; they evidence a choice-worthy therapy. Had the heart transplants been so reported, as I amateurishly figure it, we would have read in all our newspapers that the attainment was 7% three-month survival rate in 1968. In that case I must disagree with what Dr. Beecher said in calling all organ transplants a "therapy" for a desperate situation. Surely these figures show that, along the spectrum between investigational therapy and what is already an attained therapy, heart transplants should be described as primarily experimental. Then a moralist would have to say that one should not have urged on desperate men in desperate situations to choose that therapy. Rather, medical practice should pay attention to the dignity of their humanity by asking them to consent to an experiment which might be of benefit to others if not to themselves. Such freely given, understanding consent would have entered those desperate patients humanly as joint adventurers in the enterprise of medical research and advancement.

Francis D. Moore: How do you know that was not done?

Ramsey: I do not know. I would like to ask you, Dr. Moore, the same question about the case described in your wonderful book from which I learned a great deal — *Give and Take*. This was the case of the first woman in the kidney transplant era in the fifties or earlier who was subjected to whole body radiation. You describe the case and praise her great courage. That is quite appropriate provided she consented to an experiment. Not, of course, a true experiment, but surely a procedure that was primarily experimental. Looking back on it, she may have been a courageous coadventurer in medical process; and that, at the time, was what could be offered her.

Moore: Of course it was said. It is so typical of your view and Dr. DeWolf's to only give one side of things so it all sounds so open and shut. Why didn't you also tell the group that she didn't have any kidneys? That just happens to be an important part of her case which is so easy to leave out in your impassioned plea. Of course it was told as experimental. In fact, she was told that she was the first person to have had this therapy in the hope that it might help her.

Ramsey: That entirely satisfies me. Still, Dr. Moore, the purpose of our panel is to get several sides on the issues before us. Dr. DeWolf, I think, and I, certainly, am talking about a human choice to die rather than accept desperate therapy. Even if she had no kidneys, and of course I acknowledge the desperateness of the situation, I judge that the consent was necessary which you say was the basis for proceeding with the trial. Now would you say that about the heart transplants?

Moore: I can't tell you exactly what was said to each heart transplant patient, of course, but I've corresponded and talked with several of the people involved with this. It is fair to say that those patients knew what the likelihood of recovery was, at least as much as we as doctors did. You've looked at that curve after 1968, and what I said about it was that it was "too much, too soon." I didn't say that it was all bad. In fact, I said that some of the recent heart transplantations have done rather well and that (a) this should be permitted to grow, as it will grow, and that (b) of course each patient should be given a good account — insofar as his education helps him to understand it — of what the likelihoods are and what is happening.

The trouble with you both, though, is that you have to have somebody to assault — a target — so you make the picture of *all* doctors a mighty miserable one. Here DeWolf says that all doctors are keeping these "hopeless patients alive." He never stops long enough to say that some times determining the amount of hope in these situations is quite difficult. If he were to come into the hospital, I could show him some comatose patients on total respiratory support. He would say, "That's terrible, you awful doctors, keeping those people alive. They are unconscious so they can't say what they want, and their families can't talk to them." But *some of those patients recover to a very nice life,* and it is hard to say sometimes which are going to recover. Dr. DeWolf is opposed to euthanasia. He likes to keep himself very clean and not get into any really difficult problems. He should realize that withholding therapy is a sentence of death in certain situations. In certain situations it should be done, and it *is* done. The very criteria of death which he is so upset about in the case of the cadaver donors, the flat encephalogram, is actually the thing that permits the doctor in many cases to shut off the machine. Dr. DeWolf can't have his theological bread buttered on both sides.

L. Harold DeWolf: Dr. Moore I shall have to protest that you very radically misquoted me. You say, for one thing, that I was seriously upset by the criteria of death. Quite the contrary! I said I was glad that there were several criteria of death which were required to be used according to the ethics promoted by the judicial council of the American Medical Association. That was precisely my point. I approve of these criteria. I do not disapprove of them. I am glad that more careful multicriteria approaches are being made rather than the single and simpler ones of another day. Now I hope it turns out, as Dr. Beecher is inclined to believe, that the proper use of electroencephalography will be reliable. Very good, let us use it. But in the meanwhile, it is only a proper safeguard that several criteria should continue to be used.

He also radically misquoted me when he said that all doctors are keeping patients alive that didn't want to live. I said no such thing. I said, unfortunately this is happening often, and there is probably not a pastor here who visits people in hospitals who will not attest to it. I have also heard it attested to by nurses who have had long experience and who are in very responsible positions in hospitals where these things are happening frequently, and especially in research hospitals, state research hospitals and the like. Once a person is entered, he is not asked, "Do you want to have this procedure even though it may be a very desperate, a very painful one and one which gives no hope of anything more than a little prolongation of life?" Sometimes he is told that this is going to be done, but sometimes he is not even told. It is simply done. Done sometimes over the protests of family and nurse alike, the nurse often being closer to the patient through constant care even than the doctor.

Now I am not describing the kind of careful approach that Dr. Moore himself has assured us all takes place under his direction in his hospital. I am not acquainted with patients in his hospital and I don't know what is happening there. I do know, from personal observation and experience as a brother hospital patient to other patients, what happens in hospitals all too often.

Then there is this other question which one of the doctors might speak to which looms very large in the whole problem, not simply of transplants, but of a degree of all these desperate measures.

Here I must reply to a complaint of Dr. Schwartz that unwanted prolonging of dying is not the issue we were to discuss. When I was asked to read a paper on organ transplants, I said I was not especially interested in organ transplants as such, but if this was an entree to the whole issue of the relations between the technology of keeping bodies alive and the full meaning of human living and dying, then I would be glad to approach this. I noticed the workshop this afternoon, which is supposed to have some continuity with this morning session, is precisely on the question of extension of life, so this does seem to be highly relevant.

I worry about Professor Ramsey's response in that I am not happy or satisfied with the particular way of stating criteria of decision for choosing which patient is to get the help. I am not happy with any criteria that can be selected. I see no way to approach the matter with any real reason without considering quite a number of factors. But when Professor Ramsey says this should be decided on the basis of first come, first served, I know that this usually means that the people who are poor and the people who are ignorant are going to be the last ones to be considered. Usually this will be true. It is for the most part the people who are more knowledgeable who get even the beginning of medical care. In the city of Washington, the situation is desperate for hospitals trying to serve the ghetto and the deprived people of the community. The nurses there have been in a frantic position because of the impossibility of the vast need they face and the little they can do. I have not heard the American Medical Association, which is mounting its great campaign against socialized medicine, come out with anything to favor the proper care of all these deprived people. This is not an attack on Dr. Moore nor on other individual surgeons, but it is a criticism of the stance of the profession through its own organ the American Medical Association.

Beecher: Professor Ramsey, I am more than a little confused as to your definition of "experimental." You seem to equate "experimentalism" to surgical failure. I would remind you that resection of the upper third of the esophagus for cancer is, so far, invariably associated with failure. Is this experimentation?

Ramsey: It is characteristic of an experiment, surely, that one can learn from one's failures. It is characteristic of some mixture of investigational therapy that while one learns, he also treats. The patient should know where on the spectrum his case is. I'm confident the medical profession generally does this. The degree of experimentality in it, the degree of therapeutic hope: that is the question. Perhaps the difficulty is that all I know is what I read in the papers, in a certain sense.

Schwartz: But that's the trouble, sir. Why should a scholar like you pay attention to newspaper reports on such complex problems?

Ramsey: You may have private communications with Dr. Cooley.

Moore: Well, you have private communications with the "Man Upstairs" who tells you when to stop treating people, and we can't get that line of communication going.

Ramsey: Dr. Cooley was quoted as saying that it was therapeutic to give one of his patients six weeks of purely hospital existence, and Dr. DeWolf and I are attempting to affirm that there are grave moral questions about that. Also there are serious questions about the way in which donors and families of patients are induced to believe there is now great hope of treatment in heart transplants. They also read the papers. Now if Dr. Cooley told that patient that his operation was experimental primarily, then that statement should not have been uttered by him to the press. I agree with you, Dr. Beecher, that experiment-therapy is a spectrum. I'm simply emphasizing that the ethics that the profession itself says governs experimentation should, to the degree that it is on the spectrum experimental, be the ethical standard that is applied.

Moore: This quixotic maneuver of defining something and then shooting flaming arrows in it is really not a fit method of proceeding in a panel like this. How do you know what Dr. Cooley said to that patient? What difference does it make as to whether or not he said it was "therapeutic" or "experimental" in the papers? As everybody realizes, there are many operations done during periods when nobody knows what is going to happen. That, of course, was one of the main problems.

But I would like to get back to this other point which both of you have swung on pretty hard. That is the point that the inadequacies of medical care in the poverty stricken parts of this country (including the underprivileged areas of Washington and Boston) are due to the *failure of doctors*. In fact, Dr. DeWolf said the medical profession is turning its back on thousands of patients. Now that just isn't how it is. People who are studying distribution systems of medicine in this country will tell you that the problem if far more basic. Doctors can't cure poverty. To take on the American Medical Association — with which many of us have fairly little sympathy — and beat on it for this failure is equally absurd. The difficulties in getting medicine to those people are social, educational, economic. They have to do with the whole structure of our society. The concept that there are lots of doctors simply doing nothing or refusing to treat these patients has no basis in fact.

DeWolf: I agree.

Moore: These are social problems within our society. It serves no one to try to pass them off as part of this anti-medical profession line of thought. The medical profession, curiously enough, just *isn't that important!* There are other things that must be rectified in our society for these people to get the care they should have.

Ramsey: I now invite members of the audience to address questions to individual members of the panel by name. Comments are also invited, if you can keep them brief, perhaps ending by "isn't that so?" which makes it a question.

Questioner I: I should like to ask the scientists on the panel how it is that they perceive the role of the scientist at this conference. It seems the basic presupposition of the scientists is that they are providing data or education for the theologians. While the men may have nice social motives in educating the theologians, the more pressing problems of the advance of medical knowledge which may have ethical implications are not being fully discussed. The men seem to be doing some *ex post facto* kind of analysis on hypothetical situations. Now Dr. Moore in his address said that what was going on in these discussions was not addressed to the real problems. However, Dr. Moore, you didn't explain what the real problems were. In the same way, Dr. Hudson Hoagland alluded to a new understanding of the psychology or the method of human functioning based on an understanding of neuron processes. It is at that point that I think any new understanding of ethical or theological implications should be found. Dr. Moore would you explain where the frontiers are in the interface between medical science and theology as you perceive them?

Moore: First off, theology isn't the only pebble on the humanistic beach. I was surprised to hear somebody say earlier that you have to be a *Christian* to appreciate this. That is an unnecessarily restricted view. Many Jewish people and many Mohammedans and Buddhists and other faiths can understand basic humanity. I am sure that was a slip of the tongue. At least, I *hope* it was a slip of the tongue. Yet I would say that we need help from the humanists and we are getting it. We need to be helped in interpreting people's thoughts and symptoms. I think our greatest help in this area has been from our psychiatrists who are working with us all the time.

The reason that your question puts me off is that this isn't the area where the major problems in transplantation are. They are in biology; they are in human biology. That's where they have been right from the start. Dr. Ramsey said that I had wished that theologians had been debating kidney transplantation in 1956. I'm very glad that they weren't, because this complicates the issues. The biological issues are tremendous. They have to do with immunology, such as Dr. Schwartz is studying. They have to do with things which can bring to patients even greater successes than have been achieved now, and with lesser hazards. I dare say that somewhere in this huge meeting there is a panel — or should be a panel — on modern molecular immunology. I think that's where the problems are and that's where the solutions lie.

Questioner II: I sense certain differences of opinion among the panel. For example, Dr. Moore justified kidney transplants and raised serious questions about the rash of heart transplants, all of which seemed not to be inconsistent with what Dr. DeWolf said. Dr. Moore said hospitals do, in fact, often withhold therapy from terminal patients. Dr. DeWolf said hospitals should do this. Now where do they really differ? That is, is one saying they should do it a little bit more often? Is this the only difference? I don't see a really clear-cut opposition here, and I would appreciate it if you could clarify the issue.

Moore: First off, on that second point, I don't suppose there is too much difference of opinion. It's just that he gives a gloomy picture of the medical profession which is much gloomier than is justified. Withholding therapy from dying patients isn't something that lends itself to a profitable public discussion. Many people misunderstand it for the very reasons he mentioned. When it is carried out, it must be done with immense safeguards for the patient.

As to your first point, there was no rash of kidney transplantations. It underwent a very, very gradual, natural growth. My only comment about cardiac transplantation was that it was "too much, too soon." The heart is a very transplantable organ especially for those of us who have tussled with the liver, which is a much more difficult organ to transplant. I think cardiac transplant has a brilliant future, although it doesn't have much of a past.

DeWolf: I would like also to respond to the question about where the real differences lie. I, too, am having great difficulty finding out. Every time I hear Dr. Moore refer to things that I have said, he has talked about things that I have not said. I have been hearing argument against a caricature of my position and not my actual one. This matter of the Christian faith is a case in point. I certainly did not say that only a Christian can have these humane motivations. I said that for the Christian the basic motivation and the ethical criterion that I had just pointed out would be involved with the spirit of Christ. But there were humanists there including humanist philosophers, who talked with great appreciation afterwards and said that they were in complete agreement with me although they did not start from the Christian faith. I have welcomed all my life the deep cooperation of humanists of all kinds of persuasion and of Hindus and atheists and others who are humanists. Certainly I would abhor the idea of a Christian who would claim that he was the only one who had an insight into criteria for determining the answers to the problems we have been discussing.

Furthermore, there is another caricature in the idea we have word from "Upstairs" that will simply tell us when to stop therapy. If we thought that we could solve problems that way, would we have tried to spell out carefully rational criteria? We have tried to do that, and I am not quite sure where the difference is as to what the rational criteria ought to be. I am pleased to know that Dr. Moore would apparently be in agreement with me that the real concern of the physician in the hospital should always be the maintaining of meaningful life and that when the last possibility of meaningful life is gone, there should be no effort merely to prolong biological existence. I, too, am having trouble in identifying the exact point of difference.

Ramsey: The religious people here — Jewish, Christian, or otherwise — do have a concern in this culture with opening up the notion of electible death. The notion that death is a part of life is opposed to the view that death should always be opposed. This issue should not be located mainly in the medical profession. But there does seem to be on the part of some doctors a belief that these questions should not be discussed openly. The quite sane and sound practices that go on of stopping continued effort to prolong life should be opened by discussion in our society. There is a wonderful Jewish saying somewhere about the care of the dying, which says you ought not to set up a clatter outside the window because that might distract the spirit from doing what it is doing, namely departing. That is a wonderful image for the fact that Judaism and Christianity find themselves in accord on the acceptability of death. Questions arise about bodily integrity in the matter of transplants. Dr. Moore mentioned as an ethical question — which surely theologians, religious people, and others are entitled to a view on — whether it is justifiable to make a well person ill in order to make another person well. In any case, on the matter of the acceptability of death, religious men will have to cut athwart some of the basic assumptions of this whole culture, and secondarily some of the assumptions of the medical profession. One such assumption is the notion that death should always be opposed. That is the burden of some of the things that Dr. DeWolf has said.

Questioner III: I would like both Dr. Schwartz and Dr. Moore to say what kinds of considerations and help and formulations from the standpoint of theologians they are interested in having. What kinds do you think would be helpful and productive in discussions of this sort?

Schwartz: Well, as I saw the discussion developing this morning, it seems to me what might be useful is a scholarly analysis of these problems by theologians. I must say with all due respect, that I haven't heard anything except reference to newspaper reports and third-hand comments on what is really going on in the medical profession. This hasn't helped advance the cause of enlightening the situation.

I agree with Dr. Moore that the real problem we face is not a theological problem. We are not theologians to begin with. The problems we face are biological and once these can be solved, the theological problems will also dissolve because the solution will be accepted by all of us. Once we can be assured that we have an extremely high success rate with little danger to either the donor or the recipient in the field of kidney transplantation, there is no longer a theological problem. The theological problem that may have existed — for example, about when to turn off the oxygen tent in the case of a patient dying of pneumococcal pneumonia — no longer exists. That theologial problem was solved by penicillin, and I think the same thing will apply to other medical problems.

Moore: I certainly sounded negative in much of my response to Dr. DeWolf's talk. But I sense that there are many young students of theology here and it would be entirely wrong for me to sound so negative. What I would like them to do is to realize that theology — that is, looking at the world and the problems of life and death in a strictly theological framework — can be a rather limiting approach. For them to have a *broadly* humanistic and biological approach to such problems is very, very helpful. We would welcome one of them to come and work with us the way our interns or our junior residents do. This is the way some of the psychiatrists and psychologists do. Even a newspaper reporter has spent quite a bit of time with us. Come and spend time in depth. Study in the library; spend time in the laboratory. We cannot talk about these real things like arguing how many angels can dance on the head of a pin. Let's get together and see what some of the *reality* is. That is what is so interesting about life and about science. Come to work with us for a couple of years, and I know that you will help us tremendously. Then when you go and talk about this topic, you will have a broader and more effective impact.

Questioner IV: Dr Moore indicated that the problem of medical care is a general one that involves some fraction, if not the entire, of society. In this matter of responsibility which is perhaps a matter of individual conscience, do you feel that the responsibility of physicians is the same as or greater than or less than the others in society?

Moore: That, too, is an awfully good question, a very penetrating one. I would have to answer it by saying that the responsibility of physicians is greater, because you might say that this is our bit, our thing in society. But there are only a few who are very competent to speak on delivery systems for medical care. This has become a very complex socio-economic problem. We have one or two people at our medical school who are making a career of studying this and we have been meeting with them recently, because we are trying to build a new hospital. It is quite evident that they know a great deal about things having to do with delivery of medical care. Society as a whole should realize that it is a sickness of society that our infant mortality is as high as it is. You could take all the doctors in this country and send them as a crowd into Alabama, but my guess is it wouldn't help at all. You are dealing with social, economic, and educational forces that the medical profession cannot solve alone, and yet our responsibility is inescapable.

Questioner V: I am concerned by the wide difference in many areas between these ethicists and life scientists. There is one point on which we should get together and that is when decisions are made, either explicitly or implicitly, who receives treatment. The question should be pressed as to what model is used to make that decision. Some ethicists would hold that if any form of the social utilitarian model is used — and that model may be clothed in some form of first-come-first-served basis, too — there may then be an erosion of the whole structure. Will either one of the ethicists here comment on whether this is the case?

Ramsey: Briefly, I can respond to that and at the same time to an earlier remark of Dr. DeWolf. I take randomization of the distribution of a life-and-death sparse resource to serve precisely the purpose of including the poor, the not-so-bright, and others on an equal basis. In contrast, the use of criteria of social worthiness, either on the part of staff or on the part of a public committee is precisely the procedure of selection that would not apply this norm of equality in matters of life and death. Hopefully medical advance will relieve us of this problem in the future, but in the interim, we have these two models of how one goes about making the decision. One who believes in the social worthiness model has, of course, an enormous amount of intellectual labor to do with others of like mind to refine and define exactly how qualitative selections are to be made.

Questioner VI: Since this is a scientific meeting, is the School of Theology of the University scientific enough to review the problems that we were discussing from the scientific point of view, the biological problems? Perhaps the problems that we are discussing now from a humanistic point of view are problems of the department of social relations. I wonder how unbiased a theological school can be? I don't just mean a Christian theological school. Perhaps if this were a Jewish theological seminary, how unbiased could it be and how really relevant is it today to the discussion of these ethical problems? You think of yourselves as ethicists, but I am sure you will agree that you are biased in your ethical viewpoint.

DeWolf: I would wonder just what kind of bias one would find in the kinds of criteria which I proposed at the beginning. Certainly there is no point at which I suggested that Christians should be somehow favored at any point. The idea was that a whole harmonious set of values should be promoted in the whole of society by what we do, and the individual should be regarded as a person of dignity, worthy of loving-kindness and respect. This is a platform which so far many a humanist could agree on wholly. We do derive them as Christian theologians from our Christian faith, while there are others who derive them from other sources. But this would not be establishing criteria which would be somehow biased. Perhaps what is happening here — and I think it is rather characteristic of Boston University School of Theology in which I had long experience of teaching — is simply speaking for man. In the present situation when all kinds of persons are speaking for very special interests, the man who is the man of Christian faith regards himself as one whose special responsibility as a Christian is to speak for man. That is not to say that he claims exclusive responsibility of this kind, but this he has.

Moore: As to the people going into medicine, we tend to be biased toward the individual who has a strong liberal arts background. The admission statistics for Harvard Medical School favor this concentration. I don't know if this is a plot or a plan, but that's the way it works out.

The theological school should take in many people who concentrated in the sciences during college. In a sense it is a little bit easier for a scientist to have a liberal arts or humanistic background than it is for the theological student to have had the experience of doing an experiment himself with his own two hands and seeing how difficult it is to make judgments. Some of Dr. DeWolf's problems with this picture of the dying patient would ease if he just were to realize how hard it is to make judgments. We have seen situations where nearly everybody taking care of the patient thought that the case was hopeless, when somebody with maybe a special bit of knowledge said, "Look, there is a little wisp of evidence to hope." So we have carried on with this dreadful "machine living" and had a good live patient in the end. You have to have worked in biology, you have to have done an experiment on a cat or a dog or a rat or some animal, to see and to understand this. I wish   that theological schools would require science concentration.

Questioner VII: Dr. Schwartz stated that the problems which you are facing now are biological problems and that if you solve these biological problems you are therefore going to dissolve the theological problems. I sensed some of that in Dr. Moore's remarks, but I am wondering about this, because the deferral of the doctors to the arguments proposed by the theologians seems to be that doctors do indeed have a sense of ethics and that there are indeed ethics involved in these decisions. Did you mean to state your remarks quite that sharply? In terms of it being strictly a biological matter, a biological problem?

Schwartz: I didn't mean to be sharp. I meant to be incisive. Of course physicians have ethics, and I hope that all physicians constantly think about their patients in very human and loving terms. I am not sure of the origin of these ethics. They could stem from some theological principle; they could stem from humanistic principles. Doctors are faced all the time with extremely difficult decisions and, as Dr. Moore pointed out, you have to live through them in order to appreciate that things are not as cut and dried as they appear on a panel discussion. I assure you that we are applying ethical principles to these problems. What I really meant was that as science advances, the theological agonies over the problems are going to lessen. The case of the patient with pneumonia is a very good example.

Ramsey: Concerning the problem of bias, that is a human problem, and not especially the problem of the theologian or ethicist, except as he is also human. A bit of quasi-serious levity might impress that point if we appeal to no less a theological authority than the United States Supreme Court. In the case of Seeger, the Court defined as religion or religious conscience, any conscience in which there is a primacy of value or crux, so that this functions as belief in a Supreme Being having duties or claims upon us superior to all others. I think the problem of conscience and bias in conscience, however it is formed is precisely the issue that is raised when questions of bias are introduced. A person with a specifically religious conscience has no greater difficulty with his biases than any other man.

Workshops

Problems of Population Control

Irwin T. Sanders: The purpose of this panel is simply to follow up on the rich fare we have already had today and perhaps to move the discussion in two directions: one would be in terms of the kind of research that is needed to deal with some of the problems jointly of interest to scientists and theologians; the second would be on the implementation of some of the ideas that have been presented. We will start with Dr. Guttmacher.

Alan F. Guttmacher: Having been with the birth control movement as a physician since 1927, I am probably more conscious than most of you about the extraordinary speed with which it has picked up in the last decade. I am encouraged by the fact that world leaders have now taken hold of the importance of population control, when certainly the message was given to them quite some time ago.

I think this morning's discussion and this afternoon's panel were brilliant. However, they left out one thing, and that is to make more of current assets than we are doing. We should face realistically in our own country — and perhaps in all of the more developed parts of the world first and eventually in the less developed parts of the world — the wisdom of carrying out safe non-discriminatory abortion. If we were to do this in the United States, we would find a rather dramatic drop in birth rate. That certainly has been the experience in other countries which introduced it. Of course, the United States is a nation of contraceptors, and therefore perhaps the drop would not be as critical in our country as it was in Japan or Hungary. But we have to overcome our reluctance to viewing this from any other point than from the purely moralistic and ethical. We must become pragmatists. In order to meet the population problem, we have to overcome some of our squeamish ethical concepts.

Also, we should consider a wider use of and a more simple mechanism for sterilization. As you know, abortion has been greatly simplified through the aspiration technique, and we are learning now that female sterilizations can be carried out through either a laparoscope or a culdoscope, which is kind of a periscope put into the pelvic cavity so the tubes can be visualized and operated upon. At the moment it is being done in many places as a single day admission procedure. Very likely we will be able to do it as an ambulatory procedure — admitting patients in the morning and discharging them in the afternoon — and do it as an out-patient treatment. So I would say two things: first, we ought to face the wisdom and necessity for doing safe and non-discriminatory abortions and thereby replacing illegal abortion with safe abortion, and make this available to the people who need it most, because today safe abortion can be afforded only by the affluent. Secondly, we ought to go ahead very rapidly with research and pilot projects on simple sterilization techniques. Also there is an absolute prime necessity to find better methods of contraception. No one who has had much experience in this field — and I am sure most of you have had — is complacent about the pill. We certainly want to substitute something which is simpler and safer. This cannot be done unless we are really concerned and interested in curbing the world's population and can mount a point of view and a financial support equal to the Manhattan Project.

L. Harold DeWolf: In this matter of abortion, I believe too that the way ought to be opened both legally and with ethical approval by the church for abortions. We need to make it quite clear that a fetus is not a human person. Now the difficult question to my mind comes in defining when it becomes unethical to dispose of the potential human person, which this being is, up until — and for that matter even after — birth. After birth the child at first is still not really a human person, but certainly is a potential one which must be viewed with real respect and all the sanctions of reverence. But at what time before birth does it become so? There is a kind of sliding scale, actually. It is probably impossible to define ethically an exact time when a transition is made. Legally it will have to be done and is being done.

One other point, as part of the problem of confronting population growth, we must do away with or reverse our whole conception of growth as a sign of progress. This has to do not only with the growth of population, but growth in the economy. Whenever the Gross National Product does not increase, we think this is something bad. We must get away from the idea that progress is measured by increase in quantity and turn to greater emphasis upon the quality of human existence for all.

Charles R. Botticelli: I would like to take a completely different point of view. We have heard about the problem of implementation. We have had several questions asked as to what we can do about the population explosion. It has been suggested that we need a change in our attitudes, our thinking, our value systems, that we educate the decision-making people and hopefully educate the masses of people involved in populations. There are three groups of people we need to reach: those with families, those planning families at the present time, and those age groups twelve through seventeen which are the fuse of the future population explosion. We haven't spoken to this audience at all. It could be part of their elementary education and secondary education, and I plead that we speak to this group as part of implementation. We have heard of the wide spectrum of programs through the Population Council and Planned Parenthood, yet I don't believe this very young audience has been approached or educated in terms of attitudes, thinking, and value systems. With the existing programs nowadays that have a wide world audience, a program could get started next summer and be implemented within the next two years.

Herbert Morles: After hearing the very excellent and diverse speakers this morning and the very substantive discussions, the only safe statement to make at this point is to say, "I'm for sin and against motherhood." There is hardly anything I can say in terms of population control that hasn't been said, and said very elegantly this morning and this afternoon. There is a secondary problem which Professor Shinn touched upon and which, in a sense, also ties in with what Dr. Botticelli just mentioned. In the general approach, the political control — by political I mean person-to-person interaction of controlling or regulating the amount of birth in any country — will first have to be propagated through an educational process. By its very virtue here, this is an essentially slow situation. We therefore have the secondary problem I referred to: man is in the process of destroying himself and earth by an inadequate control of pollution . . . the waste material both from man himself and from his technology. We are burying ourselves in a mountain of trash. We are drowning ourselves in waste products in our harbors, in our rivers, in our lakes which we can practically walk across. We must spend a good deal of effort simultaneous with population control work on controlling the emission products from human technology and human life.

M. C. Chang: I was associated with the late Dr. G. Pincus during the past twenty years and did the animal study for the early development of "the pill." Since the pill was on the market in the 1960's, my feeling is that the present form is only the first generation of oral contraceptives. What we need now is the second and third generation of the pill; that is, we need different pills for different people, based on their physiological constitution and endrocrinological requirements, and not just one or two kinds of pills for everybody in any age or racial group. We need an early abortion pill, and we — the research scientists who are interested in population control — are working hard to find such an agent. We should look at the population as a whole rather than at individuals. In other words, antifertility measures need not be a hundred per cent effective. If certain measures can be applied to decrease the birth rate by a small fraction in each country, this would significantly decrease the number of people born on a world level. Such biological studies of population control, however still remain to be accomplished. Also, we should pay attention to eugenics, not only to reduce the birth rate, but also to increase the population of intelligent people and to decrease the population of genetically inferior people for the welfare of the world.

Charles E. Curran: The question was raised whether there isn't greater divergency between the scientists and the theologians and that we here might have papered it over a little bit too much in the panel discussion. From a more methodological viewpoint I think that this would be interesting to discuss. I got the feeling, though, that everyone realized that the needs of technology and the sciences have to be controlled in a human way. There seemed to be a general agreement on that. It is interesting that Dr. Hoagland talked about man as an imaginative animal. The somewhat abandoned definition in some Catholic high schools was that man is a rational animal. I don't know whether there is much difference between those two or not. The question of terminology certainly enters into the point there. Yet, on the other hand, I get the feeling that there is always a danger of erecting our own technology into a new Messiah. In general we speak about the limitations of technology and yet there seems to me to be an underlying current that nonetheless has almost too much of a Messianic approach to it.

Daniel Callahan: The critical question is: what exactly is the ultimate goal of population limitation? This ties in very much with the "quality of life" problem. I am struck by the fact that the discussion of the population problem has, by and large, shifted from talk of famine to talk of the quality of life. If this is indeed the case, we can't begin touching profitably on the ethical questions — and this means in great part the question of the ends and means — until we have a fairly clear notion of what we are aiming for. It could well be the case hypothetically that the loss of freedom of appropriation for some would be too high a price to pay for a gain in the quality of life in other areas. Somehow we as a community have got to come to grips with this question: just what indeed are we talking about when we are talking about a habitable human world?

G. Evelyn Hutchinson: I would like to point out to you a very extraordinary circumstance. We are sitting around here talking about human reproduction and I see twenty-four men and not a single woman around this table. This seems to me to be wholly wrong. I find it very puzzling and worrying, because all the decisions that hopefully are going to make things a bit better are going to be taken in the future by young women who are now going into colleges or high schools. What Dr. Botticelli said is very important; but it is the girls you have to reach, and by and large I have a feeling that many of them are becoming exceedingly responsive to this kind of program. It is, however, something that is presumably most unlikely to be fully promoted by the dicta of twenty-four men.

There have been some statements by quite eminent persons that we do not need to bother about population because it takes care of itself. Some of these statements have actually come from people who have great biological or medical reputations. It is most important that we think a little bit about the ways in which population does and may limit itself. In summary, it seems to me that the only ethical way the population of man may limit itself is for us to do it consciously ourselves by the smoothest, cleanest, most painless way possible, because all the other possible ways are too unpleasant to contemplate. We hear a good deal about mass starvation. At least in this country, I imagine mass starvation is totally irrelevant because long before we got anywhere near that we should have all sorts of other problems that would start limiting population in the most violent manner. Mass starvation is, no doubt, a very significant thing in India, and why exactly there should be these differences is a very interesting but possibly academic problem. The current population of Calcutta reminds me very much of what you get in any equilibrated *daphnia* culture in which nearly all the individuals are too starved to reproduce, but the moment a little bit of extra food comes along a bit of reproduction occurs. By human standards that is a perfectly horrible situation. Then, of course, there is always the question of pestilence, the various diseases which in the past have been the classic method of cleaning up large urban congregations of people. I don't doubt that if you look at a human population in the way that you look at a bacterial one it would ultimately show an approach to a logistic S-shaped curve, flattening off asymptotically. The natural ways of getting into this seem altogether unacceptable. What is worse, it is almost certain that in a human population the rate of reproduction — of addition of new births — would not adjust even by these extremely unpleasant methods instantaneously. You would get a situation similar to that Pratt or Slobdkin discovered in *daphnia;* the reproductive rate is proportional to the food supply of some hours earlier and is therefore not appropriate to the number present at any given time. The population overshoots the equilibrium points and then a big depression occurs. If the time lag is sufficiently great, you get a continual permanent oscillation with the lows very close to zero, so any random statistical fluctuation will destroy the whole population. One could continue at length on the undesirability of letting the population adjust itself, even though very eminent people have seemed to brush the question aside.

Preston N. Williams: I would like to raise up for further discussion minority group participation in this discussion. It has already been brought to light that we do not have any women around the table. One could suggest, also, that we do not have any Blacks, any Mexican-Americans, and some other minority groups. If one starts linking population solutions to eugenics this is a matter of great concern. If we proceed in the way that we generally do proceed, then we have participation by the so-called significant groups in the population — like the Roman Catholic Church or maybe the labor union, which is also Roman Catholic — but we don't have any real representation of Blacks. This is true not only in the legislative halls, but also it is true in the various foundations and in the research operations which develop the techniques and strategies. Part of my concern then is with the question of how we open the discussion up, not simply to women, but for Black women and for men who are members of minority groups.

John C. Fletcher: Like Professor Williams, I am particularly interested in the political ethics of population controls. As an ethicist, I'm even more interested in trying to be precise on whether or not our societies will be able to make the decisions that it will be necessary to make over the next thirty to forty years. What kind of human resources are necessary to be able to decide on some of these monumental questions that the panel put before us earlier — not just in population control, but in all the subjects chosen for our review here. Some of the research that I would be particularly interested in is defining more precisely what is new and unprecedented about the decisions which we face and what is not new and unprecedented. Human beings are essentially conservative when it comes to decision making. That is, they want to be oriented towards some pattern of action which has worked in the past, in their self-interest. Out of such orientation they see themselves moving toward a whole new set of strange unfamiliar actions.

Exactly what are we shooting for in population control? I want to be precise about what is new and what is old. I have heard a great many scientists say — and I heard it at the National Institute of Health a month and a half ago — that there is nothing new in any of these problems. I heard a psychiatrist say that there is nothing new at all about the problem of coercion in human experimentation with new kinds of drugs to manipulate the mind. I don't agree with that; there are some new dimensions to that particular problem. I understand what Professor Williams means when he says that ecclesiastical institutions and families and government have coerced people in the past to achieve certain institutional goals. So this is not entirely a new element to this problem, but how to be more precise. If we could be more precise and get a sense of what is really new and what isn't, this might release some courage to be able to make these decisions. My great fear is that we will not be able to make these decisions, and will be paralyzed in this passive and disillusioned kind of culture which we are building for ourselves, and who knows after that. My fear is that we will not have the resources to be able to make a firm decision.

Charles Terner: My reason for being here is probably that I have for some years been working on the biochemistry of spermatozoa of all kinds of animal species, including man. We really got into the field to work with bull spermatozoa in order to improve their fertility for the purpose of artificial insemination. We go to the other extreme now that we have a research contract from the National Institute of Health in which our obligation is to work on some means that may lead to the development of a contraceptive that works on the male germ cell. The points that stick in my mind from this meeting is the statement that was made that people want to perpetuate themselves. People want to have children and they want to know that their name is going to be maintained. This also applies to groups and especially to the minority groups. We have a problem when we get into certain trouble spots in the world where there is a precarious ethnic balance. Are we going to convince one group or the other that we are not going to upset their status, that this is not a threat to their existence or to their numerical superiorities, precarious as it may be? Examples are the Lebanons, Northern Ireland, South Vietnam, India, and there may be others. The odd part about it is that most of these people are ethnically homogenous and speak the same language. The only difference is a minor/major difference in religion. What can religious leaders do to re-educate their own people to a spirit of greater tolerance? Can it be done at all?

Aguiles J. Sobrero: Probably the only reason for my being here is that I am a Latin American and I am concerned with the population problem. I work in the oldest Sanger Clinic in the United States. What struck me this afternoon was to be reminded by Dr. Curran that man is a rational animal, and I could not but wonder, "Is he really?" When we hear how we preyed upon ourselves, probably we have to re-define ourselves and try to find a new way of understanding ourselves, ethically and philosophically. When we talk about ethics I wonder if we know what we are talking about. We talk about an ethic as if it were a rigid pattern of living, of laws and commitments that are made once and for all, forgetting about history, about how Judeo-Christian — which is the one we usually talk about — morals and ethics have changed throughout history, and how much we probably will be forced to change in the future. These to me are the philosophical causes — very difficult to define — which are in constant evolution or flux and which should be more fluid probably in the near future.

Ethically and scientifically we must define ourselves and which way we think mankind should go — our scientists, theologians, politicians, and so forth. If that is the goal, we must try to define the means. Usually we try to apply our own morals to others. And out of applying our own ethics to the others — which most of the time we don't apply to ourselves — we try to define what other people should do. Consequently we are very much against abortion and we are splitting hairs as to when human life starts and as to what is morally right or wrong without considering the situation of the individual human being who is living with the consequences.

That brings me to the practical point of my comments. We say that we would like to define liberty and we go to all extents to define liberty as we go to all extents to define our own morality and defend our own country, and so forth and so on. But I think at the same time we recognize that liberty is a big "No," or a series of big "No's" surrounding us. The richer, the more educated, the more powerful, the more refined that we are in our thought, the larger these "No's" become around us, and the closer they become, because that is the limitation of our own power, the limitation of our own efforts and the limitation of how far we can reach without hurting others. Unless we reach a state of definition in which we can talk as human beings rather than as members of this or that club or group, we will not be able to find a common way and a common answer for our problems.

Alan Geyer: One of my greatest concerns is the relationship between the population problem and ideology. Again and again we have had questions raised about fundamental attitudes or clusters of ideas, about the individual, the family, the economy and the nation, even nature and history. But these questions are raised against a background of an unwitting conspiracy in which most moralists and most scientists for generations have sort of had the notion that ideology is a bad thing. So we find it very hard to put ideas together in a very constructive and sympathetic way. This morning and this afternoon, I hear a plea for a new openness to ideas and some awareness of a desperate need now to do our homework in the whole realm of social and political ideas. The poverty of political and social ideas which this nation brings to discussion problems like this is overwhelming. It is even difficult for us to think of terms to apply to the realm of ideas. But I sense we need something like a symbiotic humanism, where humanism seems to be in good stead, and I tentatively venture the word "symbiotic" because it gathers up the notion of man's common life and the particular dialogue represented here, the kind of humanism which unlike some other varieties of humanism does stress the imperatives of community, both in megalopolis and the world scene, and which suggests this relationship between community and nature which is a very fundamental problem and has been well put before us.

So I would like to plead that we do need new exercises in ideological imagination and reconstruction. Maybe we need a third partner in this dialogue of political and social philosophers. I am not sure we have them. They are in very short supply, but with as big an agenda as we have of serious problems in this country right now and before this particular conference, it makes a great deal of difference whether we confront these ideas simply out of the heritage of a pragmatism which tends to confront problems piecemeal or whether we assume that our basic problem of attitudes and of understanding critical relationships among problems with which we are confronted.

William C. Paddock: I note here on the program, the second point: "Emerging Possibilities for Control through Increased Food Production and Contraception." I would like to speak to that one point because we probably won't get back to it.

There has been what has been called a "green revolution" — I am sure that you have all heard about it — where there has been an advance supposedly made in agriculture in parts of the developing world. Just two weeks ago at a Congressional hearing, I heard for the first time from a vice-president of the Rockefeller Foundation that because of this advance in agriculture new possibilities existed for population control, farmers didn't need to have so many children. It is the same point of view that is expressed often by the medical profession, which, of course, really started this whole problem, saying that in order to get population control programs going, we need more, not less, public health in the developing world. Mothers need to know that half of their children aren't going to die and then by sheer wisdom they will stop having all their kids. Now, this is an interesting idea. I see no basis for it in fact, however, nor do I see by any basis in fact that by increase in agricultural production population is going down. The reverse is going to be true, as with an increase in public health you had an increase in population. I don't think the green revolution is going to succeed. If it is, it is only going to be one successful battle in a losing war, so in the end, the result will probably be the same. But the time has come when those involved in agriculture like myself, or in medicine, should realize that there are some problems beyond our technical capabilities. Man does have some limitations in spite of what we are told daily. There are some things we can't do. Some problems are too big for us, and we would show a degree of wisdom if we recognized this.

Ernst Mayr: Many of the matters that we are discussing, many of the incentives in tax and everything else, will not do us any good unless the abortion laws are changed. In the 1930's I lived on a street in the suburbs of New York where every family except one had two children. With all the very insufficient contraceptives, just by social pressure, they succeeded in having small families. The one family that had four children always said that they had two children and two "mistakes." So I think a correction of mistakes is a very important thing.

In answer to Dr. Fletcher's question, "What is new?" there was a book published about forty-five years ago by a famous anthropologist who showed that there wasn't a single primitive culture that didn't have population control. Up to a point, it was what I call pre-natal birth control by spacing births, but to a large extent it was what I call post-natal birth control, mainly killing new-born children or having deliberate wars where they killed each other, all of it being methods of birth control. Now quite recently in our society, large circles including a lot of famous, outstanding people, have come out for post-natal birth control — the only alternative when the population grows too large. So let's just realize there is only one way to stop population growth, and that is some form of birth control. Pre-natal methods are far preferable to post-natal. The greatest danger is that everybody is afraid to tackle this, and we adopt a *laissez-faire* policy, and we look in all other directions and do not face this issue squarely. This is particularly dangerous in the case of the congressman, because the congressman's first concern is to be re-elected. As long as the issue is unpopular, he isn't going to come out for birth control because there might be a majority of his constituents against it and therefore he will lose his election. Most of the congressmen I have met are far more responsible and far more intelligent than we usually give them credit for. They would like to adopt these things if only it were easier for them.

Charles W. Lloyd: My interests are in basic physiology, that is, development of information leading to better contraceptives; and in the application of the human techniques that are being developed. Anyone who is working in the development of contraceptives has been comforted by the fact that we're way ahead of you fellows. We are going to have very soon much better contraceptives than are currently available. I would not be at all surprised if within the next couple of years we would have safe abortization. I know of one project that is going on which may lead to that. There are means for controlling population that are much more acceptable than anything currently available. This conference is directing itself correctly, that is, catching up in terms of finding out what people want, how to get people to use the procedures that we are able to give them.

John Rock: Today's rich fare has given me a bit of intellectual indigestion, but it expresses itself in a stoppage rather than a flux. I really have very little to say. I was concerned with women all my practical life, and perhaps I was concerned with them before I became practical. I was a gynecologist until I was put on the shelf a few years ago. Since then I have been very much interested in the fact that women can't have babies without having men, and I was somewhat surprised that researchers have not paid more attention to this. The question is asked as to new methods of research. I must suggest that the male gonads are hung outside, because if they approach body temperature they just won't function. The very easy way of contraception is preventing their cooling off. I leave that for you to think about. Long ago after we had done some work on the embryo population, one of my co-workers said to me, "John, you must be careful what you say about conception ovulation, because people will believe you," but I feel free here because I don't think you believe me.

The time has gone by when parentage can be considered a virtue. The mother should start sex education as soon as the baby is separated from her, and she does, involuntarily. Sex education should be pushed, pushed, pushed. It must include not only the physiology of sexuality, but the results of it. I think we can teach the children as they come along, so that the college girls who are going to be the mothers will continue to diminish their standards. They used to ask for four or five children, and then it came down to three or four children, and there are some surveys which rather center on three children. We can get them down to two children, that's enough, but I think that sex education in schools ought to be pushed. It has always surprised me that there is antagonism to abortion because we are sacrificing the innocent, while we have no difficulty in sending rational men into the army and sending them up to the field to be killed in the interests of society. We ought to stop talking about individual rights and begin thinking about the rights of the species and have more consideration for our species than we have for ouselves.

Arthur J. Dyck: Mr. Sobrero suggested that perhaps some of us — I'm in the field of ethics — don't know what we are talking about when we talk about ethics. Shouldn't we ask what is wrong with the world when we say that we have too many people, or that we have overly rapidly growing populations? We really do have to ask what kind of problem is the so-called population problem? To call it a threat to mankind doesn't tell me too much and I haven't heard an argument here that would persuade people that they as individuals and as individual couples ought to be doing something. The crisis of having large numbers of people so that the resources and the space of the earth are used up is really too remote. It doesn't touch us. What does touch us? What are the issues here? What is the so-called "population problem"? What are the so-called "population problems"?

It doesn't make sense for people to be asked, whether by coercive or voluntary means, to reduce the number of their children when, as a matter of fact, they are living in poverty or in fear of the death of their children. It does not make sense to ask them, whether the methods are coercive or non-coercive, to plan and to limit their children whether or not we think of these as effective demographic variables. Actually the shift to lower infant mortality rate is definitely correlated with the shift to lower birth rates in the so-called demographic transition. We do have to ask what it is we want to do for people when we want to reduce their birth rate. If we want, for example, to reduce poverty and we want to reduce death, and we want to have people more highly educated, why are not all these attacks on these problems a population policy? Increased education, as well as lower infant mortality rates, is definitely associated with lower birth rates. Why then are these not population policies: to attack poverty, to attack the inequities in education, and to attack the infant mortality rates which are very high among disadvantaged people even in this country.

If it is true that the United States is looked upon as a possible source of coercion, as a possible source of imperialistic designs in asking people to curtail or trying to suggest to people that curtailment of birth rate is essential and necessary, then I suggest that if the United States adopts coercive or compulsory methods to the extent that these would be politically unpalatable in other countries, it would be very clear to other countries just what kind of threat the United States is. So when you consider methods for curtailing birth rates in the United States, and you're thinking of the ideological threat that we pose anyway, then you have to be certain that the way we tackle this problem is a politically viable stance to take in the world at large.

If you bring a society to the point where it would be willing to accept compulsion, in a sense you don't need it. This is to say, if the problem is really seen to be such a difficult one that the individual's interests and society's interests are at one, that's the situation in which compulsion makes sense. You don't get people to stop drinking alcohol by passing laws when people are not really inclined to do so, when they don't see it as a threat to the public welfare. Those laws didn't work. If we can't convince people, if we don't know what kind of problem this is, compulsion will be counter-productive. It won't work, the laws won't be obeyed. But if you persuade people, then presumably you may, in the long run, not need compulsion or you may need just certain kinds of laws for deviants which would be relatively minor, perhaps major, I don't really know. But at any rate do you need coercion when you make your case in such a way that people are willing to accept coercion?

Melvin M. Ketchel: I suggested some time ago that we should develop methods that could be used on entire populations to lower their fertility. This bring up the point that has surfaced several times during the discussion today: that voluntary methods probably won't work. We just don't have the time. Eventually we will have to go to some kind of involuntary method. The real usefulness to the kind of dialogue we are having here is in helping us zero in on the problem of what would be appropriate involuntary methods to use under specific kinds of circumstances. There really are no voluntary and involuntary methods as clearly differentiated methods. There is a range of method going from completely voluntary to the very coercive. We heard today about some mildly involuntary methods like tax laws and welfare arrangements which would encourage people not to have more children. If it was simply a matter of comfort and convenience and perhaps something we call the quality of life, then this kind of mild involuntary method would be appropriate. On the other hand, if no matter what the green revolutionists tell us, we *do* have a food crisis in the next few years and people are faced with starvation, then it is a whole new ballgame. The kinds of coercion that we must be willing to exert in order to save what would appear to be about seventy million people a year would be a completely different order of magnitude of involuntarism. This dialogue should help us to make up our minds more concretely about what we should be working for in the event of what the future brings us.

David Keith Hardy: I'm consultant to a number of Asian governments on communications and family planning — for instance, the Singapore Conference last year on communications and family planning. I deal largely with India where I'm a consultant for the Ford Foundation to the Chamber of Populations Demographic Center. I have dealt most of my life with communications and modernization in underdeveloped countries. I suppose I am the only person here from the only rational country in the world — namely, Ireland — where we are doing what everyone else should do, which is not only keep the population in balance, but reduce it — which we do by the mores of the Irish, which are rather peculiar.

We've heard today a great deal of conventional wisdom very felicitiously phrased and everyone at the meeting — and many of us meet in conferences all around the world — constantly is convincing the convinced about a body of knowledge which is common to all of us. Yet the problem is the communications gap. We can sit for hours and talk about how effectively birth control methods are being developed. We can sit and talk about the work of the new wheat and rice programs in India and Southeast Asia. We don't really get down to the fundamental problem which is one of how you create motivation for these people.

You have only to extrapolate the figures which we all know, and I think particularly of the study we've been doing in Calcutta and in East Pakistan and West Bengal, where by the end of the century the present population — which we think is between forty and fifty million in an area approximately the size of New York State and New England — will go to four hundred million, an absolutely staggering figure which makes the demographic picture in Holland look like an extremely low density. The food production cannot possibly keep pace; it is not even keeping pace presently. In India today, the population is increasing by 38,200 a day. Add to this China, about which we know nothing, and you come to the point that unless a means can be found to communicate with and motivate families in countries in which communications barely exist — and I am excluding Western Europe and the United States — we face the Armageddon within two decades. A white enclaved world of Russia with Europe (East and West) and North America will face a totally hostile, already hostile, but by then totally hostile and famine-ridden world. A responsibility obviously derogates itself to the West — to the white world — to solve not only its own problems, which I think it is quite capable of doing, but in helping these ancient countries tackle their problems.

We have no accurate demographic study on China, figures vary between seven hundred and eight hundred and fifty million people in a very authoritarian society, who are — although the figures are so misleading and all their information is so misleading — applying a rigorous authoritarian population control with the idea of balancing their population according to the last studies at a billion. It seems excessive, but the Chinese apparently are talking about stabilizing their population at a billion. The Japanese have stabilized theirs at a hundred million. Certainly China is ten times as populous as Japan. And we have India, on the other hand, which is chaotic, theoretically democratic — it isn't non-authoritarian, it is just anarchistic — in which all the work that has been done has failed because the leadership which could have implemented a strong program completely failed to recognize the information which we are passing around to one another this afternoon. This is what I mean about convincing the convinced. We should have the Indian Cabinet sitting here, in the middle of this table being talked at by us, or to by us. You can't talk to them, you have to talk at them in the hope that some of this will penetrate. Unless this is done, no matter what is done in the more highly developed countries, the imbalance in the world is such that nothing that we do rationally can do anything except produce this enclave in which we will try to survive, for how long is uncertain. Therefore this meeting which we are conducting is simply a wake for mankind.

Garrett Hardin: I would like to propose for your consideration a time schedule of six stages that we will pass through in tackling the population problem. At the outset I want to emphasize I am only talking about the national situation. The national and international situations require entirely different tacks, because we recognize the sovereignty of other countries and by that recognition, we are precluded from doing certain things that we could do in our own country.

Sticking to the national situation, I would suggest that the first of these stages — bear in mind that they are overlapping stages — would be an ending and the abolition of *compulsory pregnancy* in this country. I use those words to stand for *abortion,* because I think they are better. Any woman who is pregnant when she doesn't want to be is being compelled to be pregnant. We ended compulsory servitude a hundred years ago. We are going to end compulsory pregnancy, and it will probably be done through the courts first and through the education of the medical profession second. It is happening very rapidly. So this is the first stage. This will automatically lower the birth rate considerably. The second stage is the alteration of our basic idea of the world from what Kenneth Boulding has called a "cowboy economy" to a "spaceship economy." This also is already taking place. This is new in the sense that for the past two hundred years we have been living in a cowboy economy. Of course, if anything has been true for two hundred years, it has been true "from time immemorial" since nobody's mind reaches back before then. Making a change is going to be a dreadful wrench, but we are beginning now the education at the university level. We must quickly bring to the grade school level and to the general public the message that we simply must make do with this world; there is no other. The third stage, and this is beginning, is the persuasive stage of population control. In other words, the appeal to conscience, the sort of thing we do with the slogan, "Stop at Two." This stage, for reasons that I have outlined previously, cannot yield a permanent or stable solution; but I agree with those who say that it is a necessary preliminary to other developments. We must start the persuasive mechanisms, get those into high gear before we do other things. The next stage will be one in which we will engage upon rather small social engineering adventures; such things as eliminating the tax deductions for children, say beyond two. If you do that, you probably have to give the family a child allowance if they have any more children, because you don't want to penalize the children. No deductions after two, and after that we send a check in the child's name every Christmas if he is number three or number four. It would be the equivalent of a deduction. No economic change, but the change would amount to a symbolic act that would have some persuasive effect. In other words, we would be saying to the family, "Any child you have beyond two, you are *not* having for the good of society. In fact, we frown upon it, but we will help take care of the child any way — *but cut it out.*"

Now, after we have gotten used to the idea that we can use social mechanisms for exerting pressure on family size, then the next stage ultimately would be some sort of coercion. What is really important here, and the thing that is very hard to design, is some sort of sanction to be levied against people who disobey the mandates of society. It is hard to imagine what the sanctions would be, but we've got to be inventive here. I think we must be coercive. But this sort of coercion probably cannot be successful unless it is built upon a solid base of persuasion first, to the point where the vast majority of the populace is convinced that it is in the interest of society to control families.

A purely persuasive approach does not produce a stable situation, as I demonstrated in my article, "The Tragedy of the Commons." If an appeal to conscience is the only control, we select for those people who have less conscience, we give them an advantage in society. This is counter-productive, just as it would be to have no laws against bank robbing. Then the people who robbed banks would benefit over those who were persuaded not to rob banks. In the same way those who have more children will in some sense gain over those who have fewer. In other words, to be quite blunt, what one has to say at some point is that in a world in which we must control population, we cannot be infinitely tolerant of acts. We may be infinitely tolerant of beliefs, but not of acts. The act of having a child is an act of warfare against society if it is one child too many. So we have to be quite blunt about this.

I suspect the way in which this coercion will become accepted will follow this pattern: society becomes aware of the fact that certain groups are not cooperating in the generally accepted ends of society, and becomes worried. To take a specific example, consider the Hutterites of the Northwest, about one million people, whose flagrant fertility is quite incredible. They are excellent farmers who produce a tremendous amount of food. They use all of modern agriculture, all of modern medicine, and breed like rabbits. They do this because they regard breeding as an absolute obligation; they must never avoid pregnancy under any conditions whatsoever — no "safe period" for them! It would be highly immoral for them to use the safe period. They can use only the unsafe period, if they insist on distinguishing. So the average number of children per family among the Hutterites is eight. Almost all live because of modern medicine. At present they are confined to the Northwest; most people don't know about them. They are only a million now, but pretty soon other Americans will become aware of them. Blacks, whites, Mexicans, Japanese, Chinese, everybody in this country will become aware of them as a threat.

This, I say, is a sort of a scenario. There will be some one group that will refuse to cooperate and thus will force society to say finally, infinite tolerance is not a virtue. We will have to, by some sort of sanction, stop this sort of thing. This means that, in the last stage, we will finally come to the realization that, in a deep sense, children belong to the community rather than the parents. The parents are something in the way of *trustees,* but they are not the *owners* of the children. For millenia we have been brought up in a society to speak of "my son," "my daughter" — ownership. Maybe we need new language to indicate the trusteeship. Once we absorb the idea of trusteeship, then I think we will be in a completely different world. I think that this is ultimately the sort of world we will have to come to if we are to solve the population problem.

Sanders: I am going to exercise the chairman's prerogative and ask Dr. Taussig if she would have anything to say and to come up and sit at the table so we can have some tokenism anyway of the ladies. Would you tell your connection, Dr. Taussig, and then give any comments you might have.

Helen B. Taussig: I am Dr. Taussig of Baltimore and have been interested in pediatric cardiology and with it, on the sideline, quite interested in the Maryland abortion laws and welfare children and welfare families. I felt a little bit incensed that women are not represented in this line of discussion. Why does it all fall on women with no idea of penalizing the young men who bring the children into the world? Certainly it is quite as much the men's fault, if not more, than it is the women's fault in the population explosion. I side always with the girl who becomes pregnant; the unwed girl is penalized in society and the boy goes scot-free. It seems to me that society ought to wake up to the fact that the boy should be penalized even more than the girl. Perhaps I would throw a bombshell into the discussion if I asked if it is really wise to have our families all limited to two children or should some be up to four and others have none? That's another thing to consider in whether two is going to be the best solution for social balance in the world. I suppose we've got to know that before we really advocate this for everyone.

Sanders: This introduces the general concept of eugenics then as was already mentioned.

Taussig: Yes.

Sanders: Are there any of you who would like to make a comment, either to clarify or to take issue or to supplement something you think needs correction?

Hardy: When Mel Ketchel was being praised this morning by Dr. Hoagland, I thought of the analogy of the use of DDT in India to the proposed use of some contraceptive in the water supply. I suppose the introduction of DDT after the end of the war in India was the most major contributive factor to the population explosion in India because of the elimination of the mosquito — malaria and all such things. Now obviously although DDT is now in disrespect, the use of DDT was an authoritarian and involuntary act performed on the Indians. I just think it is an interesting analogy even better than fluorides.

Mayr: What about the other possibilities that ten years from now we might realize some other problems arising from this, as say, the country is now realizing with DDT?

Ketchell: What we are really talking about is the long-term safety, and one can bring in the short-term safety too. Can any fertility control agents like the ones I suggested be developed which would be safe? I would profess that the answer is probably no, if one is looking for the same kind of safety that one is usually looking for in therapeutic agents. But if this were used, obviously it would be in a time when seventy million people a year were dying of starvation. Do you need the same kind of safety to prevent that kind of death as you want for a therapeutic agent? Obviously you don't. I think that it would have to be used with all of the disadvantages — safety and its coercive aspects and many others — as the balance. It is an onerous treatment. There is no getting around it. But so is the alternative, and which is the least onerous is the real question.

Dyck: Mr. Hardy talks about "talking at" the leaders of India, and Mr. Hardin spoke about "getting at" India in some other way. Now perhaps we are very fortunate that the Indians are not listening in. Perhaps they will some time when they see these tapes, and that might be a proper revelation. It seems to me that I detect here precisely what Indians should fear in us if we are going to talk that way. After all, I take it that we are concerned with the population problem because we are concerned with helping people. We want people to live a better life. Do you have to talk "at" people to help them live a better life? If you can't persuade them that you are talking about something that is better, if you haven't got enough contact with the inside of the culture that you can begin to get responses of the kinds you think are desirable, then the situation, of course, is highly limited and should be. So what we want to think about are ways in which we could stimulate self-help and the perceptiveness of these countries, whenever we are concerned with other countries. I take it that, for example, the green revolution is something that they are interested in, and John Wyon who has returned to India for a second longitudinal study after completing seven years of study in the Punjab, finds now that in this particular region of the Punjab where the green revolution has been going on, that the birth rates are going down. This surely should suggest something to us. In any event, whatever we think about the effectiveness or the ineffectiveness of improving the lot of these people, surely the population problem has as its central concern improving the lot of people, not at the expense of what they think about their own welfare.

Hardin: I propose that we restrict the discussion to the United States. We will have enough to do to save ourselves. I think it is beyond our ability to save the rest of the world.

Taussig: Is there any country that is making a more concerted effort than India is to pay the men to have sterilization? Can we say that they are unaware of their problems?

Hardin: In terms of size and magnitude of the problem, it is more window dressing. It's fine if they can enlarge it, but it is rather useless. And most of the men who get sterilized already have seven children.

Botticelli: There were several points made here about meeting our obligation to the species by remedying the home situation. It is certainly not fulfilling the obligation to the species if you create a polar situation of the hostile and famine ridden world as opposed to the patronizing and knowledgeable western world. This is the point that Dr. Dyck was making, I believe, as well. I would like to hear more comments by Dr. Hardin and Dr. Hardy on this point.

Hardy: About speaking to the Indian government, when I "talked at" them, I was referring to the Cabinet. I made a series of six television programs in 1963 called "The Population Problem" for National Educational Television, one of which dealt with India, one of which dealt with Japan, one with Brazil, one with the Netherlands, one with the United States and one with developments in new genetics. At that time we made the program in India under extreme difficulties. The Indian government was very reluctant to let us come in to make this program. When we finished, I flew back to New Delhi. Nehru had recently died and Chastri was Prime Minister. Simply to persuade Chastri to call a Cabinet meeting to look at that program — which he did very reluctantly — was very difficult. The result of this screening at the government parliament house in New Delhi was that the Cabinet just shrugged it off and said this is totally unrepresentative of India and the problems. This was absolutely typical to me of the political leadership of India. At that time we were recommending that they set up a Ministry of Family Planning.

When I talked about "talking at", I was referring to the leadership. I wasn't talking about the common man. We never had a problem — especially with women in India — in any of the experimental programs in communicating with the Indian. The Indian woman was most receptive to the idea of having small families; the men were more difficult. Men were involved in their masculinity and the residual mores about large families and farming, etc. The problem of communication was never the problem of communicating with the common man, the average man. It was always the problem of dealing with the political structure which was moribund and bureaucratic, and this is true in most Asian countries.

Sanders: I think that rather than go into detail on India, we ought to take one of the concepts that has come up over and over again today: the idea of intervention, sometimes people phrase it as coercion, sometimes as persuasion. Some of the theologians may wish to react to that in terms of the ethical or in terms of some of the political and social considerations.

Shinn: I certainly agree with Dr. Hardin that we cannot make a total separation between freedom and coercion. One lives in a society — which is the only way I know to live — at the cost of adjusting his preferences at many points to the common need. There are some kinds of coercion that are morally offensive, but some kinds are not. In part, it is a matter of our mores, but in part, it is due to the basic conception of the identity and dignity of man, which is the theme of the conference. So all my preferences are in the direction of getting the greatest total understanding and participation here. But I quite agree that in society there are some things that I have to do whether I have participated in the decision and like it or not. It is a very difficult line we are walking, and I really don't know exactly where we are going to come out. The point of Dr. Hardin's that is most persuasive to me is if we make this just a matter of conscience, then we'll only penalize the conscientious. We don't support our public schools by saying that conscientious people will pay for them. I cannot object absolutely to coercion, but there are kinds of coercion that are such an affront to people — that which involves totalitarianism — that I would rather not live than live in that kind of society. This is a confession of a perplexity, as much as an answer to the problem.

DeWolf: There are a whole series of steps here where one can start at quite a free level of instruction, education, propaganda, if you like, and move by degrees to more and more coercion. Of course we prefer the freer methods. Thinking of the church as an agency, for example, the least we can do, perhaps, is — taking a cue from the word that Lewis Carroll invented, you may remember — instead of having "un-birthdays," we could have "un-Mother's Day" and glorify restraint. At least then by degrees one can move to opening the way for birth control products and for education throughout society under government auspices, and opening the way to abortion, which I believe should be done. I have an idea that if we actually succeeded in reaching the women particularly, we would have a high degree of success even at that level, and particularly among the poor, the very people who are often hardest to reach in general broadcast appeals and scientific literature and education.

I had a little experience of this in Africa, where I spent two years at work in Central Africa. I was once addressing a rather large body of laymen and women, about half and half. They came to have some confidence in me in a two or three day conference and they asked, "Do you think we are going to be able to become prosperous like the European people? Can we have the same things in life?" I said, "If you learn to restrict your families to very small families. Yes, I can see some hope. But if not, I see no hope whatsoever." Then immediately the women began to ask, "How is it that Europeans, we understand, live together as man and wife quite all right, but they don't have a lot of children the way we do? How is this done?" I said, "Let's have separate sessions." I knew something of the sensitiveness of the people there in the discussion of such matters in public. "Let's have separate sessions of the men and the women, and I would like to talk with the men."

I talked with the men, and immediately I found I had entirely the wrong crowd. They simply were not interested. It would be nice to have fewer children, but, "Oh, no, no, no." Then I talked with the women, and they were all for it. Their whole question was: "How can we get these devices? Where do we get more instructions?" and so on. They were just a hundred percent in favor of it. They said, "Don't think we want to have children that we can't educate, can't feed properly."

I think you'd find the same thing among the women in our society. At least we can make the information available and then we shall eventually take the harder steps, which must be further down the line anyway — the sort of thing that Dr. Hoagland and Dr. Ketchell have spoken about in really mass dealing with these more difficult problems.

Williams: If one is talking about coercion, one has to recognize that coercion is unevenly applied in our society. And if you look at the six step program that has been suggested by Dr. Hardin, you have suggested a program which would have maximum effect upon those at the bottom and would allow those at the top to escape. I recall to our memory again the statement made by Mr. Shinn this morning that the threat is from the affluent; it is not simply from the poor. And if you are devising coercive means, try them first on the affluent. This is that element of the population, I think, which would be the least amenable to coercion.

Hardin: I'm not sure I agree with you. For instance, the appeals to conscience, I think already are affecting ones on top more than the bottom. It's the college girls now who are saying we are not going to have many children, we are only going to have one or two. The word gets to them first. This affects them more than the people at the bottom. The ones who are at the top of the heap are affected more by appeals to conscience, so the program I am proposing will affect the top of the pyramid first. The top will reduce their birth rate before the bottom does. Before you get down to coercion the proportion of the minority groups will have increased.

Williams: I would like to dissent on two grounds: one is that you can't demonstrate that appeal to consciences works; secondly, I would want to suggest that if you are going to use coercion, you must apply coercion to this upper group.

Hardin: Coercion to be acceptable must be applied uniformly to all. This is the only kind of coercion I am talking about.

Williams: But if you take your illustration here, for instance, to talk in terms of no deductions for more than two children and so on, you can apply that uniformly to all and all you have is an illustration of injustice as far as that mechanism is concerned.

Hardin: All right. I'll grant that point.

Hoagland: Whatever the mechanism may be, it has been well established that women with more education have fewer children. In Egypt, for example, this inverse relationship between educational levels and number of children has been well established. It also holds in other countries. Earnings in general, as expected, follow educational levels and upward social mobility, or hope for it. This is a well documented form of fertility control. But unfortunately, this process is very slow so that some form of coercion, much as we may dislike it, has become increasingly necessary.

Guttmacher: From what I have heard today, it might be that such a process would take too long to meet the problems that we are discussing now, and this is why intervention keeps cropping in as one of the fundamental parts of our problems.

Sanders: Would the Planned Parenthood Movement move faster if there were more coercion?

Guttmacher: Other groups can bring coercion about much more wisely and better than we can. I applaud the things Dr. Hardin is doing in the Echo Groups and the other groups that are taking a much tougher line. We've had significant success. We have been able, in one of the groups, to persuade our government to much more activity. We are courting the goodwill of the militants from the minority groups. If we were to take a very tough line and lead the country — two children only or 2.3 children only — we would jeopardize the position we now have. Strategically and diplomatically it would be unwise for our group to do it.

Sanders: With all the experience here, I regret very much we don't have many more hours to come back and really talk about some of these issues. We might have taken two or three and gone into them much more quickly if we had not gone around the table, but the one thing we accomplished was to become familiar with a number of people that we might not ordinarily see in some of our meetings and to know what their interests are.

Regulation of Behavior

Joseph C. Speisman: I have a few brief remarks to make concerning our approach and the suggestions made by the organizers of the conference as to what this group will be about. We ask you to concentrate on three elements. First, that we focus on the evaluative bases for policy decisions rather than on descriptive observations. We all know that we depend, in most respects, on the development of data or the development of argument, but today, where possible, we would like to assume certain background and justification for issues and get your comments on the bases for policy decision in the topic areas that we have been developing all day. Secondly, we would like to hear proposals as to how problems can be solved and decisions made — in other words, some pragmatics, some proposals for action wherever possible — and finally, suggestions of researchable problems in the humanities, in ethics, and in the life and social sciences. Those would be the elements that we felt would be of greatest value given a group of this kind and a brief period of time where you really are not going to have time to develop arguments or evidence to any great lengths.

As the workshop develops it should be a means of interchange among you and bring out the opinions that you hold, your suggestions for decision bases, and your suggestions for researchable issues. If any of you have a comment or question that you feel has not been stressed sufficiently during the morning or something you feel should be emphasized again, this would be a good time to do it.

Paul Ramsey: Before we move to questions of criteria for policy decisions, there are present here sources of additional data which we should get on the table. I have in mind two assumptions left hanging by this very stimulating day. One is that as we approach gingerly the task of walking a narrow ridge between voluntarism and coercion, it seems to be assumed that there are various kinds of nicely devised incentives which *can be effective.* I call for some evidence that this is the case. Before one takes up the moral question, we need evidence that these incentives will work. Is there not evidence, indeed, that some of the proposed incentives will be counterproductive or of no real result in the direction we wish to move?

Secondly, I was struck by the answer given to the young man who raised the question with the assumption that the location of our moral problem is whether or not it would be right for a society to put sterilizing chemicals in the water supply. Now, there are moral problems that have their residence in that vicinity, but we ought not to by-pass the prior practical as well as moral question. The problem — a paradox — is that a population sufficiently informed about the urgency of this problem to adopt that policy through democratic processes would be a society in which voluntary methods would be far closer to being effective than we have said they are. So we either have a society alert enough to the population problem that a spectrum of voluntary measures might work or we do not, and impositions in this area would require a generally non-democratic or even tyrannical society to enact them.

Now, a concluding statement on that is simply that we must always keep in mind the degree to which developed societies succeeded, for awhile at least, in bringing their population increase under control, namely Western Europe, etc. But this was done before the vulcanization of rubber or any of the modern techniques of contraception. This was accomplished by "withdrawal." The achievement of population control came because of widespread willingness. That illustrates a great dilemma before one even gets to the question of morality or immorality or the feasibility of adopting one of the combined voluntary constraining measures. If *coitus interruptus* was widely used when smaller families were desired enough, how can we say that voluntary modes of population control will not work?

Conan Kornetsky: There is a fair amount of evidence that various reinforcements will work, whether they will work in this sphere or not is another thing. They have worked at least for certain groups of people. Certainly in the upper middle class the small numbers in the family are due to various types of reinforcements, be it that they want to give an education to their children, or a higher standard of living. There are various types of reinforcements that keep families small. The point, of course, is to find the appropriate reinforcement for the appropriate population, and this may be a real big problem.

Robert V. Bruce: My fields of research have been the history of military technology, the history of science, and curiously enough, the history of urban violence, which I undertook as a change of pace but which seems to have left me in the same general field. I thought I had about boxed the compass, but it occurs to me upon hearing some of the comments already made that I could use the assistance of one of my colleagues, Herbert Moller, who is just now at the American Historical Association convention in Washington, chairing the session on demography in which the principal paper deals with the French experience of maintaining or approaching a zero population growth.

Frank R. Ervin: There is a great deal of talk about what society is going to do and what kind of society does what kind of things. I am all in favor of that except I think that one of the pragmatic problems is that — at least for more than 90% of the world, including the country we live in — society doesn't do a damn thing. Governments do things. While they are not mutually exclusive, there is not a one to one overlap between societies and governments. One of the hazards that comes up is not what society, in its wisdom, is prepared to do, but what the government which runs that society in fact does in the process of implementing the social decision. There are a lot of social decisions that I would be pleased to go along with that I would not tolerate being implemented by the government at any point in history — that's not just for today.

You mentioned the question of a society, or in my terms a government, setting about to manipulate human behavior in a way that is not coercive — such as by incentives, by models, by one thing and another. This raises some ethical issues in itself, and one of those areas not thoroughly researched is what you could call a social ecology of man. Once you intervene by establishing a new model — i.e. that desirable females are all sterile instead of all having large pelvises and so on — and you train your young men to respond to that, that kind of manipulation will have a social effect. Like all the other ecological manipulations man has ever made I doubt if we know what the other consequences of that are. There may be ripples to infinity in many areas that we had not anticipated. We thought it was fine to wipe out insects so we could grow more wheat, and it turns out that that is not all DDT does. I think that has not been investigated very thoroughly.

Kenneth E. Moyer: In regard to this problem of control and coercion, I'm not sure where incentive and coercion differ. According to Skinner, if we have good control over the contingencies of reinforcement, we can make an individual want to do almost anything. We can also make an individual want to behave in a given way with brain implants or with drugs. Now which control is more coercive? I think we need an ethic.

In the past, we haven't been so concerned about control mostly because it has been terribly ineffective. Education is a method of control we have been using for hundreds of years, but it is ineffective as a control device. Our problem today is that we are getting more and more effective methods of control. It is just a question of time until we cannot only put drugs into the water supply which will statistically reduce the fertility of a given populace, but also we will be able to put drugs in the water supply which will statistically reduce the aggressive tendencies of man. We need to develop an ethical system which will help us deal with the possibilities of absolute control, the kind of control which is coercive in that it makes the individual want to do what you want him to do. Ethically, this is quite different from the kind of control in which you get him to do what you wish because you beat on him if he doesn't. But it is no less control.

James M. Gustafson: Are there certain things we value about human beings which set limits to the kinds of controls — whether coercive or manipulative — that we are permitted to do?

I am concerned not only with the issues involved in population explosion, but also with issues involving brain surgery. We are not going to be able to settle on empirical ground what sorts of freedoms we are going to maintain for persons. We might find evidences that persons resist coercion. We might find evidences of all sorts of other activities which lead us to believe, on empirical grounds, that you cannot push people very far before they rebel and revolt. But on the other hand, there is something significant about human relationship which requires us to treat the other individual not so much as an object of manipulation and control, but as a person of equal value to ourselves. Therefore we have to engage in activities in relationship to him in the light of these convictions. This introduces an important moral dimension to this question. This isn't simply rank individualism involved in capitalistic western society. There is more at stake than that.

Joseph Fletcher: Nevertheless, we might profit at some stage of the discussion from questioning whether the insistence on the notion of freedom as individual initiative really has much more validation than the historical bourgeois tradition. I would like to go back to Ervin's reminder that Engel in *The Dialectics of Nature* adumbrated the view that freedom lies in the recognition of necessity. Isn't it at least theoretically conceivable or arguable that it is ethically regarded as a mistake to understand freedom in terms of private or individual initiatives, that although arguable in some kinds of practical concrete situations or contexts, there really is no alternative to either voluntary control or imposed control? We have to choose between the two. The only practical question in terms of Paul Ramsey's reference to the cost benefit consideration is in what respect and to what extent are we to replace our traditional initiatives with controls that are dictated by the common good.

Walter G. Muelder: You did say we must choose between the kinds of controls. It is the "we must choose" that needs a little analysis here, because this is itself a voluntaristic posture stated in terms of "we" rather than "I". But each "we" — each member of the "we" — is also a person in community. So that if we are to be dialectical, we must not become necessitarian in the strict Engles-Marx humanistic posture, because its purpose was to overcome the mechanical, impersonal, and alienative forces that were at stake in that revolutionary humanistic ethic at that time. Now I would press this ethical question, to say, "Can you be ethical?" Is the ethical question a real question unless it has a voluntary component that is decisive? Dr. Ervin, when it is necessary for someone to decide that a brain intervention should take place, who in your shop makes that decision?

Ervin: The patient makes the decision, by law among other things.

Muelder: The patient makes the decision. Would you be willing to generalize on that as a problem of social policy?

Ervin: Let me generalize on two halves of it. Unwritten law, and to some extent formal law, says that the patient undergoing such procedure has to give informed consent. The secret word is "informed." Now, who informs him? Well, I inform him, or my surgical colleague informs him, or both of us. Now it is a very difficult problem to communicate to the individual a very complicated chain of information of the logic that leads to the necessity for the procedure, the logic which outlines the hazards of the procedure, the logic which might predict into the unknown both good and bad consequences for the procedure — especially if it is a new procedure. There is a lot of complicated technical information and unwritten background to that information that doesn't get communicated. The patient is never as informed as I am in some sense.

Muelder: He trusts you.

Ervin: He *has* to trust me.

Bruce: May I ask Dr. Ervin if he has ever been tempted to press a button to make the patient reasonable enough to understand the explanation of why the button should be pressed?

Ervin: This leads to a very interesting kind of paradox. I will give you a specific example. We had a patient whom we had in fact operated on. We had done the diagnostic procedure and had wires in his brain. A guy who had a very dramatic "flip-flop" in his personality states, he was either aggressive, paranoid, litigious, difficult to deal with or he was a very sweet, reasonable, passive, dependent kind of neurotic. These were his two modes of existence. Long before he had also happened to have epilepsy which is why he had come to us. In fact, there were two patients. I had a choice as to which one to deal with. These two patients were a great stress on the wife of the single body in whom they were contained. On this occasion she broke down and wept and said, "Who are you, honey? I don't know who you are." He had gotten extremely upset on the ward. We could not hold him against his will in the hospital since our hospital is a voluntary hospital and he could only be there by his own choice. He threatened to leave and was, in fact, in the process of leaving, ostensibly to kill his wife. At least that is what he said he was going to do, and I rather believed him. In the course of the day, we managed to get him into the laboratory and stimulate this part of the brain that Hudson Hoagland mentioned this morning. In about a minute he visibly relaxed. He took a deep breath and said, "You know you nearly let me get out of here?"

Bruce: If I may quote history instead of the Bible for a change, you appealed from Alexander drunk to Alexander sober.

Ervin: Precisely, and I said, "Yes, I couldn't have held you." He said, "You've got to do something to keep me from getting out of here. I think if you had the nurse hide my pants, I wouldn't have left." I thought that was a good suggestion and followed it. We had a very reasonable discussion and he was very grateful for my having stopped him. I said, "Well, I guess we won't have to go through this very much longer because tomorrow morning we have planned to make the definitive lesion and I wanted to talk to you about that. What we are going to do is burn out this little part of the brain that causes all the trouble."

He said, "Yeah, that's great." Well, the next morning about 9:00 he was brought down and he said, "You're going to burn *what* out of my brain? Not on your bloody life you're not!" He would easily at the earlier point have signed anything I asked for. He was guilty; he was sweet; perhaps he was reasonable. I would like to think he was reasonable. But which of those two states I should deal with posed a real problem for me. So informed consent isn't all it's cracked up to be. Voluntary understanding has its problems.

The flip side of that coin is that there are certainly procedures in medicine which are known to be life-saving, or state-saving in some sense, when the patient at that point is not in a position to give informed consent. For instance, should one operate on known cancer if the patient refuses to recognize that he has cancer and to submit to surgery? This is a fairly frequent problem in cancer surgery as a matter of fact. The patient simply says, "You are wrong, I have a tumor. My last doctor told me that. It is not malignant. I refuse to be operated on." No doctor in his right mind coerces a patient into surgery at that point, but is there a kind of — in the social responsibility sense — a coercive obligation? Should you seduce him in some sense; should you condition him, reinforce him, whatever our other manipulative techniques are. That has always been answered in the negative in medicine. It keeps fairly strong constraints on itself, but not always, I suspect.

Moyer: There is another problem of coercion. If this patient left the hospital and killed his wife, we wouldn't have asked his permission to put him in jail for the rest of his life. Now we have an alternative here, not putting him in jail but having Dr. Ervin do the operation. Would that be more coercive than putting him in jail for the rest of his life? Many people feel that it would.

Ervin: Most people in our society would feel that it would.

Kornetsky: But there is no guarantee that he would kill his wife if he did go out.

Ervin: Right, nor is there any guarantee that I would cure him.

Kornetsky: That's correct.

Ervin: These are the two. But suppose we could put the probabilities at 80-20 for both of those certain other kinds of procedures?

Kornetsky: We are talking about two sets of problems. We are talking about the individual patient who makes a decision whether to have surgery or not have surgery, whether to use contraceptive methods or not to use contraceptive methods. When you begin to talk about populations, you are talking about large groups in which the individual doesn't have that immediate choice, especially when the individual is uninformed, and we have no real way of informing him properly. Then we will get into the whole problem that has come up in recent years concerning such things as the "haves" doing for the "have-nots." This is a big problem. I don't think the people of India are that happy about our coming over there and telling them what they should do, when we are not doing the same thing here. This is where the problem is.

Bruce: If I may draw a historical parallel — if neurological intervention for the development of docility in the population had been possible prior to the Emancipation Proclamation, I am sure it would have been hailed as an unalloyed boon and widely applied in the slave-holding South. We are assuming certain things to be desirable, and in the perspective of history it may turn out that they are not desirable. History might be called the analogue of ecology in the social sciences. History has to consider the effects of various sorts of activities on each other.

Fletcher: To lift our discussion out of the civil order into the military order for a minute, it always has puzzled me how very promptly most of the people with whom I've discussed this thorny question say the use of inhibitor weapons is wrong and the use of lethal weapons is right. Now, personally, I can't buy that, but many people for whom I have great respect do and I'm troubled about it. I don't want to be pushed into the position of advocacy for inhumane weaponry of any kind, but though I may be a little distorted and perverted here, these inhibitors are more humane than bullets.

Edward W. Pelikan: How much of this problem — whether it be Dr. Ervin's, whether it be Dr. Fletcher's, whether it be the point Dr. Kornetsky makes — is a question that ultimately boils down to the rate in which things happen. Dr. Ervin is concerned because within a fraction of a second or a fraction of a minute he is able to change behavior. If he were able to do this by psychoanalysis during the period of two years, the strain on Dr. Ervin and the rest of us would be substantially less. The mere issue of right and wrong must be modified by the fact that some of these things become problems and bring themselves to our personal attention, rather than to society's attention, simply because of their abruptness. The relationship of the time constant to our accepting the situation and the time constant of the procedure which can be carried out is important.

I was tempted to ask Dr. Shinn this morning if he would put his neck out on something. The way I gathered the trend of his argument is that the halftime for the population doubling is about thirty years. Presumably it will take no less than a generation or approximately sixty years in order for us to be educated away from these nefarious sex habits. The problem is one of time constants. That fact is no matter what the solution is in terms of our accepting it, there will be a solution and a new equilibrium as far as nature is concerned. Our dilemma is that we don't get in tune with the time constants of these things and therefore we see a problem. I presume the slower moving dinosaurs also saw a problem coming up over the next three hundred million years and they were scared to death about what was going to happen because the end of the world was certainly going to come about. I think the question of time constants in our social processes or intellectual processes and the time constant of the phenomena is the source of our being.

Muelder: There is more than a problem of time. There is a qualitative question here, although it affects time or time affects it to some extent. Most of the people in this room are in favor of the brain, for example, and they will extol certain levels of the brain in evolution as being in control of other parts of the brain. So it is very important that certain things get stimulated and other things get inhibited in the name of some good behavior. Now that part of the brain which gets particularly extolled is the part where people make judgments appropriate to the problems that are presented to them. That is not coercion in a manipulative sense. Thinking, reflecting, self-judgment, and self-understanding should not be put on a continuum with various kinds of coercion. Something in me protests a classification which says education is a form of coercion and brain manipulation is a form of coercion, and since they are all in a continuation of coercion it is simply a matter of the urgency of the situation as to which way you do it. There are levels of equality, of personal response that need to be kept in mind even though this should not be done individualistically, but we have the person in community.

Ervin: We would all like to think so, but can you define such a level? Can you draw such a sharp cut-off?

Muelder: Yes, the level at which you, on behalf of the health professions, are prepared to make a responsible decision leading that person who is your patient to more health and possible integration. So many marvelous values belong to the nature of personhood that we cannot abandon those in the process of trying to find the social policies that are appropriate to solving the problem that urgently needs to be solved.

Ervin: That's certainly our buffer for some time — what you and I and others will do and will not do personally. But we also know how perverted that can get. We've got a historian with us. Would you believe that in 1944 there was no *finer* medical tradition than the German medical tradition?

Bruce: Well, historians know how wrong things can go. We have that perspective. But they have been going wrong so fast lately that you don't have to be a historian to realize it.

Ervin: If you can get by with a very short memory.

Bruce: Yes.

Ervin: That is the frightening piece of it. Dr. Moyer made the point and let me emphasize it. I think Conan Kornetsky would go along with the two of us. Poor as we are in understanding behavior, we are getting better at it, and understanding means prediction, and prediction means control. At every step along the way we learn new and more subtle and more indirect and more complicated ways of defining what a person is going to do in the future and of setting up the situation to lead him to do it, whether we are trying to make him buy "Duz," or whether we are trying to make him learn quadratic equations. Some of this we can't do very well as yet, but we are coming close.

Now if those tools which we are trying to develop — the three of us, at least, consciously — to expand man's horizons and his power over himself, which I think is part of the individual freedom, then we may also provide tools for people, social systems and governments, who may be less scrupulous or less wise or less thoughtful about the consequences of what they are going to do. To take a very simple and occasionate classic experiment, if we rigged it so that you are the only individual out of the plan, and we pass a stick around and everybody estimates the length of that stick at 50% longer than it is, as we go around the table, by the time it comes to you the statistics are that you will overestimate the length of that stick, if not by 50%, at least by 20%. You are socially influenced by the fact that all the rest of us whom you have every reason to trust and respect have told you wrong how we see it.

Ralph Potter Jr.: It makes a difference that that person not know. Why is that?

Ervin: Ah, because there is indeed in man some ability to reflect and to meditate and to come to internal autonomous decisions. It is just that he doesn't do it very often. He is usually responsive to his teachers and the people around him and the ads and the television and the *zeit geist.* You can show it in microcosm in this little experiment in perception.

Pelikan: That was so back in 1944. This is the assumption that everyone's always telling you what even more of us believe is the truth.

Ervin: Exactly.

Ramsey: Dr. Ervin, you have a comparatively simple case if you can say, for example, about a given patient that there is an 80% chance he can kill his wife and there is a 20% chance you can restore him to what Dr. Muelder called personhood in community.

Ervin: Make it 55% to 45%.

Ramsey: You may be wrong to act even when your chances are that. Now we must face the urgent problem of the world's population. In doing so we begin to talk, as Mr. Pelikan does, about the time-span in which a solution must be found. We are tempted without consideration to leap to a spectrum of inducements and incentives on up to kinds of coercion because voluntary methods have not succeeded. My single point is that we should not adopt coercive remedies without asking for the evidence that they will succeed any better or as well. There are demographic variables that ought to be inquired into. Do we not know that incentives fostered by governments to *increase* population didn't work too well? Before rushing to state coercion as the obvious solution, there ought to be information, and hopefully wisdom, about some well-calculated probability of the success of such measures, that they will work in that direction, that they will not indeed be counter-productive. The latter possibility may be hard to grasp; it doesn't seem logical, but human beings are not logical. Demographers speak of some very refined studies of demographic variables. I have yet to hear these studies explained in our conference or the findings weighed in assessing solutions. In any case, from the urgency of the problem we cannot draw the conclusion that there's bound to be a solution.

Hans Jonas: Paul Ramsey's point is very well taken and I would like to elaborate on one aspect of it. In the problem of overpopulation we are essentially dealing with big numbers and not with individuals. In other words, all those methods by which we may hope to influence the behavior of individuals will not offer any security or even any reasonable hope that they will enlist sufficiently large numbers in order to cope with the numerical problem of which the population problem consists.

Now here I must confess to a very profound pessimism of a somewhat Hobbsian nature. What brings men to reason? It is fear of utter disaster, either impending disaster or disaster already there. Hoagland remarked that perhaps fifty million people will have to die before the necessity for adopting very unpalatable measures of stopping this will become palatable or acceptable. Frankly, the realistic answer is that will probably be the case, for we are faced with a terrible dialectic fear.

The influencing of behavior in which Dr. Ervin pronounced a certain optimistic belief — namely that we understand more and more of it and consequently also increase our capacity of controlling it — applies, I think, only to *our* behavior. In advanced societies, for reasons which have nothing to do with the responsibility for the future of mankind and the condition of the globe, people have adopted a somewhat more disciplined habit of procreation. In some of these advanced societies, the demographic situation is not alarming at all. Where it is alarming is precisely in those sections of society that can least afford it and which are least accessible to all those methods of shaping behavior which we may trust within our own society, including all the educational and propagandist devices which have shown the success of marketing and other methods. So the question really arises whether in something which threatens the quality of life and the future of human life on this whole planet, do we have the time to wait for the working out of those methods of shaping and recasting habits of a very personal nature — that of sexual life or married life or family life — which would get us out of the terrible perspective which looms before us.

Consequently, we must come to grips not so much with the problems of education shaping the habits of man, or of appealing to reason or a sense of responsibility, or of creating incentives of a subtle nature but with tyranny. Can we avoid granting the state the right and the power to intervene in the most intimate areas of personal life? Since averting disaster always has a precedence over any melioristic goals which otherwise are connected with the ideas of progress and beneficial intervention, and that failing other slow working and unreliable methods, we must be willing to face what action might be necessary short of letting fifty or a hundred or a hundred and fifty million people die in the next generation from mere starvation, and whether such action is still compatible with the kind of society and the kind of personal freedom which we cherish. That is the apocalyptic question which frightens me. Nevertheless I don't know whether the luxury of personal freedom and personal decisions can be maintained during such a period.

Suppose that the extrapolations are correct when they are presented to us with such urgency. You can always get people to pronounce extraordinary denunciations of personal freedom in moments of great danger, but the danger has to be very visible like the invasion of an enemy or a raging epidemic or a flood. It must be there. The farsightedness of the mass of people is negligible. We deal with large numbers of people here; we do not indeed deal with enlightened individuals. The dangers for the next generation will not, by and large, really determine the behavior of large numbers of individuals in this generation. It is only the short-term expectation, not the long-term one which can be appealed to in the name of reason and humanity. Therefore, I very reluctantly come to the conclusion that one must face up to the question of what kind of otherwise odious measures might have to be contemplated in order to avert other disasters.

Pelikan: Odious to whom? Could a conversation like this take place — and I defer to my non-medical colleagues here — if we were part of a culture in which reincarnation at a higher level of existence were accepted or if, like Christian martyrs, the culture believed that to die would be the most desirable thing possible? Suppose the mass of people are not interested and are incapable of being moved. Their definition of odious might be rather different from that of a group of college professors.

Ervin: What's wrong with fifty million kids dying? They do all the time.

Jonas: Probably fifty million is much too low a number and I merely used it because Dr. Hoagland used it. I think a much larger number would be more accurate.

Ervin: That is a 1983 figure, I think. The 1985 famine is much worse.

Pelikan: A new equilibrium will be achieved whether something is done or not done about the situation. What is it about us as well as our society which makes a certain alternative worthy of discussion?

Jonas: We can wait for nature to establish that equilibrium — for instance, by a period of really terrible distress and much dying and mutual mass-killing. Some equilibrium finally will work itself out if we don't cut it short by an atomic war. What concerns us here is how to avoid the wasteful and cruel methods nature uses to establish that equilibrium and prevent a state in which these methods of nature have come into play.

Pelikan: The formulation of the problem and the approach to the solution might be clarified if we looked more deeply into the question of why we find certain kinds of solutions unacceptable when other cultures might find them perfectly acceptable.

Potter: "Population problem" is a bad misnomer. When you look at it intensively, it becomes a number of different problems, some of which have been isolated in our conversations — the question of regional population pressures on the means of subsistence and the threat of starvation generally ascribed to less developed countries in the near future; this was branded this morning as a new problem, "world-wide population pressure" as a kind of ultimate limit of the population of the earth. In our society the same types of pressure take on more the aspects of ecological questions of pollution. Perhaps we ought to posit particular circumstances that we could envision and then starting with Mr. Pelikan's methodological suggestions, posit some types of policies that could be pursued and criticize them. In that way we would try to sort out the principles to guide us. As an extreme example, you might decide that we will reduce the population by killing off every fourth male child by lot. Then we would figure out what's wrong with that and see if we can eliminate it and thus gradually unpack what is the more humane way we ought to be. We already have lotteries connected to high probabilities of death established as the policy of our country now. So you can say, "Why is it that that is an unseemly way to proceed?"

Jonas: Even if we were to come to terms with this, the question is whether you can get those to whom it really applies — which would, not be the population which we represent here, but the Indians, the Latin Americans and so on — to let a system thought out here by the privileged nations govern there. They won't buy that. Even if you get the entire American populace to buy it.

Potter: The first part of my remarks were directed exactly to that question. You need to sort out which of these aspects you are talking about. Now if you want to talk about what to do about the Indians, let's talk about that in terms of Indian culture. Let's not confuse it with the problems of ecological disruption in the United States.

Speisman: It is worth repeating something that Shinn said this morning which speaks to this point. I think Shinn would disagree violently with your wish to place this problem in a lesser degree in a nation such as this one as compared to the over-populated one. He tried to compare the destructive use of resources in this country to pressures that are similar in Latin America or India because of the population issue, and in such you might count every American for twenty or fifty Indians because of what we are doing to our atmosphere and the overuse of resources. To follow on Dr. Potter's point, it would be worth attempting to specify the issues involved in what we are globally terming the "population problem" and then attempt to seek potential solutions and criticize those.

Kornetsky: In fact in the past this has happened. If we, for example, discovered a cure for cancer or a cure for heart disease, I am sure that people in South America and in India and in all of the very overpopulated areas would use these cures. These countries have done it in the case of malaria, for example, and it has resulted in wiping out a lot of the malaria all over the world, although certainly not all of it. But why — if we had the population control methods — would they refuse to accept this sort of "treatment" as opposed to other types of treatment which are also for the survival of the individual, if not of the species? What the problem really gets down to is why don't they accept our oral contraceptives? Why do they persist in continual sexual intercourse all the time? Their behavior is contrary to our logical system. One of the things one might look at in many of these countries is where the satisfactions of life come from. In many of the areas of high birth rate, one of the only pleasures man has and woman has is sexual intercourse. They don't have television; they don't have high-fi radios.

Ervin: Also, starvation increases both sexual behavior and fertility. It is a very simple matter to distinguish between going into Latin America or India to fight malaria and cancer and trying to get them to preserve the species. You are dealing with individual's well-being in the first case. These people — and we, too — don't give a damn about preserving the species. Let's face it. You can make all your fine metaphysical arguments, but we don't think about the species carrying on. We think about our own lives.

John Cato: One of the variables has to do with the whole question of how much we involve people in making decisions that are going to affect their lives. Obviously this is an issue that we are facing in this country, and it may well be an issue we are facing sometimes even in these more global questions. Once we deal with this question, we are then forced to lay back some of the "in-house" assumptions we have within the high-powered academic community. Indeed, I suspect that at times we are really battling "straw men" when we question things like the matter of coercion versus freedom of choice. It may well be that at the operational level, that isn't the question at all, provided we have enough in-put from the people who are involved. At some point we are going to have to question our own assumptions. What are the values by which we operate? Are we, in fact, creating "straw men" in some of the ways in which we phrase the question?

Potter: Mr. Jonas, we have available to us John Wyon who has done a good deal of research in Indian villages and might comment exactly on the point of involving people in reflection on their demographic situation — what happens, what motives move them.

John Wyon: I have had the experience of working in the villages in Punjab in India over a period of twelve or fourteen years. We went with the assumption that these people didn't understand their problems in relating themselves to their resources. We knew about birth control and *we* were going to teach them. But it turns out in fact — on the basis of detailed studies — that they not only know a great deal about how to practice birth control, but also they have been controlling their population in other ways. For example, Ralph Potter's suggestion of knocking off every fourth boy is what the Punjabi have been doing, except they eliminate every fourth girl — which is a much more effective way of keeping down the population growth. Actually there is a higher female than male death rate, which they tell us is part of the method of population control. They also have worked very hard to increase their production. In fact, the green revolution has been going very strongly there.

We are starting to work in this discussion toward the point where the real question is the relationship between how to get into consciousness and from consciousness into behavior, the relationship between groups of people — perhaps quite small groups of people — and their own resources. Either we can say with Dr. Jonas that people are ignorant and do not understand what they are doing or we can take the other angle and say we think the ordinary people do understand. Think, for example, of the effect of the famine in Ireland in 1856. There was a fantastic reduction in reproduction over a period of a few years. And likewise the response of the French people to the Napoleonic laws forcing each peasant to share his patrimony among all his sons, with the consequence of a drop in the birth rate in France. Malthus, in fact, noticed in Switzerland that when the death rate was low the subsequent birth rate was low. We have good reason to believe that if we can find out how to get the people's in-put in terms of their own social life and individual life, they can draw conclusions and modify their behavior accordingly to relate themselves to their resources.

Bruce: What in fact is the conscious rationale of birth control in the Punjab? Why does a given individual parent favor it?

Wyon: Because they are small farmers, and they want to keep the land intact from one generation to another. This is the reason only one brother gets married. Not always, but in many cases, one brother gets married and the other brothers share the wife so that in the next generation, the next generation's brothers will also farm the same land. If more than one brother gets married then they have to divide the land between the two married brothers.

Bruce: So it is a very immediate, personal and individual reason, and there is nothing cosmic involved like the concept of "Space Ship Earth."

Wyon: No, it is the "Space Ship Our Village" or "Our Village Man" which is a limited concept.

Kornetsky: What happened when the missionaries got there?

Wyon: Oh, it was terrible!

Richard E. Schultes: I have been able to observe birth control — conscious birth control — among very primitive people in a very primitive society. As a botanist I am as far out of this discussion as a fish out of water, but I have lived fourteen years in the Northwest Amazon among some tribes that had no contact with civilization. For many, many years the population has been stable. The South American Indian population is falling off after coming in contact with advanced civilizations. These people have had to practice birth control. They kill off any maimed births. They just kill them. They cannot support such a luxury. These people employ a number of plants in the belief that they control ovulation. In order to carry out my studies on hallucinogenic plants and on the contraceptive and other medicinal plants among these people, I stayed long periods of time among them to learn languages and to maintain contact with them. They use these plants. Something is controlling this population, and I am sure it is not the rhythm system! And these people, until our own civilization impinges upon them, have very few problems with over-population — until missionaries come in and cause them deep psychological upsettings. One of the first things they preach is that they must clothe themselves to be moral; a second is how sinful it is to use these plants to interfere with child bearing or contraception. We still do not know whether or not the plants actually are contraceptives, but these people know why they are taking the plants and believe that they control the population. We cannot say that they work; there is no way of proving such a statement outside a laboratory, but here we do have a people who have somehow managed to maintain their population stable.

Bruce: In the case of the Indian, the Amazonian, is their motive to make things better for themselves personally, or for their children? In other words, where does the pinch come? Is it in the generation that practices birth control or is it a case of practicing birth control to spare generations to come?

Wyon: They have a very strong concept of their own family group and their own class group.

Bruce: Is it to the father's interest, or it it to the child's interest that there be a small family?

Wyon: It is the family. The family exists in the past, the present, and the future. And what they are after is maintaining the strength and status of a wider family, both laterally going both ways in time.

Bruce: It occurs to me that the prophecy of the annihilation of the human race by multiplication might be a self-defeating prophecy. It might lead people to practice birth control so as not to subject their children to the terrors they have become convinced await them. On the other hand, if the prophecy then becomes more optimistic and parents believe that the terror has been averted, the population pressure may come again, because they will then raise children to enjoy the fruits of their being spared. That's a dilemma if it is true. It's something, I suppose, for psychologists and sociologists to address themselves to.

Speisman: Even though we seem to come to the conclusion that the appropriate and enabling methodology is one that is reasonably direct and reasonably personal and that fits with any given cultural pattern, it does not remain concrete. You still come out with abstraction of the family, or of an ethic, if you will, that enables this process to go on.

Fletcher: We may have reached a stage where we might try an analysis, expressed more or less ethically. We have addressed our thinking today to two closely related problems — (1) population and attending questions about fertility control, and (2) the problem of behavior control. We have been saying — without much overt disagreement in any case — that questions of freedom and personal initiative don't represent any kind of absolute or perfect right, so that sometimes it might be ethically justifiable to invade purely private choice for the sake of a broader common good. Then the question would arise — leaving aside for a moment the whole problem of fertility control and looking just at behavior control — when or under what conditions or for what pragmatic reasons would chemical control or electrical control or genetic control or, indeed, cultural control be wrong? I don't know that I would go as far as Horace Skinner and say that a family is a behavioral technology. But there is some truth to it, certainly in terms of conditioning. The answer to questions posed in this fashion should be in terms of very concrete contextual situations. If we are agreed — and this is what we should be clear about — that there is nothing inherently or intrinsically evil or wrong about the control of behavior by chemical or electrical or genetic or cultural means, then should we not be trying to specify some kinds of situations — either actual or hypothetical — in which we believe that ethical insight and temper would favor control and some which would oppose it, and then examine the grounds upon which any such ethical reasoning is brought to bear?

Cato: What is at stake here is how prepared we are to be open to the future, which is a great phrase the theologians like to use. If you really take that seriously, then the answer to the question you are raising is, "We don't know." All we can do is pick off some criteria in terms of what basic mental health is — non-involvement with the law, not hurting oneself, etc. — but beyond that we just don't know, so that what we have to raise are the questions about our assumptions with regard to what is "the good" — what is the good man and the good life and the good community. We are going to have to continue to come back to that point.

Ramsey: As an ethicist, generally I like to discuss what is good — situationally or otherwise — and to avoid discussions of comparative odiousness. But I am still trying to learn what the experts believe *will work* and why. I don't mean in wonderful, primitive illustrations — people in the bush or in nice rural situations where the generations are intact. I mean, rather, population control measures that will work in the world-wide metropolitan civilization we are in. Let me take just two things that have been mentioned today. First, it was said quite rightly that the younger generation in our own country is taking the lead in awareness of the ecological problem. There the impending disaster gets closer in sensibility and perception. My question, however, is: is there the slightest evidence as yet that this will produce something like a postponement of the age of marriage in this civilization or to greater responsibility about sexual intercourse with imperfect contraceptives? There were other things mentioned which seem morally acceptable and non-odious procedures in themselves. You put a negative income tax exemption on the third child. Or when the people reach old age and retirement you put on them certain disabilities if they have acted with population improvidence in the previous course of their lives. Concerning that second suggestion, are we really resolved no longer to build floors under those who act unreasonably? This is like using negative income tax on a guaranteed income to get rid of our terrible welfare system. Well, fine! But there are bound to be some people who are profligate. Do we really mean not to let another welfare system develop? We could leave that to private charity, the churches, etc. So we could say that in a meager way we will sustain people who have four or five children, disadvantage them only a little. But do we mean to be cruel to "unallowed" children, or do we naively believe that acceptable constraints will work because we count on people to act logically? That assumption may be compared to the assumption that liberalizing abortion laws will lower the rate of criminal abortions. It seems not logical to assume otherwise. But there is plenty of empirical evidence that there is serious question about that assumption. So before beginning to discuss moral issues — such as eliminating the fourth male child or the fourth female child — we need to determine the range of things that we have reason to believe *will work* in a world-wide, metropolitan civilization. If the feasibility issue is reasonably resolved, then we could far better approach the question of social and moral acceptability of proposed measures. It is the question of practicability that leaves me somewhat the pessimist.

Bruce: The most effective approach should be to emphasize the threat to the welfare of the children, and perhaps this is something of a self-correcting mechanism at work, poverty is relative. If it is a mark of poverty not to go to college and college tuition rates keep going up the way they have, that may be a positive incentive to have fewer kids.

Kornetsky: The poor, of course, have always been the ones that have more children. We're beginning to touch on some of the real issues here. We can't export birth-control to India and South America like we export Coca-Cola. We can export that and people will drink it there because we drink it here, and they'll only drink the birth-control pill there when we drink the birth-control pill here.

Sometimes we end up talking about a particular sub-group of people in the United States and the sub-group is composed of the people we know, the young people we come in contact with, the protestors who are the upper income group. We don't touch the mass of people at all who may have different ideas, different mores, different goals and different aspirations. They are not the people we come in contact with except in a very peripheral way. Until we understand that total problem, how to deal with this in our total population so we can make an impact in this country, maybe we cannot make an impact in other countries. Of course, then it may be too late.

Moyer: There are several different problems. One problem is population control in the United States. Another problem is population control in underdeveloped countries, such as India. It isn't at all clear to me that the population control in the underdeveloped countries is dependent on the taking of the pill here in the United States. It is much more dependent upon the individual's perception of some reinforcement to her for personally taking the pill. I'm inclined to believe that people do not drink Coca-Cola in South America because it is drunk in New York, but because Coca-Cola tastes good. Now if we can make the pill taste good, or make them perceive that taking the pill is beneficial to them as individuals, they will take it whether it is taken in the United States or not.

Pelikan: Mr. Schultes makes the excellent point that so many primitive cultures have been in equilibrium with their environments for a long time. Precisely whose problem is this lack of equilibrium? And why do we conceive of it as a problem?

Muelder: Now we get back to the ethical vision of the ethical issues. We are still talking at two different levels. I would be very glad to speak to the policy level that Professor Ramsey is urging us to speak to, but have to declare myself on what I regard as a more fundamental ethical level: to control behavior — including population control — as a question of social policy made in ways that would be acceptable given the dignity of human beings, that is one level. But to control behavior in such a way that one takes away from the future the capacity to reconsider is another level. Whether the policy was good enough is a question of a totally different dimension. I want to conserve the capacity of the future to reconsider whatever decisions we may have made — good or bad — in the present generation. The kinds of control that are appropriate to each of these should be distinguished from one another, with a different answer depending upon which level we talk about.

Speaking on the policy control question and not taking away from the future's right to reconsider or the capacity to reconsider, from the ethical point of view today, mankind is a unit. It is the patriotism that the young people dislike, it's the capitalism the young people are protesting against that allows us to talk about privileged America and our rights to have bigger families than somebody else. Empirically, concertly, existentially, as well as the standpoint of the future, mankind is a unit. These different countries are going to have their revolutions. They are having them now. They are going to continue having them, and they are going to state their revolution in terms that are meaningful to them. Consequently, we do have to ask the question for ourselves, "How do we as privileged people, at the moment, participate responsibly in their right to have the same quality of privilege that we have," if that turned out to be good. Our willingness to keep questioning our own hierarchies, while those other revolutions are going on, is important, since mankind is a unit and therefore all people have fundamentally the same claim on dignity or have the same dignity which gives the same claim on everybody else.

Now I see no way of moving to the future without a great deal of social control from the point of view of policy. Our nation is exercising too much governmental control? Good Heavens, too little! You medical people want a great deal more help from the government, but you want the kind of help that lets you keep your autonomy in terms of the merit of a case.

Perhaps we need to relax the abortion laws or to modify the abortion laws. As an ethicist, that is not a closed question in my mind — in fact very much an open question. It raises the issue: what do we mean by a human being? Later on, before these sessions are over, we are going to talk about prolongation of life and that also raises the question of the beginning of life. Life begins before there is human life. We are sometimes in the middle of life as human beings and — getting back to the brain question as it throws light on this — there is a stage in the development of the embryo and fetus where you can't say it is human life in the sense in which you are trying to save the brain of some person to operate fully. There is the stage where it no longer functions as a human being, but there is the semblance of a brain there. I am saying this to show that I am prepared to talk about all kinds of controls in terms of a social policy and the education that goes with it, as long as we do not confuse that with the question of the kind of control that takes away from the future generation's ability to reconsider.

Fletcher: Have we been talking about any irreversible methods? I don't think any method has come up that is irreversible.

Ervin: We were talking to biologically irreversible efforts. The question is whether we were talking about any politically irreversible process. That's where the social control issue comes up.

Fletcher: So man would become so habituated to whatever system was devised that he could not change it?

Ervin: I don't know if there are any politically irreversible processes. I'll bow to the historians on this.

Bruce: Politics are the art of the possible, and many things are possible.

Freda Rebelsky: There probably are some psychological irreversible processes — for example, the atom bomb and the notion of killing so many people at once; or vaccination which probably seemed very coercive at the beginning, but once it was done people modified their points of view so that it became natural; or integration seemed coercive to some people at the beginning and as they get used to it the framework changes. It's a little bit like the point about how perception can be manipulated. As you institute measures to control population — which you may decide are necessary to avert a catastrophe even if they are tyrannical — you may be led to think about children differently or to think about population differently or to think about the family differently. But we make these choices all the time anyway. When you go into an Indian village and bring them a net to catch enough fish in one day to feed the whole village for a week, you are probably making great changes also in the religious system, the social system and everything else, and you are willing to do it. Why are some so unwilling to do it in relation to population? But maybe I am mishearing.

Schultes: I am very glad that you brought up that question of vaccination. I started thinking about this when Dr. Jonas hinted that we might have to take — you said "tyrannical," I would say "dictatorial" — measures in human life. As a botanist, I know nothing about your fields. Democracy is a luxury that many people oftentimes cannot enjoy. Thank God that vaccination was not invented yesterday at a time in history when people could sit around talking about the "ethics" of it. It was invented in a time when officials could say: "You must be vaccinated or you don't go to school" or "You must have it so that you will not be a menace to your neighbor." We, as intelligent human beings, have just got to get away from so much of the permissiveness that our own democratic ideals naturally bestow in us. In the use of natural resources, for example, there is no room for democracy. We cannot permit uncontrolled use of soil leading to its erosion. A person may own a piece of land or the government may own a piece of land, but we are derelict if we permit the owners to do what they want. It will not be there for future generations. I am glad you brought up this question of vaccination, because it may take some of my colleagues here down from the clouds and make them face reality.

Potter: It is ironic to have that comment here in Massachusetts where there is the famous case of *Jacobson vs. Massachusetts* about the ability of the state to compel vaccinations. That case then later came to play a significant role in another case — *Butt vs. Bell* — in which Justice Holmes decided that compulsory sterilization would be a permissible step in society. He rested that in part in a concluding sentence saying that the right of the state to give compulsory vaccination can be extended to require compulsory sterilization for those who would bear children, but are forbidden by the state to do so. About the only place to go to get any substantial body of reflection on compulsory means of population control are the cases debated by eugenists, lawyers and others around the turn of the century or the first two or three decades of this century on the question of involuntary sterilization. It is not the case that only recently ethicists have raised these issues, because they were raised at the time vaccinations were introduced and have continued to plague the courts for a number of decades, not only in our own state, but also in the nation.

Moyer: The fact is that our culture does accept vaccination with relatively few people fighting it. We also coerce individuals into going to school. People are not permitted to decide whether or not they are going to send their children to school. There are a few cases like the Menonites who protest this, relatively unsuccessfully. So we are using the same kind of system which is already accepted by the society.

Potter: Yes, but then you come back to Paul Ramsey's first question. If you can conceive of techniques that are going to be fairly successful in inducing people to limit the number of their children, the hard cases will be only a small fraction. The really hard thinking comes in deciding what you do with someone for whom all the propaganda — maybe even subliminal advertisements and everything else — is not effective. They persist in invoking the right to have the privilege of determining the size of their family. They may be a very small minority; they may not be a demographic threat; but they can still be a significant political problem.

Gustafson: Some would say they can be taken care of electrically, however.

Potter: That's just the question. Can you go that far without throwing in jeopardy a number of other rights or a number of other issues?

Ervin: That's my social-ecological point. These things do have impact.

They have impact on attitudes towards children or subsequent laws, etc.

Potter: Yes! If you could just isolate this issue and isolate the techniques used in dealing with the issue, it would be simple. If there is no carry-over to other areas of conduct of the pattern of thought that legitimates certain sanctions. Should we do that with smokers, too?

Ervin: Let me raise another point, because it seems to me that Dr. Wyon told us something that we are ignoring. We have bounced between the biological and the ethical and left out a piece of the real world which I think can be identified as political. What Dr. Wyon said about the Punjabi and what Dr. Schultes said about the Amazonian Indians has to be taken with considerable respect. Indeed, the human animal is not a hell of a lot more stupid than other organisms, and in the right circumstances where he gets his feedback about his environment and is in intimate relationship with it, the evidence that we have heard cited, as well as other evidence, indicates he will come into reasonable equilibrium with it, including population equilibrium.

Now Ramsey dodged that issue, not entirely inappropriately, by saying that we live in a metropolitan world, which implies to me a loss of some of these feedback controls and decoupling from the real world. But does one possible solution to this problem involve participatory democracy and the ownership of land and of the control of one's own resources and microcosms in a very intimate kind of way, and then the using of the immediate awareness and wisdom of the individual, plus some education, to bring things into balance? Maybe what we ought to be talking about is a sizeable political and social revolution, and not how to build new gimmicks into the existing social structure. Shinn touched on these issues — and not erroneously — this morning when he said that one of the problems arises when the Indians or when the urban Black population in this country or when the South Americans say, "You middle-class Whites do not want us to reproduce." This is the wrong issue, but there is the question of whether there exists a touch of racism, or a touch of elitism, or a decoupling from the real world of politics, land ownership and self-control and a disregard of that issue in most of the talks about population control. That is one thing that really has to be considered. If the Punjabis could control population, the Hindus could, particularly if they get rid of a few of their ideological hangups. That is an agenda item that is not to be neglected for the future.

Bruce: A key word here is feedback, a means of bridging the gap between the two themes of discussion: neurological intervention and the population problem. Perhaps we are underestimating the power of feedback, and if we do underestimate it, and even short of electrical intervention we develop highly sophisticated — what you might call programmed — operations on the human inclination, we may lose the benefits of feedback.

Possibly freedom has not merely an ethical value, but also a pragmatic value that is without the freedom to adapt: we'd be lost if, for example, for the sake of preventing a population explosion, we enlisted all the sophisticated resources of brainwashing and set them in motion. This may be what Dean Muelder considers to be irreversible, that perhaps the greatest danger is not so much failing to find a way of persuading the population that the population should be reduced, but persuading it too well and too irreversibly, too permanently, that it should be reduced. My questions with respect to the Indians have been directed towards the notion that perhaps we underestimate the will of people confronted with an immediate disaster, as in the cases of the Punjabi and the Amazonian Indians, to take measures for themselves, if they happen to know the measures, whether it is eliminating every fourth female or using certain plants.

It may be that what this conference is coming around to is the notion that what is needed is not high-powered pressure, but the dissemination of information and the dissemination of the means to act upon the information and leaving use of it to the interest of the parent, not necessarily just his interest in himself personally, but also his interest in the welfare of his immediate family to use and posterity.

Ramsey: I wish that were true.

Kornetsky: A point of information, was the birth rate lower or higher thirty of forty years ago in places like India and South America or is the population explosion a function of a decrease in infant mortality?

Wyon: The birth rate, if anything, has come down, but it is the death rate that has fallen radically.

Ervin: And the geometric progression of a absolute number of births is still upward?

Wyon: Oh, of course, the actual number of births has gone up. Also the population has increased as a result of fewer deaths.

Potter: In regard to Paul Ramsey's issue of "metropolitan societies," it seems a helpful way to progress would be to study, in very fine scale, the payoffs for individual couples in particular social settings, the way John Wyon has done in villages of India. There are two types of situation-circumstances in which people are unlikely to limit the number of their children — when things are really bad and they suffer from despair and therefore don't bother — and the other when things are very good indeed, and you get something like the Bobby Kennedy syndrome, where they have a great number of children, and in between there are circumstances where people restrict the number of their children for one reason or another. Kingsley Davis made a list of those circumstances that are present where you have people restricting the number of births in their family, as they have very successfully in Hungary. It reads like a chamber of horrors — for instance, if housing is made impossible to come by so that people have to move in with their in-laws, or if job prospects are restricted, or if maternal health care is not provided, then the birth of another child makes the situation intolerable.

Ervin: Sounds like a typical American inner city.

Potter: But then Davis comes up with the observation that no government is willing to implement these policies for demographic purposes. The severity of the issue rests at the point that the things that we are pledged to do for other motives — for economic and political betterment — may also have the effect of increasing people's inclination to bear children, to enjoy this good life which they share. So it becomes a severe problem to give them other motives to limit their children while you are creating a situation in which life seems to be so good it should be shared with more people. In a sense, we know what keeps the birth rate down in a metropolitan society, but we don't want those things.

Ramsey: You seem to reverse things a bit, or give us a chicken and egg problem. Instead of our seeking ways directly to limit population, you seem to be saying that really to attack the population problem one must go to work on the problem of bedrock poverty. Are you saying that in a metropolitan civilization it is a solution to the problem of poverty and despair that alone will make the limitation of family size a desirable goal for most people?

Potter: There is a complete despair which causes people to say, "Why bother to limit?" But a lesser degree of hardship would seem to be effective when people see some chance of their children getting ahead and they make them "intensive crops" and pour a lot into each one. This has been the technique of Jews in America who have a very small family size with very intensive education aiming at critical positions in the social structure. In contrast with that, I've had debates with the Black students who are resisting what they think is a genocidal policy of having birth control clinics in Black areas. They want number in order to increase their political effectiveness in society, taking the alternate tack than the Jewish community has.

Cato: I'm happy that Paul Ramsey was the one who raised this because I'm always accused of paranoia when I raise them as a Black person. But it is a real issue that there are many people frightened to death about what we are cooking up around this table, or what they think we are cooking up. My plea would be for a variety of experimental modes so that no one gets the notion that you are going to go gunning after any one community. If you are going to deal seriously with the question of the metropolis, then you have got to deal with the question of community control in suburbia and in the inner city and all around the lot. What saves us from some grand political scheme is the fact that we have many things going on. We're looking at them all tentatively and are not freezing out any possibilities.

Muelder: Isn't it here that the distinction between society and government comes in? We have many modes of social control appropriate to sub-groups within a total society, and that is different from an overall state political control concept — although the two are not absolutely separable. They reinforce each other appropriately and are in conflict appropriately.

One of the things that moved me when I heard the addresses was that with all of the illustrations given and the factors presented, we have a problem of cumulative causation. One should look at all the variables moving in a particular direction and reinforce those which are responsible from the use of that general term, and try to inhibit those variables which tend towards irresponsibility. Some of these variables will be more appropriate and acceptable to the Black community at its present state in the development of American society and their locus in that society taken by and large. The Jewish community has already been referred to; certainly rural Appalachia is one kind of area. The poor in the great cities is a different kind of situation. A mining camp is certainly different from rural areas. There are many modes of social control that are appropriate, and one should set in motion any cumulative causation of those variables that move in a generally constructive direction. The accumulation of these many variables may end up with a total socially good effect.

Pelikan: The thing that has been bothering me was the outrageous presumption on the part of many of us that there was indeed some specified level of equilibrium, some specified time course that this had to take. This seems a terribly presumptuous thing. I think Dr. Muelder and Dr. Cato have given us the way out by using many flexible approaches. Perhaps to be very ultrabiologic, to let the best possible equilibrium be assumed — and unfortunately it may mean the starvation in this part of the world of a certain number — with many who might indeed have starved as well.

Kornetsky: The trouble with that is that the equilibrium won't be a static equilibrium.

Pelikan: It never has been.

Kornetsky: And it will continue to change because we keep pouring in other ways of saving lives of people.

Pelikan: Someone this morning pointed out the fantastic and sudden perception, particularly on the part of young people, of the importance of ecology. People are becoming aware of their existence in a dynamic biological situation, which is something most of us around the table only discovered after we had gotten out of college.

Schultes: You also assume that there is such a thing as a stable biological equilibruim. The very fact that they are called dynamic means that they are not stable. Man is a part of nature. This is certainly something that many people often forget, even biologists.

Kornetsky: Yes, but let us say advancement has ceased and we do not discover any new ways to save lives. We use the methods we have now. We would achieve an equilibrium in the world at a certain time which would then stabilize except for minor fluctuations. However, what happens is that the "have" countries keep feeding into the system continually. I'm not sure where this leads. It is not a dynamic equilibrium.

Pelikan: It is no equilibruim. It becomes part of the feedback. It was only the obscure professorial types back in the nineteenth century who raised the Darwinian question of what you are doing when you save a lot of people. This is "'cardtable talk" nowadays. It is part of the feedback that is being built into the system which some people are proposing.

Ramsey: I thought that the time scale you referred to was set by horrendous projections we often read about, both with respect to the ecological disruption and the population problem. I would be very happy with the kind of things that you are now saying as the terms with which we must work, with multiple solutions, multiple population, and as actively as possible on all fronts. From the other sort of prediction, given very little time, one readily concludes that although a measure violates the human, that's the way we have to do it. I protest against that — especially when it is added: nevertheless we will fail or are likely to fail.

Pelikan: I want someone to say, "The reason I am around this table is that I am scared to death, not for society, but for me and my kids." That is why most of us are here. That's why we find that a certain rate of population increase is terrifying. If you fail to recognize that, then you are tied up in many things that imply that there is an optimum rate that can be set by people sitting around a table.

Speisman: There was an optimum rate which was set this morning, and that was zero.

Jonas: Equilibrium can also be terrible. Equilibrium doesn't in itself mean that it is a good thing. There can be equilibrium between numbers. The barest, most miserable subsistence level would also be an equilibrium. Equilibrium will work itself out automatically, but we must ask what kind of equilibrium.

Potter: I want to know if Dr. Pelikan really means to espouse what sounds like straight unvarnished Malthusiaism, the saying that we mustn't help out with poor laws because the poor were preordained to be poor.

Pelikan: No, no! That's why I suddenly find myself allied with Dr. Muelder.

Potter: All right, but are you? Because I thought you were saying that if we intervene at all, we mess things up.

Ervin: Are you saying, "Let many flowers bloom"?

Pelikan: But now we can begin to think of practical alternatives, such as Dr. Ramsey wanted. Certainly we as educators must encourage the ecological approach to the solution of problems. We must certainly work as hard as we possibly can for greater understanding of ecology as opposed to dead biology. We can certainly work, both as biologists and theologians, for continued recognition of the fact that these are not separate fields. Now even as individuals we can see courses of action.

Potter: But having intervened — let's say with medical care and public health facilities in underdeveloped countries and so forth — and thus having destroyed an earlier equilibrium based on high birth rate, high mortality, are we obliged to do something more now? Are we obliged to intervene once again or to allow this ancient equilibrium to revert? Is that ancient equilibrium less desirable for some reason than new prospects or what?

Pelikan: I don't know that this is good or bad or the kind of thing that should be done on the question of equilibrium. But certainly there are countries that are able to decide — and have begun to decide — the caring capacities of their own land and the resources that are required from either outside or inside in order to achieve their level of equilibrium. These are things in which we should help.

Potter: But should we keep out of their hands any destabilizing medical inventions that we now have?

Pelikan: Heaven forbid! However, at the same time we should point out to them, if they do not know, the consequences of unbridled increases of population.

Potter: So, sir, you wouldn't deny then that somehow there is a good attached to preserving an existing life. Would you continue to press for that where possible?

Pelikan: It is eminently desirable, though that is partly one of those culture-bound things that we have acquired over the course of the last several hundred years in a certain part of the world. I am sufficiently democratic that I do not want unnecessarily to impose that point of view on people who conceivably might have a completely different way of achieving equilibrium.

Kornetsky: Are you saying that we should go on the best way we know how and somehow develop an acceptance of this? We still have the problems, but now we feel better about them?

Bruce: This exchange suggests to me one possible answer to the question that was posed in the beginning: what research is needed? I don't know in fact whether it is technically possible, but we have come to have faith in the omnipotence of computers, so maybe using them would make it so. We might try to build some concrete alternative models. We have been talking about the differing cultural ideals and objectives of various societies. It would be an interesting and useful thing to attempt to work out a description in concrete terms, in terms of the typical family in a given culture, of what it would mean for that family in the future if it and other families had two children, if it had three children, if it had four children. What this would mean for Indians might be one thing, and for Americans might be another. However, having said that, I'm inclined to think that they might not believe it if we did give them all that information.

Kornetsky: Do we know why birth control methods have failed in these countries? I heard some examples of some small subcultural groups where they have birth control that does work, but in the large masses of people do we know why it has not worked?

Wyon: Speaking for Punjab, the people have been using birth control for years. The idea that we are the great Westerners with all of this modern technological birth control is a very nice fantasy for us to indulge in, but it just isn't true. They have many methods of birth control — rhythm, abstinence, withdrawal, induced abortion and also recently, delayed marriage. We discovered this year to our amazement that the average age for marriage for women in the world of Punjab has now gone up to over twenty. We knew it had been rising in the late 1950's, but it has gone way up. They have all sorts of methods of birth control, and they have been using them and are using them increasingly. The birth rate has actually fallen in the last ten years quite definitely.

So the question that arises then is: if they know how to practice birth control, why don't they practice it more? And this is where you run into the ecology. It leads us to the point that Dr. Muelder was suggesting in regard to the urban United States. Also, it has some relevance in that there is a possibility of working with social units on the Indian scene — getting them to collect information about themselves, their births, their population structure, working out with them their land, etc. — so that they see more clearly the inter-relationships between their own group and their future. This is the diagnosis, which is a phrase that hasn't come up yet, although we have talked about treatment. Maybe we ought to start with a diagnosis of the ecological situation which seems a perfectly feasible concept to develop, and, as Dr. Muelder said, why not with the Blacks, the Jews, the Irish, or any other group of people. Dr. Pelikan said that he is only concerned with himself, his own family, his own children and their future, but here we are discussing with him as a group what it all means to us. This could occur in all sorts of groups that can be formed on the basis of religion or ethnic origin or local neighborhood and so on. It is possible for social units to start to grapple seriously with the implications of their own population increase and what it means to them and their children.

Ervin: Maybe we shouldn't talk about India by the hundred hectare units.

Speisman: If any of you feel that you have a summary statement of your own or a comment that might tie together some of the elements that we have been discussing, it would be enormously useful for the conference. I have to express some of my own confusion and maybe this will summarize something.

We have made a couple of points that are worth bringing out. One is the point that Ramsey raised initially, which is what will work, and the second one is the focus on solutions that fit particular community or cultural patterns. As far as we have been able to determine at this point, solutions will be successful only insofar as we are enabled to both define and work within some kind of cultural or community pattern.

The earlier discussion, however, is where my confusion comes in. We have lost a little bit of the urgency that was expressed this morning. We are now talking about comfortable, compatible methods that we all would agree with anyway since we've been raised in a tradition that says hold, educate, look toward the future. Without trying to overstate it, what I heard this morning from presumed experts is that we don't have that kind of time. That, in fact, there is the potential of two-dimensions of feeding a population and of having a population starvation. There is no longer any potential of remaining irreversible whatever methods you use. So while I certainly resonate to the concept of understanding a particular group, community or cultural approach as the only way to provide educative means for solutions, what about this urgency? Is it gone only in our minds, or is it overstated?

Pelikan: Isn't that part of the question of whether one should prepare to accept things? If we are willing to accept the question of very personal urgency, a dire threat to us as individuals, we automatically find certain kinds of things to be more acceptable regardless of their intrinsic rightness or wrongness, however that might be defined. If on the other hand this is a purely biological problem with the human content left out, we can wait for things to achieve a new equilibrium. Again, I would like to know why we are here. If we are going to adopt one position, then almost anything becomes acceptable, as it has become acceptable in enforcing public health measures. As soon as the group decides that they want to do something badly enough, forget the principle; we can find a way to do it. On the other hand, if we are going to be purely biological, let's forget about it and wait for things to achieve a new equilibrium.

Cato: This is the only kind of question many of the people I know can relate to: the matter of urgency, the notion that we can deliver a number of services in this country once we put our minds to it. But rather than dealing with questions of population control, let us concern ourselves rather precisely with that matter of how we are going to deliver better medical services to the city. How are we going to develop some alternative ways of growing food? How are we going to handle the question of artificial foods, and so on? As people, for instance in the ghetto communities, look at the enormously wonderful things we are capable of doing in outer space, they say right away, "Well, why not here?" So this kind of question that we are dealing with today is really at a level of abstratcion that one finds very difficult to relate to.

Jonas: I don't see what abstraction there is about the prospect of a very closely impending ecological crisis of this planet. What is so abstract about it? In the face of such a prospect, as laudable a thing as the improvement of medical services recedes somehow into second order, though it is close to everyone immediately concerned. I don't see that this is so abstract. To be scared is a very legitimate attitude to take here. One needn't be scared about oneself and perhaps not even about one's own children. We may, here in America, be spared the impact of this for another generation — maybe or maybe not. To be scared about the condition of this planet is an entirely new situation. This is the first time in the history of mankind that one can speak in these terms and that one *must* speak in these terms and very concretely!

Moyer: There is an urgency. If we believe the prognosticators, in the next ten to twenty years hundreds of millions of people are going to die of starvation. Many people are not willing to accept that biological failing of the equilibrium. The ultimate equilibrium may be the absence of *Homo sapiens.* Many people are not willing to just sit by and accept that. As Dr. Speisman said, there is an essence of crisis, and we do not have time to sit around and wait for education to take effect. As I pointed out, it is most ineffective with our current state of knowledge. Therefore we are pushed into a situation in which we must use extraordinary controls and extraordinary methods of control. These are the things we should consider, because some of these controls — according to the ethicists — must be more acceptable ethically than others. Perhaps we need to decide which kind of available controls — and many are available — are more ethically acceptable than the others. That is the crisis we face.

Wyon: Could I just comment on what is happening in a country like India where the government has accepted and is acting on the presupposition that the population growth is an extremely urgent problem? They are, after all, one-sixth of the human race and the government is taking this extremely seriously and is acting with the help of outside countries, such as ours and Sweden. They put into action a country-wide birth control program with great force of ads on the billboards, on the radio. With every movie you go to see there are ads for family planning. There are red triangles everywhere in India, on the back of every bus and every rickshaw. They offer rewards to people who have sterilization operations done or who have intrauterine devices inserted. They give rewards to people who get others to go to have these things done. They give one or two awards for doctors.

What is happening? Well, as we measure it now, it means in these villages — particularly in the Punjab — about four or five per cent of the couples with a wife of child-bearing age have now had a vasectomy or tubectomy or have adopted the new methods. At the same time we personally came across the resistance to it, and there are many other supporting reports. The village people say, "Oh, you're Family Planning people. Go away! We don't want you. We don't want to be sterilized." The initial subterfuge is that when the Family Planning worker comes and says there should be six or seven people from the village to have vasectomies, they say, "O.K. He'll go and he'll go." The old widowers will go or somebody who wants ten rupees will go, or else they make up the figures. We heard of a doctor who gave two authentic reports for three months and then she was reprimanded by Family Planning people. For the next three months she just made up the figures. She had made so many visits; she had done so many operations. They thought she was fine.

Moyer: Then the education is not very effective. Then we must have much more drastic methods. And if we must have much more effective methods, which ones are ethically acceptable?

Schultes: I am not sure that education is not effective. It has to be the proper kind. The Roman Church has been very effective in its own kind of education in Latin America and in Europe. It is a kind of education, albeit it is indoctrination. It may not be what we would like, but it has worked. Go among these people and you find fear, a fear of everything.

J. Robert Nelson: There is great irony in this historical event in which we are now involved. I think we all agree with Dr. Jonas that we do face unprecented crisis, even impending catastrophe for the human race, and precisely at the time when significantly large numbers of people on this planet are discovering the possibilities of freedom, emancipation, the truly human life we speak about, and all the other good virtues which some of us — at least in a certain tradition, largely the Judeo-Christian tradition—have been nurturing for centuries. Now suddenly the irony is that we are going to have to accept restraints and suppressions upon these very aspects of freedom and initiative and opportunity which we thought were so good. That is why I agree fully with Dr. Moyer that some kind of scale of desirability or odiousness — to put it in the negative sense — of those things which we can have and enjoy and those things which we cannot, must be worked out, and not only worked out theoretically, but also given some social and political implementation. Whether this can be done by one nation, however, is the really critical problem. Here I come back to Dean

Muelder's very proper emphasis that we cannot think simply as Americans here. We may be internationally-minded Americans, but even that isn't enough. Our supreme loyalty is to the whole human race of which we are a part.

So far not a word has been spoken referring to a fifth of the human population, namely China with its vast unmanageable populations. Yet we are somehow all part of their problem, too. The fact that we are politically divided from them — the United States refusing acceptance and so on — simply makes the problem all the worse. Therefore, one other aspect I would inject in this problem of irony with regard to our discovery of freedom: the technological era into which we are so rapidly being catapulted is one in which the freedoms are going to be more and more restrained and invaded. If we believe some of the prognostications of cybernetic experts who tell us what the computerized society of the next few decades is going to be, we know that such things as private responsibility and private interest will be invaded more and more by electronic devices. We already see it in the wire-tapping. All of this presents in Dr. Pelikan's terms, a cause for being "scared to death," but not just individually, rather scared corporately to death, which is another factor.

Cato: I am a little puzzled that no one here seems to be aware of the supreme irony to me that in the light of the triple evolutions — weaponry, cybernetics and human rights — we are leaping to these grand solutions when there are a number of middle range solutions. The fact that we aren't discussing those raises the question whether there is a culture-bound character to our science. That in fact, there are some value substances that are hidden and that we would think we were guilty of those if we didn't raise questions about medical care, the fact that people are dying in the ghettos, the fact that there are chronic illnesses there — lead poisoning and drug abuse— and the fact that we aren't putting our brains to work in those areas. It strikes me as ironic in the extreme.

Ramsey: That's not ironic, that's symptomatic.

Muelder: In any case, it may be symptomatic. It gets back to the point I was trying to make a little while ago. We Americans like head-on attacks on problems. We do not like to think in terms of complete variables, which, in the context of the problems in the long run, may have more to do with an issue than the most obvious and immediate thing. We want to get a job done. *Now* it happens to be population.

So we think about population control. This is important, but if ecology means anything to me as an ethicist, it means that we are operating in highly complex systems, every part of which has an effect on every other part of the system. The most obvious symptom may not turn out to be the most crucial in the long run. It may be something that is skin deep when something else may be more symptomatic. Americans have not wanted to think about their social system. They love it as it is. They want one little reform after another. What we are confronted with is a question as to whether we need or do not need to think radically about our total social system, which will then get at the question of medical care, which has to do with all of the power structures of our society.

While it may have seemed a bit complacent a moment ago when I was talking about doing to each group what is acceptable to it, we have an expedient responsible alternative. While you are in the process of getting the whole thing moving, the Chinese are not going to ask us how we want them to do it. India has more communication with the West and therefore there is more communication about this problem. South America is in a different mode of revolution from China. It is only part of realism to recognize that the actual responses of people in the different parts of the world are what they are prepared to do. Therefore, we need to study those not in terms of simplistic solutions — just because we middle class suburbanites like to do it one way or those of us who started our families in the depression did it one way or now our children are having theirs in another mode — but in terms of strategic response that is more flexible, that doesn't turn out to be the more radical one in the long run, but the deeper and more effective one? I would like to submit that that has at least a popular social hypothesis about it.

An Observer: I'm not an American; I'm a Canadian and I have two children. I felt that two children were quite enough, so I went to my doctor and I asked to be sterilized. He said, "Certainly not! You are in a perfectly healthy condition." I went from place to place in quite a number of large cities in Canada. I don't know what it is in the United States, but in Canada it is against the law to be sterilized.

I work in a rural school in Nova Scotia, and as a school psychologist, one of my jobs is to keep records. I've seen familes of twelve and fifteen children. Their teeth are rotting in their mouths because they are malnourished. The women come to school periodically. They are pregnant again for the sixteenth time and I asked, "Why are you pregnant again? Why don't you do something about it?" They tell me their doctors have refused to do anything for them. I have heard this story time and again.

In India, you mentioned sterilization. That is usually men they prefer to sterilize by operation because it is easier, is that correct? Now, gentlemen, you are men yourselves, what is the self-image of a man who cannot perform or who thinks he is not going to be able to perform if he is sterilized? Now, for a woman it works a little differently. She can still feel feminine even though she is not procreating at that particular moment. I can speak from experience in this way. Therefore, gentlemen, if you want concrete suggestions, allow women to have control of their own bodies, so that when they may go to their doctor and say, "Please, Doctor, sterilize me; I know what I am doing, I am an intelligent woman," they will be able to have it done. Have the medical profession also take into its own hands sometimes the decision for this poor, miserable pregnant female, year after year after year giving birth to feeble-minded children — and how else can they be but feeble-minded, because she herself is feeble-minded — and during deliveries slip a tube in or something so that this does not happen again. The point was raised over the possible compulsory sterilization for the mentally retarded. Is this in force now? It is not in Canada, I know.

Potter: In a number of states there are laws.

An Observer: I had a horrible experience. I went to a wonderful school for the mentally retarded in Turo, Nova Scotia, and it was a model institution. After we talked, one of my questions was, "Where do you get your people from? Where do you draw from?" And he said, "Oh, well, people get referred by the schools, and then of course we have the children of our graduates."

Speisman: It might be commented to the organizers of our conference that we need more female participation. Gentlemen, I am not sure that we are going to go beyond this point.

Problems with Organ Replacement

John A. Mannick: "Problems with Organ Replacement" is a broad enough term to satisfy almost anyone who wants to talk anywhere in or about this field. With a group of this size, there will be a wide range of ideas about what ought to be discussed here and we would like to allow for a maximum latitude. I suggest that we follow in the footsteps of this morning's panel, where it seemed fairly clear to some of us in the audience, and I suppose to the panelists themselves, that there are questions in the minds of theologians or people dealing with the problems of ethics in our society concerning organ transplantation, and particularly the protection of the rights of the individual involved in organ transplantation either as a prospective donor or as a prospective recipient as well as the families of these two chief actors in the drama. Ethical questions as to the behavior of transplantation groups in the country with regards to these problems have been raised. Many of us in transplantation have the distinct feeling that part of the problem is information and pertains to our communication with the public — and the theologians present as a segment of the public. Many of us would appreciate the opportunity to hear in precise terms what is bothering the theologians about organ transplantation. Because I had the distinct feeling personally — and I know I share this with many of my colleagues here — that a number of the problems raised this morning are, in a sense, straw men, and that if we can satisfactorily lay them to rest in these somewhat more critical surroundings, we might accomplish some real good. I welcome any kind of dialogue carrying on from where we left off this morning with regard to the problems bothering people about how we're behaving in treating patients with this new therapy, this technique of organ transplantation.

Henry K. Beecher: Are there any Jewish theologians here? I would like to put a question to them if there are. If there aren't, I can state the point of view of the Central Conference of American Rabbis which comes into an impasse it seems to me. This has not been discussed and is in contra-distinction to this morning's sessions where a great deal was said about Christianity and not much about Jewry. As I understand the stand of the Central Conference of American Rabbis, they say that the three worst things that you can do are: first, lose a life; second, commit sexual sins; and third, idolatry. Then a little bit later they say it's all right to take an organ out of a cadaver, but you must never, never take an organ out of a living individual. It seems to me that this is in direct conflict, because if anything works, we know that the transplantation of a kidney from an identical twin to his brother is a going proposition. So if they deny this possibility then they have denied life to the twin, and it seems to me, that is a conflict.

Mannick: This is a good place to open. Is there anyone here among the theologians or ethicists who has any grounds for worry concerning the donation of a kidney by a living individual to another member of his family for purposes of a transplant? Does anyone here have any philosophical or ethical objections?

Francis D. Moore: Does the Central Conference of American Rabbis object to blood transfusion or skin grafting?

Beecher: No, I think not, as far as I know.

L. Harold DeWolf: It's no issue as far as I'm concerned. In fact, I have no theological misgivings at all about organ transplants as such. It's only particular conditions and relationships that I am concerned about.

Mannick: Could you be specific about the conditions that are bothering you?

DeWolf: They really have to do not with the organ transplants peculiarly at all, but with heroic procedures both in the cases of people who have no qualitatively meaningful life and possible prospects as far as the best judgment of everyone involved goes, and also as compared with the massive needs in our community for other kinds of medical service, so that you may be having many people dying in order to try to extend the life of a few.

Beecher: They are utterly explicit about this. They say you shall not take an organ out of a living individual.

DeWolf: I don't question what you say. I simply don't know. I'm saying as far as *my* theological position is concerned, I have no misgivings. I would go further and say that even on the matter of taking organs from animals to transplant into human beings, I still have no misgivings at all. I don't have that kind of understanding about what the body is.

Mannick: As I understand it, your objections are the fact that perhaps we might apply transplantation to people whom we have no justifiable hope of salvaging. Could that be regarded as a correct statement of your position.

DeWolf: This is one. It applies no more to organ transplants than to other therapeutic measures.

Mannick: And the second is: can we afford all this?

Walter G. Muelder: Perhaps the question is being posed in the wrong way this afternoon as was also posed by implication in the wrong way this morning. The question is not whether physicians are under attack by theologians or ethicists for something they are doing or not doing. The question is: by what ethical methods do we approach such problems? What are the models with which we work? What are the criteria which we could talk together about, which should be considered when decisions are being made? These are common problems. Now great trust is placed in the medical profession to be self-policing. No one is attacking this. I don't think the problem is attack or defense. The problem is that here are complex ethical questions which are often ambiguous at the point when decisions have to be made with risks being taken. The theologians recognize that ethical decisions are like this in life. The physicians *have* to act and *do* act. So I suggest that we talk a little bit in relationship to these and related problems. What are the ethical factors that bear on all of these questions? Do they have a priority? How are these priorities set? For any one profession in society to assume that it has the right hierarchy of priorities on the questions which concern that profession is something that needs to be examined together.

Fritz Bach: One thing which would be very helpful here is to separate theology and ethics. Perhaps we are all — if there is such a word —

ethicists. We all grow up as an ethicist and we all handle our affairs keeping certain ethical considerations in mind. Theology — at least as I understand it — is a very distinct area of study which many of us would not feel competent in, but in ethics at least we should all be very concerned. That is where we have our common ground work of discussion, the ethical considerations.

Now there was a conference held recently — which Dr. Moore would be much better at commenting on since he chaired that conference — in which some of these very questions were raised. Namely, on what basis does one determine who gets an organ or who goes to dialysis. The first thing we should remember as we start this discussion, is that there are certain medical considerations in transplantation today which are used or can be used to select the recipient of an organ. This is usually the case when we speak about kidney transplantation. We are selecting the recipient for the organ when we are talking about non-living transplants. These considerations are both medical consideration of the state of the patient, whether this is a patient who will potentially do well with a kidney transplant, and the question of having the right donor-recipient match. If you have the right match there presumably is a better chance of success. At least these are some criteria which we can start on. Over and beyond that, of course, there are the much more general criteria which are not only being battled out in the problem of transplantation, but in the problem of eugenics and euthenics and the problem in general of what kind of society we want to have. These are discussions we should be having.

Mannick: All right, we are going to be talking about ethics. We're decided about that. My opening remarks were meant to imply that there are some ethical considerations that are of real concern to the theologians which perhaps might not be of such concern to them were they aware of what's happened since these issues were raised in the field of transplantation. I am thinking specifically of the idea of selecting kidney recipients by means of social worth. This — as all transplanters here know — is a procedure that has been abandoned for more than a year in the one place where it was applied — namely, Seattle — because of the moral considerations that were above and beyond the capacity of anyone on the committee to come to terms with. I think that I speak for those of us here who are engaged in this business by saying that none of us try to do anything more than the lottery of first come, first served, and therefore, I don't believe this particular ethical bugbear is with us any longer. That's the sort of thing that I meant. Dr. Reemtsa, I know you felt there were some issues raised that were no longer a major concern with the transplant group. Can you elaborate on that?

Keith Reemtsa: In dealing with these problems personally with the patients and their families, these concerns are not of the same moment that they appear in a discussion. That is to say, when we deal with a patient with renal failure and his family, we have certain methods of treatment which are available and which to some extent are availing. We have certain information which we can provide to help them with the decision. So that many of the concerns that are expressed — such as the changing identity of the person, the definition of death, the selection of who shall live, the prolongation of life, the right to die, the matter of informed consent — are in a sense solved issues. There isn't any transplantation center in the world that does not rely on these criteria. We all work in something of a public fishbowl, so that if you have concerns about appropriate ethical safeguards being applied, the best safeguard is the experience of the groups which is really open to all.

A more important matter is the one that was raised on the bases upon which ethical considerations are made. Although many may think of ethics as a standard, as a series of standards, neatly wrapped and taken off the shelf on appropriate occasions, in actual fact — at least in the scientific community — ethics are a continuously evolving series of standards which are greatly influenced by results. Now this sounds like an empiric approach to ethics. But if a certain type of transplant works, this over a period of time becomes an ethical approach to that particular problem.

Both our medical approach — which is mostly keyed toward the treatment of episodic or catastrophic illnesses — and our Judeo-Christian ethics were formulated in times for the protection and procreation of the race, when the great enemies were the devastating forces of nature and diseases, etc. Now we are in a very different social situation in which the opposite problem prevails. That is, figuring out some way to do the reverse, to limit the apparently unlimited expansion of people and yet find some way to live within this environment and with ourselves. Perhaps the soundest basis we can provide for determining this ethic is a scientific evaluation of the results of these various pilot projects, or, if you will, models.

Paul Ramsey: If we search deeply enough, in a significant measure we can identify something — if you get below the level of codification and the particular "prohibitiva" that Dr. Beecher read — that is really quite definitely at work within the medical profession. It would be worth identifying it — if you will not bristle at my use of words — as an ethical impulse. This is to say, wouldn't it be the desire of kidney transplant teams to move, by the fuller conquest of the immune reaction, to the exclusive use of cadaver kidneys, as over against familial donors, which are now significantly better? I would identify that as an ethical impulse. It bespeaks recognition of the fact that this is a new thing in medical history, the impairment of one human being's bodily integrity for the sake of another. Now that is in the Jewish and Christian ethical tradition, and it is not only the Jewish — in some quarters at least — that would conclude as Dr. Beecher read to us, but the discussion of the problem of mutilation comes up especially among Roman Catholic Christians. Some of them had a hard time even justifying blood transfusions.

Now what's at work underneath is what, in effect, doctors think. Indeed as you know, whenever the first kidney transplants were made here in Boston, there was a declaratory judgment warranting medicine in taking this step of removing a kidney from a well twin and giving it to the one that would otherwise die. This judgment involved both patient consent and a comparison of injury and benefits. That's the positive ethical judgement that we have in common here. I'm not sure whether this estimate still pertains, but at least I read someone's estimation that though the impairment of the donor twin is minimal, it is not negligible. Didn't someone estimate that it is as if the donor twin — or the family member — for the rest of his life would drive to and fro to work eighteen miles a day the rest of his life on our throughways? That is not negligible. Maybe you have reduced that now. But in any case, if you have, you are doing something more than just being technicians, you are acting as doctors ministering to the flesh — if I may use religious language — in acknowledging its integrity.

Now on the other side, I don't think a doctor is ever going to do what I have heard some of my fellow moralists discuss as if it might be the good and charitable thing to do: allow a living man to give a heart to a recipient — as if that could possibly be for us human embodied beings an expression of a soundly based charity. Now there is what I'm trying to circumscribe: that we all recognize in some measure the moral requirements of the integrity of the embodied personality, even when there is an overriding consideration — as in the case of the familial transplants — we think that the cost can be estimated to be worth the benefit. It was, as you know, a rather strange way in which the Massachusetts Supreme Court reached a decision regarding transplantations. It said that the donor twin really got a benefit: namely, he was relieved of the psychological trauma. I don't particularly like that way of justifying it, but in any case, they were seeking to conserve something about the wholeness of the individual in this way of reflection.

Mannick: Dr. Curran, who has, of course, participated in some of these decisions might straighten us out a bit on just how the law and ethics interact in this consideration about the *primum non nocere* idea in therapeutics and in regard to transplantations in particular. What about the rights of the donor? Is the law taking into account or is the law acting ethically in this case?

William Curran: In general the law reflects what is the predominant ethic of the community. In a more pluralistic society this is always much more difficult to do. The law tries to reflect it. In the case of which you speak, the law was cautiously moving forward and trying to allow this act, the transplant of a kidney, to be performed. It rather automatically limits the scope of the availability, perhaps, of the donor group to persons over eighteen. Therefore, younger children can't be used, or adults if they are under some other kind of legal restraints. This is still a serious issue both in ethics and in law: the involvement of children, the involvement of prisoners as donors or as subjects in experiments.

It is unfortunate that in some of the cases of heart transplants — the cases in Texas — that a suicide was used and that in two cases homicide victims were used. A murdered policeman was used in Boston for our first liver transplant. A certain amount of the use of donors in this field may have been questionable: that some of our early work involved children, that suicides have been used. These kinds of questions have some serious ethical considerations in them. We should get away from the use of "marginal people" or second-class life. It reflects back into the early middle ages when the main source of anatomical studies were the homicides and the suicides. We moved away from this into a more voluntary kind of society, a more voluntary action. These are perhaps some of the things that will come in the future. However I would caution you as far as law is concerned; I would caution you not to enact into law ethical principles in every one of these areas. For example, to enact into law the requirement that no physician who was involved in any way in the "procurement" of the donor organ can in any way be involved in its later transplant.

This has been adopted in many parts of this country as a part of the law. This is very questionable. There can be a situation where a physician is involved in caring for the donor, as in an emergency ward, and, at a later time, he may be involved in another place in helping with the transplant, merely by notifying a transplant unit of the availability of the case, or helping to prepare the body. There may be legal liabilities imposed at a time when these things are not clear, when these kinds of adaptations in law are quite premature. These principles may be perfectly good ethics if you wish to follow them in particular circumstances, but to go to the extent of translating all, accepted at the moment, ethical principles into a law of the state seems to me to be ill-advised.

Mannick: Dr. Russell, you have been pioneering in this whole field of transplantation. How do you react to the idea just put forward by Dr. Ramsey, that it is an ethical step in the right direction, perhaps, to start downplaying the living donor as opposed to cadaver donors in kidney transplants?

Paul S. Russell: I echo his approach entirely. He has identified the source of this so far as we are concerned very properly. It is interesting to me that this comment about the potential living-heart donor is a real one. Christian Barnard received quite a stack of letters from all over the world from living people who wanted to give their hearts. This takes us back to some very interesting things that Dr. DeWolf was talking about this morning about to what extent we are the captains of our own bodies. Should we allow this to take place? If we carried this through, we might aid and abet suicide under many situations and maybe we should do that. Dr. DeWolf, you have properly identified the questions that all of us have regarding what the objectives of medicine should be surrounding death or impending death, and it seems to me that we are all able to identify bad deaths, the types of deaths — perhaps extreme ones — in which medicine should intervene and make things different and medicine does make a big effort to do that. But you imply there is such a thing as a good death, that there is something we should strive for as a total community. Perhaps eventually since we all die, there is something that is sort of a nice balance and that — if we could have our choice — all of us in this room would die according to a nice packaged plan, in fact a plan that we might even be able to subscribe to in advance, as you suggested we might be able to do. In other words, if we could write down a set of circumstances, that we might get to a place where we would be willing to just put our signatures at the bottom of it, and then the doctor would take care of things. It would be, in a sense, a rather nice planned suicide which would be good from the social point of view and good from the point of view that I have been trying to grope for in regards to the definition of the kind of death that we want, so to speak. If we in medicine need help, which perhaps we do, surrounding the question of death, it would be in this one area where we would like to ask how we reach the proper definition of a death toward which we would all like to tend?

DeWolf: I did expressly exclude the person willing to take his own life from his right of the individual and indeed his responsibility to be the steward over his own life. My list should not be considered a kind of package formula for how I now propose to die. The question is quite out of my hands. But simply because of my own particular medical history, I can predict the fairly high likelihood of certain kinds of physiological incidents which might occur which it would be known very quickly were going to mean that I could not return to any kind of really meaningful and useful life. I have seen it in my forebears, and there is, no doubt, a bit of heredity involved. I would be quite willing to state that under certain circumstances — in fact I have stated to my wife — that I would just as soon she wouldn't be in too much of a hurry to call the doctor and turn things over to him. That might relieve him from the task of having to make these decisions.

Moore: This leaves her with the responsibility, though, of a very tough problem. Because if you are referring to having a stroke, a transient occlusion of your carotid artery can look exactly like a stroke and be completely reversible. You are taking liberty there with your wife's medical judgment.

DeWolf: Well, I know she will use judgment, and no doubt she will be consulting a doctor very soon.

Moore: But you just told us that she shouldn't consult a doctor under certain circumstances.

DeWolf: Under certain circumstances, yes. Well, let me be explicit. My mother awakened during the night and found no sign whatever of life in my father. The doctor came and he found no sign of life in him, but he succeeded by heroic measures in getting him to live a very wretched half-life for a few months.

Moore: So you are asking your wife to decide whether your death is just like your father's death, which is a troublesome and difficult decision to ask her to make. You are putting her in a very difficult situation.

You say that you don't want to have anything to do with suicide, but you are quite prepared to tell the doctor not to do anything to keep you alive under certain circumstances. Of course that's tantamount to suicide. He may join in the decision, but you are being inconsistent there because you're saying that you don't approve of euthanasia, but there are many situations in medicine in which simply doing nothing amounts to killing the patient. One must be very careful of these things. You can't compartmentalize these things so easily.

DeWolf: I agree and I certainly realize a doctor has the most agonizing time, that it is a difficult discrimination to make. I want nothing that I said to indicate that I think these problems are simple; they are immensely complex. I have entered into them through study, mostly of medical literature, not newspapers, but medical literature, which are agonizing at best. I am only entering in as a proposed kind of partner in the process of trying to find ways of resolving these. But Dr. Moore, too, has said that there are circumstances under which he would not further continue treatment, because this person has now reached the point where it is impossible to do more than interfere with his dying and that is an irreversible affair; and I would agree. That can be separated from euthanasia. I ought not take more time at the moment, but I would be happy to tell why if the opportunity seemed appropriate for me.

Mannick: Dr. DeWolf, this is your opportunity. Why is this separate from euthanasia?

Helen B. Taussig: Why is euthanasia bad?

Mannick: (a) Why is euthanasia bad, and (b) how is the proposed mechanism you have in mind different from euthanasia?

DeWolf: There are various considerations, but one that seems to me especially easy to explain, and important, is this: the relationship between a medical doctor and his patient is an extremely sensitive and important one psychologically. I do not want any situation to arise in which a patient will come to a clear consciousness out of delirious agonies of pain and see the doctor offering him a medicine or starting to give him a hypodermic needle and he is going to think at the moment, "Oh, that man is here to kill me." There are enough people who get these paranoid delusions at best without our allowing them to be fed them by doctors sometimes becoming deliberate agents of death. There is a great psychological and hence ethical difference between ceasing actions which are designed to prolong the dying of a person, and, on the other hand, the deliberate taking of a positive action of giving a treatment which is designed to take his life.

Mannick: Dr. DeWolf, perhaps what we are discussing here is the ethics of consent in regard to all varieties of procedures — the most experimental, and the most mundane. I wonder if we could hear now from Dr. Fletcher, who has done a good deal of work in the ethics of consent, with regard to any problems he sees in the specific issues of transplantation by the patient and the consent to donation of an organ by the family of the cadaver donor. I know that these are all areas that you have thought a great deal about.

John C. Fletcher: I haven't done any work on the consent process in transplantation. My work has been in the consent process for non-therapeutic studies.

I have noticed in my studies of the consent process that one could generalize from the non-therapeutic situation to the therapeutic one of organ transplantation and say that denial plays a tremendous role in illness generally. Patients and subjects in experiments do tend to deny a great deal of what they are told in the consent process as it goes along. Many patients withhold from the physician a lot of what they *do* understand, so that the communication process between the physician, who is in charge of getting the consent, the donor and the family of the recipient, and the recipient is a very complex psychological contract which is very open to the problem of denial of what one is told. We theologians have to be tremendously sensitive to the kind of data which has been reported by psychiatrists who monitor the consent process here in Boston as elsewhere, and have pointed up the role of denial so that what comes out in the newspaper or even in a court trial, where consent is a problem, may very well stem from the role of denial on the part of the patient as well as the doctor in the consent process. This would be one key problem that I would point to in the consent process.

Mannick: What do you mean exactly by the role of denial? Could you be more specific?

Fletcher: Denying how sick one is in order to get life-saving therapy.

Mannick: The patient is simply not listening to the doctor when he tells you that?

Fletcher: I imagine that is right. I've never been in on a consent process for transplantation. I've never witnessed it myself, but I have read and talked with physicians who have informed patients about the statistical chances in the early days of kidney transplantation in which there might have been a very poor match, and after it was over — or even during the process — the patient would have forgotten that or would have denied the fact that his chances were very slim.

William H. Goldwater: There is a great deal of trust in the communication between the physician and the patient in these situations as, for instance, in the following situation that I ran into earlier this year. One particular day I was in a certain city speaking with some people in an experimental ward where certain drugs were being taken. It happened to be one of these prisoner situations. I talked with the physician that I was visiting around with and with a couple prisoner subjects, and in speaking with them I got the distinct impression that they had a vague idea that they were taking a pill that would not be harmful, but was like aspirin essentially. Several days later I was at a conference that some of you attended in New York City, and I heard a leading physician who is in charge of the grand program in that institution speak rather elaborately of the fact that every one of these prisoner subjects was given an elaborate description of how these drugs did or didn't work. This, of course, made me smile because the prisoners' own statements were at much more of an elemental level. Here is where we run into that problem that was referred to in terms of what does Cooley tell his patients and so forth. So much depends on the trust the subject, or the patient if you will, puts in the physician. There is a lot that you cannot put on paper, but is a spiritual sort of thing.

Robert S. Schwartz: This was very interesting to me, but I'd like to hear your comments on another aspect of this problem. I have been in the position quite often of having to offer an experimental drug to a patient, and the patient accepts this because he wants to be liked or admired by the doctor. He wants to be a good boy; he wants to be patted on the head because the doctor is a figure of authority. Whatever the doctor recommends to the patient, he immediately agrees to and covers up, or denies, the potential harm that may come, all in an effort to be liked by the doctor.

Fletcher: I have seen this in talking to one patient interviewed after she had given consent for a study. I discovered she had an enormous amount of doubts about entering into it. I had observed the original sessions, and I asked her why she did not bring up any questions at that time, and she said, "Well, I didn't want him to think I was stupid." But I found that when doctors do get feedback about both what happens and doesn't happen, that this is of enormous significance in getting consent. They respond quite readily to that situation — go back to it and try to clear up the missed communications involved. It could be that the psychiatrists who monitor consent processes — as well as others who are interested in this problem — may be formulating a new kind of role in the medical research situation of ombudsmen or facilitators of better communication between people — people on the inside of the problem, as well as people on the outside who don't have access to the medical situation but do need to know pretty explicitly about what is happening in there. Society has an enormous amount of interest about what is happening in there. Unless we are inventive enough to release information that's reliable about what's happening and take our licks, as well as the joys in our successes, then perhaps society won't be reassured that every kind of precaution is being taken.

Mannick: Now we are getting at one of the real ethical problems that we face in transplantation as well as other medical frontiersmanship: just how good is this informed consent we are all very confident we have? I know a lot of people want to speak to that.

Moore: Dr. Goldwater has such a good point there. It ties in with what Dr. Fletcher was saying, too, about this interesting concept of denial and selective forgetting. We see it all the time with patients with malignancies who, at some stage, want to know what the trouble is and what their outlook is. If they are people with a reasonable education and emotional background, we like to tell them and we do. We don't ever take hope completely away from them, but we let them know that they have an advanced tumor for which we have no cure. The thing that is so striking and very amusing about that is that within two or three days they often will have forgotten it or blocked it out completely. They will not tell their families and their family will ask, "You told mother what the trouble is?" This is an interesting property of blocking out something you don't really want to know, and I think it enters into the consent process: the patient who wants treatment badly will block out part of the black side of the picture that the doctors try to give him.

Mannick: Dr. Beecher, this seems to me your field, and I know a lot of other people want to speak to it, but what about this informed consent?

Beecher: Again and again I think we are deceiving ourselves if we think we can very often get satisfactorily informed consent. It's the goal toward which we strive, and in striving for it we get a positive value. The positive value is that the subject knows, because of your inquiry, that he is going to be the subject of an experiment. I can tell you hundreds of examples where they haven't known that they were subjects sometimes of deadly experiments, and so I think there is a value in striving toward this goal. But we are deceiving ourselves if we think we ever achieve it in ordinary circumstances, in any reasonably complex situation.

Hans Jonas: Dr. Moore, does this blocking out apply independently of the intellectual, educational standard of the patient? Is it independent of it?

Beecher: Absolutely.

Jonas: You would say that even if you had informed a philosopher who had during his life accustomed himself to the idea of dying — the philosophy being an exercise in dying — even he would succumb to this, as it were, biological compulsion of forgetting?

Moore: Not all patients do this, of course, but I have seen many people with really a superb educational background who simply block out, and if they don't want to spend time thinking about it, and they don't, it is gone in a few days.

Mannick: Dr. Curran, how about the legality of all of this informed consent we are talking about?

Curran: Let the record show that I raised my hand! The first mistake we can make in talking about informed consent is to look upon it as a means by which a physician transfers his responsibility to the patient. This is a great mistake. It is not possible for a physician who determines upon a course of action and realizes that there are risks involved in it to transfer totally his responsibility to make a judgment as to whether or not the patient should enter it. To remove that burden from himself and place it upon the patient is a natural desire. Informed consent, however, merely allows the patient to participate, but it doesn't mean that he takes the responsibility fully himself. The physician must act within the realm of acceptable medical practice even in involving the patient. It must be reasonable for the patient to consent or not to consent. It must be a question he can understand and answer. It is not necessarily a part of the informed consent that he understand all of the objectives of the experiment. All he basically needs to have conveyed to him are the significant benefits that he should weigh against the risks. That really is basically all he needs to know. It is a simple concept. If it gets to a point of complication, then I am not sure you can say that is something that can be transferred to the patient for decision.

Beecher: But no one knows the risk.

Curran: If no one knows the risk, then there is a responsibility on the physician to determine whether the act should be performed at all. But he can't answer that by throwing it onto the patient to decide.

Mannick: How about the idea of a little child, a sibling of someone who needs a transplant — not just a kidney transplant, but for example, a bone marrow transplant — Dr. Bach? What are the ethics of the decision to put this well sibling to sleep and take bone marrow out of him and other assaults of that sort? How can you justify this ethically? You are going to help the other sibling who needs bone marrow, perhaps, but how about the one who is giving it, as a child? How do you resolve this?

Bach: I wanted to ask Professor Curran this very question, because here it seems, for the moment at least, the only donor that we know is acceptable with some degree of confidence — and there are not statistics worth mentioning yet — is a sibling. And very frequently the way in which one can treat the diseases successfully for a brief period of time, is by using a sibling donor, frequently under the age of twelve or fourteen. This has been done. There are seven cases now where apparantly the recipient is doing very well. In no case, as far as I know, was the sibling donor over the age of fourteen, and yet he was clearly put through a risk, a risk of very light anesthesia, a risk of having bone marrow taken. Slight, but informed, consent had to come from the parent. I don't think in any of these cases that the child was old enough to be really consulted, except that in every case that I know of — and certainly in the ones we did — phychiatrists did interview the child extensively and gave an opinion whether they thought this child could be used.

Mannick: Were there any of the cases brought to court?

Curran: No, not yet.

Mannick: The mere fact that this possibility exists for the sibling even if he is an adult, doesn't this finger him in a sense already? Does he really have any choice once the possibility is presented? Is he under such pressure that he can't make a free choice?

Bach: I don't like to tell anecdotes in medicine, but I do want to tell one case of my first real endeavor to get informed consent from a twenty-three-year-old sibling for a kidney transplant. As I sat there saying to him, "You know if you don't want to give this kidney to your poor dying brother (I didn't say that part) all you have to do is tell me, and nobody will ever know except for you and me," but the rest of the sentence wasn't honest when I said, "that you didn't want to." I think — as you've told us, Dr. Curran — that we have to make the best attempts we can and there are all kinds of psychological problems within that framework. Most of us have accepted for certain cases at the present time that it is justified to use a living donor. Now maybe not all of us have accepted it.

Mannick: Dr. Muelder, is this the sort of ethical nitty-gritty you were after this afternoon?

Muelder: Yes, the method by which one arrives at this, because if the ethics of the medical profession in dealing with these questions are valid, then they can be publicly discussed on the basis of merit, reason, and criticism. It may be that those then in the theological world who have made this a specialty, who study sensitivity to human beings as their life's vocation, may raise questions in a way that enters into the whole matter without any assumption that they have special sources of information going into it that are ethically compelling — and I deliberately put it that way because sometimes we are, in theological ethics, approached as if we assumed that. Now, since the value of human life is one of the "givens" in this, and the variables draw from the center, everyone wants to take this seriously, and it gets to be then the problem of the limit. If I may still make a comment or raise a question about the case that was just brought up now, a typical case . . .

Moore: Is that a typical kind of case?

Muelder: It is a typical *kind* of case in which parents are asked to make decisions about minors which involve dis-values or risks to some, values to others. What are the kinds of questions, not what are the kinds of answers theologians bring to this, or ethicists bring to this, but what are the questions that should be pressed before one rushes into that final decision?

Moore: Without commenting on the "rushes into" part, which seems to me to be a little loaded . . .

Muelder: I didn't mean it in that sense. But there is an eagerness in the life scientist by nature of their being in it to get on to new things. Now, this does not mean that it isn't responsible, but a life scientist is not a life scientist if he doesn't want to work on something that hasn't yet been done.

Mannick: Dr. Taussig, you've been innovative in all kinds of things in life sciences. What about the ethics of all this?

Taussig: In the early days of the "blue baby" operations, the patient's parents wondered very seriously whether they should approve the operation. We tried to paint the picture black and really didn't know what the risks were but said it was a fifty-fifty chance. I think perhaps it was painted too black. The parents would say to me, "What to do?" And often I said to them, "I think it depends upon your philosophy of life or upon your religion or what you believe is right. Are you going to say that if the child has an operation and dies that you were responsible because you gave permission for the operation? Or are you going to say if the child dies without the operation, you were withholding hopes from him?" Often I've said, "It depends on your philosophy of life as to whether I would urge you to take the risk. I don't believe the child is going to get well without taking a risk." But then it comes down to saying what are your own beliefs and what is right.

Curran: The point has been brought up at least twice of the possible involvement of some "ombudsman" in helping to make these decisions to protect the donor. I bring it up in regard to the comments concerning the use of the psychiatrists. It seems to me that a psychiatrist is not being used for that purpose here. The psychiatrist is largely being used to help make determinations as to whether or not the individual can understand the circumstances and can make a reasonable judgment. I look upon him as almost part of the transplant team; that is, he is interested actually in encouraging participation. On the other hand, an independent scientist, or an independent person who can achieve some degree of expertness in the reasonableness of the judgment itself as to whether the risks are too great for the individual to take — this is the ombudsman concept. It involves a community representative in helping to arrive at certain kinds of conclusions. Now, there are two ways in which this can be done. In our legal cases here in Massachusetts, we sought the help of the court, not merely to help in a particular decision — that is, to know whether or not it was wise to enter — but to set a general principle from which we could then act in the interest of other children and other donors. We didn't mean to have to go back every time to seek judgment. To make progress in science, to make progress in medicine, and to have every single decision individually reviewed by an outside figure would create a mechanism which should be questioned.

James M. Gustafson: I'd like to pick up on Dr. Taussig's remark and tie it into this problem involved in donation and pressure on siblings. Dr. Taussig suggested, to me at least, the way in which the person responds to medical intervention, experimental or otherwise, would be dependent in part on certain kinds of fundamental beliefs or philosophies of life. I take it that that is one of the hardest dimensions to get at when we are talking about ethics of medical care. I'm not proposing that there is a single philosophy of life which is the right one to have, but I am proposing what persons believe — what convictions they have about what is right for them to do and what is good for them to do — is a part of the context within which certain things are not only medically easier, but within which certain things can be judged to be morally right, at least for that particular person. I was very interested in the discussion in terms of the sibling donors, and I suppose many people around the table know about Renee Fox's interest in this kind of question, particularly her perceptions in a very astute way of the very psychological pressures that you alluded to on sibling donors.

There is in the Western religious ethical tradition a very strong support in favor of donation of something of one's self for the sake of the other. It's present in Judaism. Rabbi Simons from London recently did an article on Judaism in which he picks up what has been the traditional Christian thesis of giving up your life for the sake of a friend, and carries it through certain stories that one finds in rabbinic literature. He suggests that in Judaism while there is no moral obligation for one to give up his life for the sake of another, nonetheless there is a kind of possibility — in a sense, going a second mile — in which this is something that is not only approved of, but really lauded within Judaism.

Certainly if one looks at one of the central themes of Christian ethics, which might have some effect on certain people who take these things seriously, there is a central theme that it is a good thing to do, to give up something of one's self for the sake of the others. Now, Professor Joseph Fletcher indicated in a letter published in *Religious Situation* in 1969 that in a sense one of the reluctant virtues that the Western religions have been talking about for a long time is the willingness — right? — to give of one's self, some aspect of one's self for the sake of the other.

I want to enter in here the suggestion, you see, that certain people believe certain things to be good. If one can cue in on what they believe to be good, or what they believe to be the right kind of conduct for them to engage in on the moral sphere — not talking about the legal sphere — then certain things are going in favor of certain sorts of procedures.

Mannick: How about this pressure for a donation?

Charles Curran: I would want to comment on what Dean Muelder said. Our topic being the Identity of Man—between the panel I was at yesterday and the one today — it seems as if it were two different "Men" we're talking about.

Yesterday with the social sciences, we were talking primarily about the needs of society, etc., and today the medical scientists are talking primarily about the good of the individual patient. This comes up in terms of the ethical discussion, because today the discussion has been almost entirely in terms of consent. I believe this is very important. I don't want to overestimate it, it is not the only aspect to be considered, but this was very interestingly brought out yesterday when people were saying that because of societal needs it might be necessary to require that families only have two children. This is a little bit of what Paul Ramsey was driving at when he said there is a value of bodily integrity which is an element that enters into the discussion, not only concerning consent itself, but on all ethical and philosophical points involving life and death. Consent, as an issue, merely gives us a good focus on these other problems as individual in nature rather than societal.

Ralph Potter, Jr.: It is not enough to talk about the reactions of each individual through his own framework of values, although that's certainly important. We are clearly dealing with the nature of medical practice as an institution in a society, as a set of practices of agreed-upon expectations concerning what people will do in certain roles. Each of us — since we live behind a veil of ignorance and don't know what facilities we will need in the future — have a stake in knowing what the shape of this institution will be.

John Rawls, and other moral philosophers of late, paid a good deal of regard to institutions in ethics as the very nature of setting up a particular institution like promise-keeping — or medical practice in this case — that would thereby rule out certain types of rules, certain appeals, certain arguments that you can make. So, for instance, if I promise you something, I rule out the possibility of later saying, "I'm sorry I don't find it convenient now to keep my promise." This contradicts the very nature of the contract that I entered into with you. We ought to look at medical care in that way. When we enter into the institution of doctor-patient relationships, we rule out certain types of arguments, certain types of procedures, and one that ought to be ruled out — as Father Curran may be delighted to know — is euthanasia, and having a physician now change in his role by an appeal to the individual case of that patient, that rather he has an obligation to future patients who will relate to other physicians differently, if that practice enters into implied contractual situations.

So there is a public issue here. This is a warrant for all of us talking about the practice of medicine, and it is an institution of which we will avail ourselves some day soon or late. We have a stake in knowing what will be built in, what will be the expectations, what facilities will be available to us when we inherit the need.

Jerome L. Krasner: Norbert Wiener was primarily known as a mathematician, but he was a great biologist and his last work before he died was *Our Garden Golden,* which touches on many of the same things we have discussed here. He made a couple of the points that are germane to some of the discussion. His point was: our ethic is based on our knowledge, and we have to assume that our best knowledge in the given time constitutes the basis for an ethic, such as to do a high-risk operation. At least in Wiener's mind, one had to look ahead to say, "What does the future hold?" If it comes to the point where we have a tautological case one hundred percent, there is no question of ethic any more. Is it a question of the individual or the question of humanity for the future?

Wiener commented on something that Dr. DeWolf alluded to in this and what I might amend to call "a prescription death." Wiener didn't discuss it in these terms. He discussed it in different terms, but if the biomedical field gets to the point where the extension of life becomes indefinite, where the physician has the option more or less to terminate or to keep a guy going, it's germane here. Because Wiener commented that the physician now is put in a very delicate position because he becomes both the curer and the executioner. What happens to the relationship between the patient and the physician? Nobody's talked about the poor physician trying to sit here amid the ethic and maintain his own ethics.

A problem which we are experiencing today — and I am sure these gentlemen here can vouch for this — is the attachment of electronic means or mechanical means of resuscitation or monitoring, and the ethics implied upon the manufacturer if something is wrong. Whose fault is it? Is there an ethic that must be adhered to that doesn't mean that FDA takes over bio-engineering? There are problems here. I throw these out for subjects of conversation.

Mannick: We ought to leave, if we may, the subject of consent. We've discussed it perhaps to the extent that the time allows. Let's proceed onward with some other questions, also ethical, which pertain to this panel and the general subject of problems with transplantation. In discussing ethics, one of the things that was raised by Professor Potter was the question of the contractual-implied relationship between the doctor and the patient. Dr. Russell, do you have some remarks in that regard?

Russell: Will you elucidate further for us what, in your mind, does the contract consist of? It is extremely important to us at the present time. We want to fulfill that contract, and we want you to know that we want to, but we've got to know what it is. My feeling is that the contract that might be expected by Dr. DeWolf is, perhaps a little bit different than yours and maybe his idea of how the doctor might help him or others like him conceivably is different from yours. From his remarks this morning, he thinks part of this is due to aging and different perspective and all of that we have to take into account; but I wonder whether you could clarify further what you think that contract should be and what the implications are when you walk in the door.

Potter: Let me say that the subject of the whole conference is the nature of that contract. That's what we are working out and that's why the public dialogue, although difficult and vexing at times, is so important, because that is the only way of establishing common expectations that keep us from second guessing fruitlessly later. I don't have any well worked out scheme for what ought to be in that contract. There are some things fairly obvious that are already mentioned. They are very broad principles that are already common expectations. It is only around the fringes of those that we have these difficult and doubtful cases, and the only cure I know for that is to persist. I've never had the opportunity to take the type of invitation that Dr. Moore issued this morning: to come and spend several years with the hospital, and I'm just not versed enough. I've also enjoyed good health and haven't been close to medical practice at all. I have not even formed what you would expect to be an average layman's concept of what it ought to be. I'm pretty sure about how it comes to pass, and that's through this kind of conversation.

Gustafson: I wonder to what extent we could get at what is an important question from the side of the physicians: what they conceive to be the limitations of their obligations or responsibilities to the patients. Just in terms of conversations in the university in which I am housed, one of the most thorny problems we find is that many physicians have an overwhelming sense of almost unlimited obligation, and the society presses more and more obligations on the physician for the patient. It might be useful if we could clarify what are the limits of the physician's obligations to the patients.

Mannick: Dr. Schwartz, what about this: the limits of ethics and the obligation of the physician and how should we be talking about ethics in this regard?

Schwartz: I would want to come back to a point that I touched on this morning which has, apparently, scandalized many people, but nevertheless I feel that it's a point that is the underpinning of everything we are talking about: that is, a system of ethics — and I parenthetically would prefer not to use the word theology since I don't have a good understanding of what theology is — based on facts. This is what I meant this morning when I said rather sharply that theology will dissolve with the facts. I think Dr. Taussig's comments bring this out very clearly; because obviously in the early days of cardiac surgery, she and her patients and her colleagues were terribly concerned with ethical questions about this daring operation. Yet today the medical profession and the legal profession would accept it as unethical if operations were not carried out on a patient. So that the ethical problem has reversed itself completely because of facts and knowledge, and not because of anything more mysterious than that. We are going to see the same thing in the field of organ transplantation. If we can lick the problem of cadaver tissue, which we may be able to lick within the next decade, then the ethical question of transplantation will undergo a radical transformation, and we won't be sitting around discussing whether or not we should use Brother John's kidney, but the ethical question will change. This same principle which I feel to be central and very important is at the basis of the meaning of the contract between the doctor and his patient. It is what available facts the physician has — not theories and not speculations, but hard facts — and what facts are available to the patient, and whether or not there is a mutual understanding of these facts as Dr. Fletcher emphasized previously. This is at the heart of the whole question.

Reemtsa: I'm very much in support of Dr. Schwartz's remarks: namely, that there can be and there should be a factual basis of ethical value. That is the title of the book, The Scientific Basis of Ethical Value, in which Bentley Glass proposes just this view: the pragmatic point of view, if it works, is ethical. That is why I must take exception to the suggestion that now, on the basis of some consideration, we should move from related donors to cadaver donors. That is by no means an assured conclusion. We should make efforts in both directions; but until we know what those results are, we are not justified in directing our efforts purely on theoretical or theological considerations without scientific data. In the future we will probably look back on most of the issues we are discussing today as rather minor ones, such as consent and that sort of thing.

What really hangs us up now and will in the very near future is the fact that we will soon have to make choices between the rights of the individual and the rights of society. So far in our expanding pioneering efforts this has not really been necessary, at least not in hard circumstances. We have had the view that a man could have as many children as he wants. He can pollute the atmosphere and the river and so forth. Now this is even true as a medical situation, and as Dr. Moore pointed out this morning, we are not really competing with the care of patients in the ghetto, because most of us are not qualified to do that, those of us who are also doing the other work which has been mentioned. Nevertheless we must face the fact that in the near future there will be competition for these very scarce resources. We will compete not only in organ transplantation versus the ghetto, but it will be versus atomic submarines, versus Mars explorations, Vietnam, etc. I would like to focus on the ethical considerations that will help us in making judicious choices in these large areas of private rights versus societal rights. Again, I would emphasize that this would have to be determined on the basis of evidence, on the basis of the factual accomplishments rather than on preconceived notions.

Mannick: Dr. Moore, I know you have to leave us, and this brings us up to something that I know is very interesting to you. That's why I would like to hear from you on it. It's something we should be discussing this afternoon at some length, the whole question: can society afford us transplanters, anyway?

Moore: I'm glad Keith Reemtsa has brought this up, because I know we are all maybe groping for what is the biggest ethical and theological issue that we can deal with here today, and I would say it is precisely that issue: is it right for this country to spend billions of dollars trying to put men up into the solar system and various places while *we* cut back budgets? Now we happen to dislike seeing the transplant research budgets cut back. We are all big enough people to realize that that is only one part of a much bigger picture of health sciences in general, biomedical sciences in general. It is very shocking to me that the biggest cut was suffered by the National Science Foundation, which is really the grandpappy of them all. It is the basic science on which all of us rely that took the biggest cut. None of us, I think, could get very enthusiastic about the Vietnamese war; nonetheless it is in the picture. The thing that is most in competition with us is the space race. We have got to come out quite clearly and say we do not think that that is a valid alternative to working towards the welfare of the people here. What we are talking about today is the ethics that attend a very tiny effort in biomedical science, yet it's symbolic of the whole picture. The problem is that *we* would put the priorities with people here now on earth; and it just so happens that the Senate, for reasons that I don't fully understand, has put the priorities on the exploration of the solar system. It's very interesting. Those moon rocks are fascinating, but are they all that important in terms of competition here?

Jonas: Dr. Reemtsa, what exactly do you mean by rights of society versus rights of the individuals in the context of organ transplantation, and where do the rights of society come in here? Can society afford to waste tissue of dying persons that could be used to help salvageable individuals? Are you suggesting that there is a right of society or even an interest of society involved in the saving of individual life at the cost of somebody else, or where does this alternative come in — society versus individual — in the context of organ transplantation?

Reemtsa: My remarks were not confined to organ transplantation, although this is an area that has focused a great of attention. My concern with private versus public rights is more in the future areas than in the specific problems of transplantation. There are some conflicting rights in this area, but they are relatively unimportant. The use of cadaver organs as it is done by the French in harvesting organs from victims of accidents without consent would be an example of a public form of acceptance which is perhaps more advanced in other countries than it is in ours at this present time, but we shall come to that. Again, most of the problems that we are talking about in transplantation will be resolved, or at least minimized, with the improved biologic information which we have. Does this help?

Jonas: Not entirely, because a conceptual scheme is somehow thrust up in which there is construed some abstract right of society as a whole on resources of individuals for the benefit of curing certain individuals. Is this the opening of a door to a possible overruling of private inviolabilities and integrities in the name of such an abstract as the public weal? I recognize that the public weal, where there is — for instance, in the case of vaccination — a rather clear danger to large numbers of people through infection and where one can force an individual to undergo a certain procedure so as not to be a danger to others, that is a clear cut case. One can define this area of compulsion very clearly in terms of a public danger. But in such cases as the extension of the life span of certain sick individuals, to construe as it were, a public right on the resources of others to help them to survive is in my opinion a distortion of concept.

Reemsta: It is definitely a distortion, and I meant it as such. I am suggesting that we are going to have to "distort" our views. We are going to have to get away from this inviolability of the Judeo-Christian concept in which man himself is "the" unit with dominion over fish and fowl and creeping things. We are going to have to change all that because the circumstances are no longer ones in which the human race is struggling for its very survival against nature. Now it is struggling for survival against itself. It needs a new framework.

Alan Geyer: Until the last couple of sentences, the occasion for my remarks had passed. They helped to make the effort more timely, if not the substance of it. At the risk of some caricature, we have had lifted up before this consultation two rather contrasting notions of the truth about man and what the future of the process of discovery of that truth is. Dean Muelder suggested in his opening comments that as knowledge accumulates, the mystery deepens, and he repeatedly used this phrase. Dr. Schwartz suggested what seems to me to be almost an opposite way, that the essentially mysterious elements of life are diminishing as facts accumulate. I'm not on intimate enough terms with the medical profession and with its intellectual and philosophical life to know how typical Dr. Schwartz's comments are. But at any rate, there is a real issue here as to how we look toward the future of the truth about man. My own biases in this area are shaped perhaps not only by having been through a process of theological education, but also as a social scientist. The knowledge or the conviction that the mystery is deepening has become more and more important in the field of political science and sociology in recent years. In the face of this, the task of theology has become not less important, but in some ways it has become more important and much more difficult. Some of the questions pressed on theologians and moralists here have perhaps urged the theologians on to a broader conception, a more demanding conception of their task which is less imperialistic than theology once was, but in which the theological questions are opening up in a new way and in which the role of theology, in a sense, will grow.

To reopen a possibility Dr. DeWolf alluded to this morning in his opening comments: he said something like this: "If time permitted, I could lay out in a more elaborate and systematic way the ethical assumptions and criteria which I bring to this discussion." I wish time did permit this morning. We do keep coming back to this queston: what are the criteria and what are the assumptions which we bring to the kind of issues that we have been talking about this afternoon? Now, you may want to put this question to him or you may not, and even if you do, he may not wish to respond.

Mannick: That leaves me a lot of alternatives. Before I exercise any of them, I'd like to ask Professor Shinn how he reacts to these reactions.

Roger Shinn: As related to what I have already said, I am interested in the discussions we have had of facts and values. In one sense I welcome it because we are still close enough to the recent past dominance of a logical positivism with its absolute separation of facts and values that I'm glad that that's not been the stance here. There has been a real sense that facts and values are related, and that certainly any policy decision must pay great attention to the facts, and that factual developments do change the nature of decisions. They remove some problems. All this I very much welcome. And yet, I find a little difficulty in seeing how any body of facts per se add up to a basic value commitment. Here I'd just build on what Dr. Krasner was saying from Wiener's final book. Wiener's point was — and as you say he used the computer as a symbol — you can computerize a great deal of decision making — that is, projecting that such and such acts are likely to produce such and such consequences — and when you've done it all, only a human being can make a moral decision, because when you are asking what will work, you are asking what will work for the good of man. If Wiener is at all right, there is something of a tragic quality built into this. For example, as Dr. Krasner said, suppose you prolong a life indefinitely, don't you face another new set of issues? Isn't one of the services we all perform to the human race that of getting out of the way so posterity can have a chance? Don't we have to confront the relation between our deepest desires and renunciation of some of our ambitions? A man's decision on all this depends a great deal on his basic symbolization of life — his own and other people's — and his most deep-rooted loyalties and his sense of what it is to be human. If sheer human survival is our only value merely because of the accident that we happen to be human, it's got no more ethical qualities than a wolf's desire to survive. But if it is because our humanity represents something else that we conceive imaginatively in all kinds of ways, then you are down at the point where ethics — the decision as to good, bad, right and wrong — does depend upon certain root apprehensions and loyalties about the nature of life and man.

Mannick: Dr. DeWolf, what precisely are the ethical considerations that we should have behind us when approaching specific problems such as asking a person to donate an organ, such as deciding where transplantation gets financed as opposed to something else in the country, such as deciding whether we give all of our country's medical resources to health care delivery, and none to research, etc.?

DeWolf: I can't set forth the basic Christian ethic in the time allotted, and that's what would be required. But I do want to support in theory just a bit further, by example, what Dr. Shinn said. This is basically what I intended to respond to this challenge, this relation between facts and values. I want to call your attention to this fact presented by Dr. Moore, when he spoke about the space program and competition with the health programs of every kind. The space program works and so does the health program work, and you cannot decide which one you want to have work until you decide what kind of goals you want to reach. What are the ends? What are the values? Which are more important? What are the proportionate values? If it is true that human meaning and value is, in the broader sense, of more value than simply the narrower range of intellectual human values and some others that are involved in space exploration, then it would seem the health program ought to have priority. Similarly, to turn to another point that I have wanted to press and to which I haven't heard too much response, there is this question of the proportionate — I emphasize *proportionate* — priority given by the profession to public health and to the care of the individual. The individual is of priceless importance; but *all* individuals are important, not just the one who is performing at a given moment, and there is therefore a very real problem.

I agree with Dr. Reemtsa, and this has to do with basic Christian ethics, and with humane ethics which have been developed in the West largely under the influence of the Judeo-Christian traditions. Much of Western ethics has emphasized the dominion theme: man's dominion over nature. I'm personally a member of a theological and scientific team, a group called the Faith and Nature Group, which is trying to work through to a more meaningful relevant understanding of man's relation to nature in the present new situation. The facts certainly change radically the way in which the basic values which we adopt through this whole Judeo-Christian culture apply in a given situation. Even the Bible has other themes besides dominion. It has also the statements that God made this and that, and not man, and saw that this is good. Man must learn to live with them, to respect nature, and to be a practical ecologist and not simply ride roughshod over everything for his own short-term benefit.

Mannick: Dr. Schwartz, how does does Schwartzian factual ethics solve the problem of who gets the money in the scientific community as regards health care delivery, transplantation, research in immunology, etc., which ought to come first?

Schwartz: You've all witnessed today the evolution of a new philosophy. Before I answer that, I would like to say, suprprising as it may sound, that I really do agree with Professor Shinn. I like his remarks and I don't think that our positions are either-or positions. I'm not in favor of computerized man nor do I practice computerized medicine. Medicine is an art which is blended with science, and it's a humanitarian art, if you will. So I agree with everything you say. As soon as we begin to lose sight of what the basic elements of humanity are, we are finished.

About priorities, the emphasis has been misplaced here, and unfortunately Dr. Moore has left. I'm sorry that he picked out the space program — it's such a convenient whipping boy — but that's not where the emphasis ought to be. If we are sitting around here discussing theology and ethics and morals and so on, we ought to take up a different order of priorities — that this country is supporting the most monumental military machine in history. We're just sitting around accepting it. If we ought to protest against something in the federal government, in the federal order of priorities, let's talk about that, not about the space program. This country has enough resources to support both a space program and a meaningful health program. By meaningful program, I would include what Dr. DeWolf is concerned about and we are all concerned about, namely, bringing medical care to those people who don't have it right now. We are the richest country in the world, and there is no reason why we can't do space exploration, bring back moon rocks, and take care of a sick people all at the same time. But we are going down the drain on an eighty billion dollar a year military budget, and it's a disgrace to our ethical standards, if I may speak sharply and decisively.

One more comment which is based on this idea of ethics based on facts. If we are going to have an ethical system of medical practice, we are morally obligated to generate facts continuously. If we stop generating facts, the ethical system is going to fall apart. Now the crunch is on. There's a squeeze on the generation of facts which has come down from the federal government. This is immoral; this is unethical. We can't deal with sick patients who are presenting new, challenging problems to us unless we have those facts, and those facts are not going to become available with the rapidity that we require under the present system. This very distinguished panel should voice very strongly their objections to the priority systems, not in terms of space, but in terms of the self-serving military system that this country has built up.

Mannick: Dr. Goldwater, as the representative of a rapidly disappearing organization, the National Institute of Health, would you care to comment?

Goldwater: Actually this business of selecting national or health priorities is one that we have been up against in the government for the past five years. In answer to this business of priorities — and whether it's the war system which constitutes a minor portion of that total defense budget, or the choice between, let us say, various kinds of transplantation or medical care systems — we have to go back to something that Dr. Moore himself said today. He raised this question this afternoon, but he answered it this morning. He said that our culture, our civilization, our society in this country is not attuned to the commonplace sort of medical care. We think of the heroic; we think of the glorious, the steps on the moon and so forth. This is what attracts people, that attracts Congress. If it attracts the public, it is certainly going to appeal to the congressman to vote for it. Now this is my thesis: this is the way that the heroics of the transplanters got extra money for the National Institute of Health, the Arthritic Institute and the Heart Institute, because this is the kind of thing that made the headlines. This is a simplistic sort of analysis of the situation, but it doesn't take too much thought to see how it works in terms of the appeal to the congressman and how he is going to get his votes. As far as the space program, we had the Kennedy dictum: "Let's reach the moon by the end of this decade." I heard this morning that we are going to reach Mars by the end of this millenium. So this is the kind of thing that you have to bring into context.

But coming back to the challenge we have with our current social system in this country, we have to consider that we, as a society, have to set our priorities, just as yesterday some of the programs that I was concerned with dealt with the question of how you have to get these things in line with those people who are going to use them. The people of this country have come to realize that certain things are good for them and certain things are better and certain things are not as good. It is just a matter of, perhaps let us say, the theologians having to take up a certain amount of work that the medical scientists cannot do and to inspire the people of the country to something bigger and better on the behalf of society rather than just the individual, and get us to a point where we can do both of these things again, the basic research and the practical and applied.

Ramsey: On the priority problem, I think we ought to ponder this more deeply than we have so far. It is not only the space program that is the whipping boy, but the military establishment is also. We all have our priorities — things that we would exclude in order to make it credible to believe that we could do the remaining ones. Let's just take the quality of life in urban America, the pollution. Try to calculate what enormous social responses would have to go into improving that. It is not at all obvious, to me at least, that the budget of the National Institute of Health, the graph of it, could have kept on going up. In other words, even on things that we could all agree are vitally important things for our civilization to move ahead on, we will find ourselves in conflict. We are going to find this having to be worked out crudely and in the political community. To assume otherwise is like somebody addressing the first grade in a school, and saying, "In this country every one of you could become president." We really mean any *one* of them could. Now any one of these things we could do, to the limit of desirability. It is very difficult to believe that even among things enlightened people would agree were of urgent importance that we are going to have the resources to do them all. The medical needs of the world at large — let's put in foreign aid or whatever one would do to really transmit abroad things that would service human needs — are going to be a part of the priority. In other words — and this may be giving up on the game — that civilization is not a population engaged in the focused enterprise. We are bound to live with the situation in which there is justification and an urgent need for moving on a multiple number of frontiers and we are going to have to fight this out in terms of the political process and hopefully improve the ways in which such decisions are made.

The proximate ethical principle I want to make — in addition to the things mentioned by Al Geyer and DeWolf and Roger Shinn, for which I think there would be profound religious backing — is a kind of extension of meditation upon the patient-doctor relationship: the whole business of the need for a consensual community as we proceed in the practice of medicine. I'm not talking about just the patient-doctor relationship in the old style, but the fact that, for example, Medicare and Medicaid are giving the patient in the ward an individual physician who is responsible for him, plus the problem of how you are going to really train doctors. Medicine is an art, it's a manual art often, and there comes a time when the young surgeon has to be left alone in the room. If there is justice here, as there should be, it is going to call for far greater consensual community on the part of those who occupy private rooms to be willing to be a part of this process as a kind of partnership across the generations. We who have benefited from past training in the manual art of medicine need to be willing to engage with the medical profession that this continues to be done. I don't know whether I could go along with this, but how the devil do you train and keep training enough people to be able to do heart catheterization if *everybody* makes the demand for the one who really knows how? There is a first time for doing that, you know, and it is a dangerous operation even with great skill. So here we are in the consensual community I am talking about. We'll have to accept, to a greater degree than we have consciously done, the necessary fatalities for a not quite so good performance.

Mannick: Dr. Reemtsa, we are all aware of the great problems in regards to training composition, the ethics of all this, but to get back to the ethics of transplantation, and specifically, the ethics about how do you decide whether we ought to spend money on transplanting or on health care delivery in the ghetto, if the choice were ours, what about this question? How do you resolve it? Is it really a specious question even?

Reemtsa: Speaking in the context in which I work, it probably is a different question than in other areas. We work in a very limited geographic area, defined population. We have facilities for both dialysis and transplantation so we have no problem really in making some of the difficult decisions. I would, however, comment on this matter of delivery of health care since this cliche has become embedded in our political and medical lives. Many, particularly outside the medical profession, have the feeling that this "delivery" of health care is something just like that. It is neat packages of health care which are being sequestered in medical centers, and all we need do is load them on pickups and dispense them to the ghetto. But the delivery of health care in America is a non-system at the present time. It comprises multiple methods, none of which is totally adequate to the needs of that particular area. However, this cannot be solved in isolation, and as Professor Ramsey said, this requires an enormous consensual community effort which includes political and social and economic changes which must coincide with these medical developments.

I support Dr. Schwartz's view of the importance of continuing inquiry, not only to give us a continuing broader ethical base, but also to emphasize the fact that most of the diseases which we are now treating, we know very little about. The diseases killing us fall into two general groups: one of them we know about and we don't do much — we eat too much, smoke too much, drink too much, drive too fast — all of those things we understand even though we still do very little about them, but that isn't really a doctor-patient sort of thing.

Mannick: And parenthetically it is very hard to blame the medical profession that human beings are dying from those causes.

Reemtsa: Right. In the second general area are diseases on which we have such inadequate information that we can do little about them — cancer, hypertension, stroke and so forth. Now in between them there are certain things where the ministration of the physician makes some difference. But for us to forego continuing research and inquiry into these very major problems would be a disastrous decision. It would be like what the British did in the seventeenth century, building fever hospitals to treat malarial victims instead of looking after the mosquitos in the swamps.

Mannick: Are we saying from the medical side of things that perhaps the public has spent all of its time focused on the package payment for the fee for treatment, and has ignored the fact that the medical bill has two other large items on it, one of them being how we are to pay for medical education without which the fee for treatment is meaningless and the other medical research without which none of this is energized? All of us who are here on the medical side of this panel probably feel strongly that these two aspects of the present and future problems in medicine have been greatly underemphasized in public awareness.

Goldwater: Speaking of kidney, heart and so forth, transplantation and replacement, what about the preventive aspect? I don't think we have even gotten to that — the value of preventive programs in women, for instance, in kidney disease. The potential that that has for cutting down all kidney disease, including the need for kidney replacement by machines. The same may go eventually in behalf of cardiac diseases, cardio-vascular diseases. A great deal of emphasis has to be put on the preventive aspects of these long-term degenerative diseases, rather than just the cure at the end stages as it were.

Muelder: To come back to the points raised by Dr. Schwartz and relate them to the question of priorities, one of the moral laws that I would subscribe to among others — a procedural moral law, not a substantive *a priori* answer — is that one ought to consider the foreseeable consequences of alternative possibilities and on the whole approve of them in making a choice. Now as we get more facts, and by this you mean predictions, we are able to handle that part of the moral life which has to do with anticipating the foreseeable consequences. Then of course, we have to evaluate them, whether one set of alternatives is as acceptable to us as the other. Dr. DeWolf and others are pointing out that predictive alternatives do not evaluate themselves. So we come back, then, to the question of what is one's hierarchy of values or one's system of values or realm of values. I'm not trying to press one model more than another. Those of us who work in theoretical ethics as well as applied ethics, know that a great deal can be done here, but sooner or later you do come to this question of priorities. If there is a valid question of priorities between the space program or anything and investment in heart transplants, then there is a real question of priorities. The question then is: according to what criteria are these priorities placed? They don't order themselves. This becomes the social ethics question par excellence in the world today. What are the priorities before the world communities? What are the priorities before the American community? To what extent the personal or the more general? But the general social is always made up of persons. We are simply not firewood laid in the fireplace of society. If the individual has no value then the society has no value. We cannot deal with simple alternatives. But let me just press it, if it is in order to press the priority question, to society as a whole between NASA and organ transplants, in order to raise the question between more socialized, in one sense, and less socialized or more personalized medicine on the other.

Now the medical guild has its own order of priorities. It likes to debate these things among themselves rather than to have too many outsiders enter into the debate until the facts have been established. Then the public is invited, more or less, to accommodate itself to what has been shown *within* medical practice to be acceptable *to* medical practice. It is at least conceivable — and I'm pressing only to method, not attacking the profession — that in a more and more complicated future-society the public may insist on some priorities that the medical guild does not like. One of these may be that we can't afford organ transplants. It is conceivable. Even though it may be factually established that it can be done, and it can be done well within the medical frame of reference. Now all of us together in society today have to help answer the medical priorities along with the medical profession. We are in a situation today where we have to take seriously the theme of the consensual problem and we have together here the medical profession, theologians, ethicists, business people, all kinds of professions. What kind of community do we want and what kind of people do we want in that community? We are stuck with a problem that no longer will isolate itself as simply "the" theological question or "the" medical question. We know what the population problem is; what we need is to change the social attitudes towards it. Won't you theologians go out and help change that because somehow you are the inspirers of society? It may be that we don't want the role of being the inspirers. It may simply be that we want to participate in the role of the priorities.

Mannick: I wonder whether you are not commenting very much as one of our top science writers did at the end of the Senate hearings concerning transplantation, stating that witnesses testifying against scrutiny of their own field seem to be saying, "Daddy knows best and daddy will tell you when it is safe for you to play with this dangerous toy." They produced no convincing evidence "daddy" really does know best, but they did make the senators thoroughly angry. I suppose that's really what we are talking about.

I wonder if we could raise one final issue and that is the question of identity. Enough people have raised it, that we ought to talk about it. I don't believe that there is anyone here among the medical men who thinks that the fact that you have somebody else's organ makes your problem of identity any different than it was when you started, and I'm sure that the public has had some misgivings that this may be so. I don't believe any of us in medicine think it is so. Dr. Fletcher, will you talk a bit about this and your observance of this problem.

Fletcher: I wanted to raise a question for facts and to try to get some sense of whether or not this question was researchable. It's a question that has popped up in all kinds of literature surrounding transplantation, probably based on the presupposition that what happens to my body affects the way I perceive myself. What happens to myself probably has some effect on or some expression physically. Psychiatric reports have shown individuals who have renal transplants do suffer some kind of trauma. I read one report where women who received transplants of a male kidney, or of another kidney, felt that some strange new organ had been introduced into their bodies and even entertained fantasies of being pregnant. Male donors who donated kidneys had some fears of being castrated. Those people who try to think ahead to mechanical organs — like the possibility of an artificially replaceable mechanical heart — have hypothesized that the anxiety of carrying this mechanical organ and being so totally dependent upon it, would indeed affect the person's sense of basic security or identity. Now, I ask those of you who have been involved in a series of transplants over a long period of time — and if you have studied it — has there been appreciable change in the recipient's sense of identity, and how do you go at that question?

Mannick: My impression has been that the patient's greatest fear is one of rejection which is haunting him all the time, and that this has subjugated anything else that I could perceive. Dr. Russell, are these people worried about their identity being changed when they get new organs?

Russell: I think they are. It is quite right, as you have observed, that people have found this out by talking to patients and inquiring as to their reactions. From a strictly biological point of view, there is no reason why, physiologically, they should be able to detect that their blood is being brought to the normal state by a structure which was born and raised in somebody else, any more than if it had been in themselves. So that I think it is a problem of accommodation to something which is completely new, as Dr. Moore emphasized this morning.

The whole procedure of life being dependent upon something that came from somebody else is quite new to all of us, and it is not surprising that, as you say, fantasies might arise from this. We are going to have to learn how to accommodate to that if we want to persist in organ transplantation, just as we do with lots of other new medical problems. Take patients who have electronic pacemakers, now a very wide-spread thing. They rely on this for life. They have to come to terms with this, and they do have fantasies about it — about getting too near to the TV set or something like that, all sorts of things which they might be worried about which may or may not have a basis in fact as we know it. It is something we will grow out of, all of us, as we get more accustomed to it. This is only one example of how we're going to be more and more dependent on unpredictable outside forces that we must come to terms with.

Fletcher: I'm worried about helping to create more multiple dependencies than we already in fact have. I am very interested in trying to analyze the source of the enormous amount of violence and aggression that is present in our society today. I agree with Eric Fromm, that one of the reasons is that people have become so passive and dependent that they engage in violence to prove to themselves that they are alive, that there is no other way to compensate for the fact of feeling so empty than to engage in some destruction to prove negatively to yourself that you are human. Another reason is probably a great sense of disillusionment on the part of many groups of people in our society of tremendously high expectations, and in certain groups, very low rewards, which increases the sense of frustration and does lead to more aggression and violence. The transplanted population is very small indeed. I also know from studies of patients on long-term dialysis that they do have problems with dependence. They come to have a high sense of aggression about being there, the struggle with the problem of being dependent. I wonder if we are not contributing to a whole new form of illness through increasing the sense of dependence upon technically elite special groups with special sources of knowledge that are hidden behind screens. It is very difficult to get in and find out what is really happening to people.

When I raised the question of identity, it's not just if I were transplanted tomorrow, would I think that I was Suzy-Q because I got her kidney rather than John Fletcher's. But transplantation is a part of a process in which we are indeed changing the identity of modern man, in which we are beginning to get the feeling that our personalities and our bodies are endlessly revisable. This is part of the motif behind transplantation. Part of the religion that supports it is that we can change ourselves extensively, world without end. We may be doing violence to some of the limits of the possibilities of changing human nature that are involved in changing our identity, corporately as well as individually. That worries me about organ transplantation.

Mannick: This may be a good note, that is, a questioning note, to end this conference. This afternoon we have explored certain areas where ethical considerations are operational in transplantation. Perhaps they were not some of the areas that were conceived of in the public press, but beyond those, where we really do find ourselves in true dilemmas, where solutions are not apparent. One thing is clear: Society is not going to allow us in science and transplantation to proceed alone to reach answers to these questions.

Problems with Genetic Manipulation

I. Dorothea Raacke: This workshop on the Problems with Genetic Manipulation will continue the interface between theology and science and focus on the problems that might arise if scientific developments are allowed to take their place. It was said this morning that feasibility means practicability. The time scale is not so important, because the purpose of conferences such as this is to make us aware of the problems that we are going to face. The time to discuss them is long before they are at hand, for when they are already at hand there is always an air of panic about such discussions. The fact that the problems in this particular workshop are *not* at hand — as for example, the problems on population explosion are at hand now — gives us more leeway in discussing, perhaps in a calmer way, the problems that are going to arise. Dr. Ramsey, will you begin the discussion?

Paul Ramsey: If the geneticists will bear with me, I would like in the genuine spirit of inquiry to put before you a point that for me seems to be decisive ethically. Before rushing to a balancing judgment about the goods or ills of a program of genetic engineering for mankind, we ought first to attend to the problem of the first trial. I have in mind the difficulty of proving it will ever be morally right to learn some of the procedures that may in the future be possible through genetic manipulation. In this I bring to bear a sense of the value of the individual — you can say Judeo-Christian western humanist, if you wish. In this view, the individual has sanctity and ought not to be absorbed or used for the sake of over-arching community values. Let us suppose a case of what you might call negative eugenics. The idea behind genetic engineering is to knock out a deleterious gene somehow for therapeutic purposes, not for overall species purposes. The therapeutic objective arises because our genetic knowledge tells us that a couple has a high probability of producing a child who will suffer individually from a serious defect. However, am I not right that in getting to know in a first trial whether one can knock out this deleterious gene, scientists cannot know the gene with which it will be replaced — if that is the correct language — or the side effects, even genetic side effects or other effects that they may at the same time produce?

I'm accustomed as a moralist to balancing judgments. It might be true that to allow a child to come to birth suffering from that genetic illness would be worse than any damage that may genetically be introduced in the first trial. But why should that child ever have been conceived? To avoid the moral objection arising in the case of the first trial, to bear our ethical responsibilities to the first mishap — which would be a life having sanctity like any other — geneticists will have to become more pro-natalist than the Roman Catholic Church ever was. Why? Simply because the indicated treatment in the case we are supposing is not having any children, sterilization, using three contraceptives at once, or hying them away to a nunnery. In other words, you have to assume the existence of the life you are going to be working on, if you are ever to begin a line of balancing moral judgments. Otherwise, the claim is absolute that a human life is not to be manufactured. It strikes me that our genetic information should go to warrant genetic counseling and even some pretty extreme social measures to *prevent* that genetic catastrophe. Unless one is going to make the astonishing assumption that the child already exists and is defective, then one wonders why is it being made in order to learn how to correct its defect? Why suddenly this presumption about there being a child that is not born, on whom we must then, are able then, are warranted then in making a kind of balancing judgment between illness and the hazards of treatment? For me the problem is the first trial. As a moral test this applies to many areas, if one does not dismiss the cruciality of the vital sanctity of the single individual in our ethical heritage. The question is how one learns to do many currently forecasted procedures without violating a human life. I assume everybody here knows that moving from microbes or mammals to the human in experimentation is always a step that has its risk. However small these risks, they are risks to a life that from the Western ethical point of view, has infinite sacredness. Such a value should drive us to those other indicated preventative measures and will not allow genetic engineering on gametes.

Philip Morrison: What about somthing more neutral, like sex determination?

Ramsey: That doesn't introduce this sort of problem. It may introduce others.

Raacke: How is this first trial different from any first trial in medicine? Presumably the gene one would try to extirpate or modify would be on a desperately ill individual who could not but gain from such a procedure.

Bernard D. Davis: If Professor Ramsey were at a university that has a medical school, he would have a very rich field for consideration and discussion, because, in principle, anybody who tries a new surgical operation tries it on somebody. He tries it first on experimental animals.

Ramsey: I have not been understood. If genetic surgery means — and I understand it may embrace this — working on an already conceived embryo or fetus by whatever operations, then it would be on all fours with the first trial of an investigative therapeutic operation. There the individual is already in being. One works on him at grave risk, and so forth. To "operate" on a child "preconceptually" is another matter.

Davis: Well, I'm afraid then, you *are* misunderstood. Or to put it another way, I really can't understand the problem. I don't see any difference. Obviously before anybody tried this on human beings, there would be extensive tests to see what would happen if we tried to introduce DNA into the sperm cells of lower animals and then higher animals, up to monkeys. The comparability of operating on the sperm cells of lower mammals and human beings is much greater than the comparability of moving with a drug from one kind of animal to another, because there is a great deal of species specificity in the response to drugs.

Neil Todd: Haven't we already faced the blunder in a rather remarkable way, not with genetic manipulation, but in treatment with something like thalidomide, and survived the shock? In other words, a mistake was made despite all the pre-testing and planning. It was an unprecedented disaster in medical science, but we don't scrap the whole program. We all respond to it in somewhat different ways — embarrassment, chagrin, despair to a certain extent. The first blunder made in a genetic manipulation cannot be any more or less of a disaster than the kinds that have already been made. In other words, we can live with the problem, and we must live with the problem, of making mistakes. That is part of the trial and error system. That is much of what science is about.

Isaac Asimov: The universe does not consist of scientist alone. Scientists are a body that is embedded in the large sea of a non-scientific public. Every mistake increases public distrust of science. We are living at a time when we are dangerously near a catastrophic public distrust of science, and I hate to see anything happen which will encourage this further.

Todd: Science has vindicated itself on numerous occasions. Many things have been done and accepted, such as the Salk vaccine and a whole catalogue of things that have reduced misery. The public, if they are not yet aware of it, are prepared to be aware of the hazards that go with the benefits, unavoidably sometimes, because we can make mistakes.

Asimov: Unfortunately the public doesn't approach this always in the cold light of reason. To use a not completely accurate analogy, it has never been possible to avert anti-Semitism by pointing out all the good Jews.

Ramsey: This is not a simple question of a mistake. In the case of thalidomide — I'm surprised you introduced that — that wasn't being given for the sake of the child. A truer illustration would be some procedure formerly used to increase oxygen supply to an unborn child, later discovered to be injurious. That was a mistake. A tragic mistake, but not immoral. One was making an effort on behalf of that child, let's say, or the woman who was pregnant. In the case of genetic engineering upon germinal material, one begins to operate on a life that does not yet exist. There are far less hazardous remedies to prevent the transmission of genetic defects, e.g. three contraceptives at once. Otherwise we must be extreme pro-natalists in order to justify the first trial. Our premise would have to be something that Christianity has never believed, namely, that every woman should have a child by any means. Procreation is rather where one bears responsibility for the species, as Father Curran said earlier. The indicated treatment here would seem to be — for both the child and the species — the genetic death of that couple as over against the kind of mistake I'm talking about, which is not just a mistake comparable to all others.

Raacke: You are advocating eugenics as against genetic engineering then? You are saying we should forget about the genetic engineering and stick to eugenics or to a kind of eugenics?

Ramsey: Eugenic counseling, all kinds of things; but until I see the answer to the moral objection to the first experimental trial, I conclude that genetic engineering should not be performed upon sperm and ovum. That chooses for another the risks he alone must bear.

Todd: How do we distinguish that from making procreation possible through medical manipulation of geneotypes that would normally be excluded and thereby producing geneotypes that we know in advance are "defective," as, for example, diabetes?

Lynn S. Margulis: Any medicine before the reproductive age that allows the continuation of people who are going to perpetuate whatever they've got wrong with them — diabetes, muscular sclerosis, there are thousands of examples — and keeps in the gene pool people who would, under ordinary natural selection be selected against, is in a sense already genetic engineering. Of course it is a deleterious kind of engineering.

Morrison: But it's more than that; it is also individual therapy.

Davis: It is the value we place upon the individual that permits us to allow the continuation of people with defective genes. We're also aware of the fact that we can later intervene to stop reproduction by them.

Margulis: The relevant issue is much broader: there is only so much land and there are so many people trying to grow exponentially. Which ones are going to be those allowed to grow? At present those with the money who can afford to get through to a reproductive age are the ones leaving the genes to the next generation.

Jerome Gross: The highest birth rates and the fastest doubling rates are in places like Latin America and India and China among the poorest.

Margulis: Yes, and from an evolutionary point of view, these people are the most successful.

John Cato: In a sense the eugenic thing is going on now. With reference to the Black ghetto, for example, the fact that there is bad housing, poor nutrition, poor delivery of medical services, etc., suggests that we haven't got the moral fibre to deal with that issue. I, therefore, am very skeptical about letting anybody deal with the other issue in terms of selection of population and so on. I leave it to my theological betters to lay out a rationale for it, but it strikes me that this is the real interface which challenges both theologians and scientists. It is an interface that has to do with our advocacy — as someone put it earlier in this conference — on behalf of man rather than on behalf of our technological competence. That is one of the great fears that I felt throughout the conference.

Raacke: What specifically was your fear?

Cato: The notion that we are all quite competent in our respective fields, but in a sense we are more prone to push the progress of science or theology rather than raising what strikes me as a significant policy question. We need to continue to press those policy questions so that we are not in the position of — five, ten, fifteen years from now — saying what a horror we unleashed.

Salvador E. Luria: What has just been said touches the center of the problem. That is, the question of considering issues of scientific or moral policies as if they were the issues involved in this whole problem, which is clearly not the case. May I expand a couple of minutes on this point? It struck me this morning when Dr. Davis, in his relatively optimistic presentation, stated that the dangers that may be faced are not terribly serious. This is based on the assumption that a hypothetical humanity will apply, in a rational way, the technology which is likely to arise from science. That is extremely difficult to believe looking at the world in which we live. The usefulness of a conference of this kind — and of all discussions of genetic engineering about which I have been speaking and writing for many years — is the warning that any technology that science generates is at least as likely to generate dangers and unpredictable deterioration of the human society as it is to be of benefit.

Let me divide the possible application of genetic engineering — intervention at the level of genetic material or at the level of nuclear transplantation — into two categories. Let's call them the positive, therapeutic or eugenic applications, and the anarchistic, destructive or degenerative applications. As far as the first class goes, there is no question that there will be pressure to go ahead when these techniques become available. Here the only reason for fear is the fact that in a not too socially responsible setting, they are likely to generate even greater problems than those posed, for example, by organ transplantation, which have already created problems of a social nature that hospital administrators know very well. Roland Hotchkiss put it in a very good way: new developments are likely to be used for the usual mixture of uninformed do-goodness and personal profit in any society that exists today, whether it is economic profit or power profit. The real danger is that once one opens this kind of gateway, it is much easier to develop destructive uses. From the example of what happened with atomic energy, I see very little hope that any of the societies existing now are going to be sufficiently pre-adapted not to make destructive uses of new technologies. Neither a society that sends intellectuals into exile for criticizing the government, nor one that drops billions and billions of dollars worth of bombs on Vietnam can be trusted with the power of a new technology that can go to the very roots of human nature. For this reason this kind of conference is extremely important: to warn that the problems are not scientific, the problems are political.

I am always skeptical when I hear scientists talk about the possible benefits or dangers of some technology, because this is not our decision. I am equally skeptical when I hear theologians dissect the moral aspects, because I have seen what happened to the German theologians under the Nazi Reich. The only ones who really got into the battle had to take the political route, and Dietrich Bonhoeffer paid in front of the firing squad for having made that decision. Very few theologians raised any questions about the use of the atomic bombs over Hiroshima and Nagasaki, which, after all, was not purely a scientific or physical decision. It was in part a biological decision to use a mass-destruction weapon on people of a certain race. There is a tremendous responsibility that we take if we, as scientists or as theologians, give to the public the impression that the problems that are generated by genetic engineering — or the possibilities of genetic engineering — are such that scientific or moral solutions can be found. The solutions are political and the decision will have to be made at the polls or at some point of authority. They are not going to be made around the conference table.

Raacke: I didn't have the impression that this conference was one of making decisions. It's supposed to be illuminating.

Luria: Conferences are very useful. They can point out the issues and present the problems of responsibility for making political decisions. That is the good that can come from this kind of conference.

Paul M. Doty: If one interprets genetic manipulation broadly to include all attempts to control the outcome of the maintenance of fertilization, then there are three grand levels one can discern: the first one is the attempt to eliminate defective offspring either before fertilization occurs or shortly thereafter. This attempt to correct and eliminate what is obviously agreed upon as defective by wide margins from the norm is one level of operation, and that is what genetic counselors address themselves to. This is what is gradually beginning today. The second level is perhaps a more informed revival of eugenics as a philosophy, and ultimately as a mode of operation for larger and larger groups of people. Thirdly — in the far distance, at the turn of the century perhaps — comes the true genetic engineering, where one attempts to improve upon existing genes and eventually attempts to carry on the evolutionary process toward higher processes that are no longer possible, because we are no longer operating by the natural selection principle. Each of these three levels can be called the manipulation and engineering of the genes. We have the problem of how society is going to face them, and what the norms are going to be and what political problems are to be solved.

In the foreseeable future of the next decade, we will be faced almost entirely with this first problem of how to diminish the quarter of a million defective offspring that are produced in America every year. At this level — insofar as it now goes on through genetic counseling and so forth — it is more insulated from political pressure than any other act which people undertake, so I don't see the fear that Luria holds before us when we address this first problem. This is the only problem that we are going to face in the coming decade in a substantial variety of forms, and these range from genetic counseling, which would urge two couples not to have offspring, to the other extreme of sex choice by means of prenatal examination, revealing the sex of the embryo and followed by abortion if that was not the sex the parents wanted. It is in this range of situations that the practical problems will come. I do not see how it is going to be coupled to the political climate, but I do think it is going to be very related to the moral climate.

Jack B. Bresler: In the area of socio-genetics and regarding the question of genetic engineering as a form of manipulation of genes, some ongoing social influences are already, and have been for some time, changing the human population pool considerably. For example, take the question of artificial insemination: if you compare the donors to the males that they replace, you probably think that you are dealing with a more intelligent group than the males that they are replacing. This is engineering; this is manipulation already; this is going on constantly. It has been said that celibacy in the Roman Catholic Church has depressed the population intelligence, because it tends to remove the most intelligent from contributing to the human gene pool. On the other hand, in the Jewish tradition the scholar, the rabbi, was always encouraged to reproduce and always given funds so that he could. Demographic studies in Europe at the time show that the rabbi usually had more children per offspring. So this was an influence that has been working all the time.

Recently in a genetic conference in Princeton, there was a discussion of mating. Sociologists and geneticists now indicate that intelligence and education are emerging among the strongest devices for the selection of mates, so we are restructuring the genetic pool along intelligence lines. There are quite a few who do believe that.

Harold P. Green: Since I'm neither a life scientist nor a theologian, I can only hope optimistically that the reason that I am here is because everybody recognizes that after the theologians and life scientists decide what to do, they will need lawyers and legal systems to implement their decisions.

As a lawyer, I tend to be rather conservative, because I recognize the need for reconciling the objective of stability with the objective of change. I've been rather disconcerted since I have been in Boston at the AAAS meeting beginning last Friday and have watched some of these students in action. I've been rather dismayed to find that by and large I agree with their conclusions. I agree, for example, with Mr. Shapiro's conclusions, at least in part, although I don't agree with his rhetoric and I don't agree with his reasoning. He may have reached the right conclusions for the wrong reasons. Essentially, I agree with what Dr. Luria had to say.

I was impressed this morning — as I was when I read his paper in *Science* — by Dr. Platt's description of the kind of geometric advance we have had in certain technologies in the last thirty years. I don't think, however, Dr. Platt stated the matter quite strongly enough. I would state it in a different way. Go back thirty years in time to 1940; ask yourself how much damage could an evil or demented person have inflicted upon society in a single act. The answer is quite trivial as compared to the situation today when an evil or demented individual can quite literally destroy the entire world in a single act. We have developed at least three technologies in the past thirty years — or that are being seriously considered in any event — which I think are many orders of magnitude different from any kind of technological development we have ever had in the past. One of them is the general field of bio-chemical warfare agents. The other, of course, is nuclear weapons. A third, possibly is the development of drugs which operate on the mental processes. Genetic technology is certainly in this category. The technology which has not been developed, but which I am sure will be developed in a matter of a few years and which I fear more than any of these, is a technology which will permit us to read other people's minds. This will be a catastrophic development.

These technologies are particularly difficult from the policy standpoint for two reasons: one, the very magnitude of their consequences is staggering. Secondly, there is the question of their timing. They have come about very quickly from their early conception to their practical application. Only thirty-two years ago it was authoritatively estimated by a commission established for this purpose that typically there is a time lag of at least thirty years between the development of a technological idea or invention and the time the social effects begin to be felt. We know this time lag has been tremendously shrunk, and today the social consequences are almost instantaneous upon the invention itself.

Now the problem, as Dr. Luria has pointed out, is what do you do about technologies of this magnitude to bring them under effective social control. Let me state a couple of axioms: one, you can produce just about any kind of technology or technological result you want by pushing the button on the resource machine — the main resource is money. If you spend enough money and marshal enough resources, you can — at least in time — produce any result that you want. But there is no button you can push which is capable of securing wisdom or sound political or social judgments as to how these technologies can be used.

This brings us to two principle dangers with respect to the technology to the magnitude I've been discussing particularly genetic technology: we run the risk that we may destroy ourselves before we can bring technology under adequate social control; alternatively — and I think it is an equally great concern — in an effort to bring technologies of this magnitude under effective social control, we may destroy our freedom. The real question is: are there any technologies, or any scientific developments which should not be pursued despite their benefits, because of their potential to destroy our survival, or our survival with freedom? I think it is axiomatic, as Mr. Shapiro said this morning, that what is feasible, we are going to try to do. If we can prove that we can do something that is useful, we are going to make use of that technology. Actually there are some questions we want to ask ourselves: do we really want to be able to control the climate, with all the social, political, economic implications that brings about? Do we really want to be able to develop a technology which would permit us to read each other's minds? Do we really want to be able to affect human life by genetic intervention? It is never too early to start talking about these questions, because if one permits vested interests — including the vested interests of scientists — to develop in these technologies, they are very difficult to turn off once you let them get started. The solutions are never all black or all white, they are always in gray area. There is always latitude for temporizing and saying, "Well, that's not the problem now. Let's put it off five years until the problem is more real and more significant." Therefore, it is at least worth considering the proposition that maybe in some way or other with respect to a technology like genetic technology we ought to talk about, if not prohibiting it, at least discouraging it.

When I say prohibit it, it sounds terrible, because that is freedom destroying, too. I don't like to destroy any freedoms. We shouldn't interfere with the scientist's ability to think, to study, to research, to invent. However, there is one very effective way to slow down technological growth. The way is to turn off the money machine. And the way to turn off the money machine is for the United States Government, perhaps, to adopt the policy of spending no money or substantially less money, with respect to these technologies. You could even do it more dramatically. You could spend more money in other technologies to divert scientific talent away from genetics into something unrelated like increasing the food supply through non-genetic means.

Now what does this accomplish? Any delay, any slowing down of the process of the development of the technology like this, is good. It's good for two reasons, or one reason mainly: it gives more time. It gives us time to develop more experience with the technology and in how to deal with it. I suspect, for example, that we might have made some wiser decisions with respect to nuclear technology if what has developed in the past twenty-five years had taken the two hundred and fifty years that it would otherwise have taken without World War II and so on. Hopefully, with a greater degree of time, we can develop the greater degree of social wisdom which is necessary to deal with the technology. Or to adopt a more pessimistic view, I suppose that that is responsible for the enormous hypertrophy of a few scientific activities. It was not and it is not that way at all. The scientific community can say in advance very clearly, as Professor Luria said, not to do those things, to stand aside and keep from doing those things that are going to lead to uncontrollably rapid technical change. But generally speaking, what happens in the *Bacteriological Review* or in the *Physical Review* is absolutely not going to make anybody seriously concerned about threats to moral or scientific activity unless a second step is taken, an indispensable step, marshalling a lot of social pressure, money resources, etc. Maybe science is self-serving — I certainly would not be able to defend myself on the charge entirely — but the fact of the matter is really the other way around. The enormous pressure on the part of several great nations to invest thousands of millions of dollars and engage tens of thousands of persons at all levels, up to millions of man years, made these things possible. Those are decisions of political nature. They have nothing to do with the call of the scientific community *per se:* "Let us have a thermonuclear test." There *is* a Dr. Strangelove, but he clearly does not speak as a scientist who has taken a scientific point of view; he is speaking as a man of affairs.

Gross: Professor Green has obviously raised a number of interesting questions. One that he has emphasized, as have other people at this meeting, is who should put the brakes on and what we should put the brakes on and how far, but no one has discussed who decides what we shouldn't prevent. There are some things that should move very fast, technologically and scientifically, and if they don't, we may not survive. All this discussion shouldn't be on what we should be holding back, because there is a positive decision to be made. Apparently Professor Green's fear is direct communication between minds, and perhaps many people might go up in horror if it was actually proposed that they might do this sort of thing. But let us look at that particular problem a little bit more closely. Fred Hoyle produced a rather dramatic and interesting description of our method of communication and why this might be the limiting factor for survival. He pointed out our thoughts are electrical. They go down to a pair of oscillating Ribes from which you get a vibration of the air which transmits a kind of Morse Code. This then goes into another system essentially the reverse duplicate of it and which has to translate the code in terms of a long history of experience of that particular individual. Maybe one percent gets through and maybe that one percent is distorted. It is quite possible that the very intelligence the human being uses to do such remarkable things with such great power and with a minimal input and his ability to communicate well with his fellows are really at the root of most of our problems. One man's idea becomes impossible to transmit to another person — particularly if those people are at the position of wanting to press buttons, and more particularly if they have the power to do it. Essentially our problems are because there are people who can press buttons with great power, and it is impossible for people to communicate adequately with them for a variety of reasons.

I would like to propose the opposite point of view from Dr. Green's — and in fact society has been doing this — that of trying to improve in every conceivable way our ability to communicate with each other. We haven't really tried to improve the machinery of communication itself. I would propose, for example, that we might be better off if we were able to develop a technology whereby we do speak in Gestalts to each other, by patterns, that we have the opportunity of convincing each other by the total picture that we might be able to present. I am not saying that this is what we *should* be doing, nor am I saying that it is even feasible. But we should not allow the control of what not to do to be held in the hands of some few people, any more than we should allow the control of what we should do, and this should apply to genetic engineering.

We are not in a position at the moment to predict whether or not, for example, cloning of human beings is necessarily a bad thing. We respond automatically to the idea that it is a horror, but I wonder if we thought it through very clearly whether that might not necessarily be true. For example, perhaps we might have a good look at the way identical twins communicate with each other — and perhaps identical triplets — if we really would like to understand what the cloning machinery really results in. But again, I'm not suggesting we do. I'm saying that these ideas which look so horrible to us really should be considered carefully before we decide to prevent their development.

Luria: You are going back to the question of which things may be good and which may be bad, and the point both Mr. Green and I have been trying to make is that what is good and what is bad depends on the setting and depends on who chooses the values. The point that needs to be emphasized is that we are assuming, in the rational spirit of the eighteenth century which does not hold any more for our society, that humanity somehow will make the right decision. We have seen almost nothing but the wrong decisions because of political and social reasons.

Asimov: It is fascinating to me to hear laymen work up science fiction plots. It is not the question as to whether we will have or not have telepathy. Just as some people are more articulate than other people, some people will be more telepathically proficient than others. You are going to end up with a wide variety of telepath proficiencies in which, perhaps, you will have several different levels of society — the complete telepaths, the partial telepaths. You can't foresee the difficulties that might arise. All you foresee are very simple possibilities, and when you plunge in, the difficulties will overwhelm you. With the best will in the world, we can't foresee very much, and we have to grope.

Gross: I'm only saying the risks may be greater by *not* doing certain things.

Raacke: We have had a number of discussions on the necessity of saying "no" to research that might have a bad outcome. But I haven't heard anybody really say what, if anything, are the bad things that would come out of the types of genetic intervention that we talked about this morning. Maybe we should concentrate a little bit on that end of things.

Luria: It would be possible to make a virus to be used against the people who have a gene or a set of genes which is very high for a particular skin color, for example. That is perfectly conceivable. It is probably much more conceivable than the ability to inject a gene or to correct the gene for diabetes in human sperm or in human eggs. These are the dangers! The dangers are very immediate — just as it is easier to explode an atom bomb than to use atomic energy.

Todd: I find Professor Green's remarks impress me as highly reactionary. He suggests that we stop research because a delay or a slowing down would help us to make a more rational decision. Gunpowder was invented in the eleventh century and we are still finding ways to use it and they are not terribly rational, so I don't have too much confidence that a delay is going to help.

Another thing lacking from the discussion is some perspective on the nature of man. I have one which is not as definitive, but one which will help us understand something about the creature we are talking about manipulating. I see *Homo sapiens* as a somewhat aberrant Pleistocene relic which has survived into the Holocene, or the present. That is, he probably should have been judged least likely to succeed by his contemporaries in the Pleistocene and predicted to have become extinct along with mammoths and saber-tooth tigers. Nonetheless, he has survived, and he has, continually throughout this period, widened the taxonomic gap between himself and his nearest relatives. That is one characteristic of what has been happening to man.

Homo sapiens has done this gap-widening, if you will, through what we call aggressive behavior. He has in the past, extinguished or been responsible for the extinction of other men, either of other species, sub-species, perhaps even of genera, once the world was populated by "men," in the sense that there were many representatives of the family hominidae. Today he is a monotypic creature. In that sense he is even more peculiar than the rhinos, of which there are three species, or the elephant of which there are two. Anyway, he did this by so-called violent, aggressive behavior and such an assumption is not without some empirical and theoretical basis. In fact this aggression and violence has led man to his dominate final position, and therefore *ipso facto,* such behavior, in a certain genetic-evolutionary sense, must have been and will remain adaptive until some different selection pressures arise.

Notwithstanding the peculiar problems that have come to pass with a rudimentary control of atoms and genes, a recognition of the problem cannot erase the genetic conditioning. It can only open the door to some sort of control, if and when an understanding of the mechanisms involved reach a sufficient degree of sophistication. One of the roots to this sophistication is to challenge various assumptions and examine new perspectives. The characterization of man as aggressive and violent is a relative sort of thing. Many other species have evolved ritual displays to arrest violence short of severely damaging another individual or producing some lethal result. While this is true, it is not universal. Even among species which have such elaborate mechanisms, damage and death do occur as the result of direct confrontations. Even if no immediate physical injury is inflicted in such encounters, if one individual is denied food, shelter, mating privilege and so forth on account of the episode, the gigantic result is nearly identical to a lethal struggle. In either case it places the more aggressive individual at a selective advantage, and it is something of a paradox that more aggressive behavior is not manifested in many species which have evolved for prolonged periods of time under such pressures. Now the proclivity or propensity or the capacity of an animal for aggressive and violent behavior must be constrained by a sheer physiological limitation as well as by innate behavioral mechanisms of a genetic nature. I propose that man is not more aggressive than other animals, but is in fact less easily intimidated. This distinction may prove to be highly relevant when the neurophysiological basis is subjected to some sort of genetic cure.

Luria: What is the evidence that man caused extinction of the related species by his aggressive behavior? I don't know of any such, but I'm not an anthropologist. I don't think there is any such evidence.

Todd: Yes. There are human remains from places like Olduvai, charred human remains that suggest that perhaps man was even cannabilistic in some situations.

Morrison: But not specifically other hominid species.

Todd: We also know that different populations — and I don't want to defend a particular taxonomy — were sympatric in these areas.

Morrison: There is some question as to whether it was not mating and mixing.

Todd: But this swamping of another gene pool still served, as long as genetic introgression was possible, to widen the taxonomic gap.

Davis: This is by definition. This is how a species gets established, by widening the genetic gap.

Todd: Yes, but in this case this has come to be an intentional sort of thing.

Davis: Aggressiveness is not proved.

Todd: I'm saying aggressiveness is not proved. I'm saying perhaps it was not being intimidated.

Bresler: I think you are possibly on treacherous ground in using man, or "the man that existed millions of years ago," because although we like to use the taxonomic designation of *Homo sapiens,* there are some reservations as to whether you can include the man that existed three or four million years ago, the proto man, in the same species as you would today. There have been enough changes so that just basing a lot of the evidence on what happened to proto man and relating it to today is treacherous ground.

Raacke: We still haven't decided if there is anything bad in genetic engineering that should be stopped or whether genetic engineering in any of its manifestations — including selective mating, as Dr. Davis pointed out — would, in fact, change any of the values that are particularly human, as Dr. Gustafson said, or whether we can just let the developments develop. We haven't addressed ourselves to that point.

J. Robert Nelson: Let me pick up your reference to human values, because I think this is important in our consideration, especially in view of what Dr. Todd described as the nature of man. His description is valuable to the discussion because it points up more sharply some of the different perspectives we have on the human person. It has shown not only the generation gap, but also the intellectual and conceptual depth which separates a good many of us in our modes of thinking. His essay on man is exceedingly interesting from the scientific standpoint of physiological-psychological development, but it has very little to do with the humanity we are talking about. That is to say, I can't see the kind of man you have been describing. Whether or not he is affected by genetic manipulation or even some forms of maltreatment or impairment wouldn't matter very much, because you haven't really touched upon who man is and why there is any meaning to our existence anyway. This is what we are groping for. We who claim to have some kind of knowledge in the realm of theology do not claim to have ultimate answers. We are groping along with everybody else to know who we are and why we exist and what our future may be. Therefore our discussion on the role of genetics in all this should touch more upon the question of human value, of authentic humanity, and not only upon the physiological development.

Todd: Perhaps there was too much preamble to my remarks and the last sentence was too telegraphic. It is genetic manipulation of behavior which has characterized recent human development. A number of people have mentioned how behavior is manipulating genetics, and perhaps, genetics has been manipulating the behavior. We have to know where some of the bases of this behavior reside. The issue has been raised that the decision is a political one, that we can't trust the politicians to make a moral decision. That's really what people have been saying, because we interpret them in a sort of general way as being the aggressive, hostile man.

Preston N. Williams: I want to ask a question about development of genetics as a science. We are suggesting that in order for the science to develop — at least in the present day — there must be a large input of funds, there must be a bringing together of large resource pools of talents, and one must be aiming at some sort of development which will have consequences for the formation of the total gene pool. That suggests that genetics is primarily a social science and the consequences which one should aim for are social in nature. Is this what genetics is all about? Or when we talk about present day genetics, are we talking about something that is therapeutic, that does involve genetic counseling, that means more to individuals than it does to social groups?

Newton Morton: For genetic counseling, the purpose is — at least nominally — to affect a particular family for its own immediate objectives.

Raacke: But genetics is not just genetic counselling, is it?

Morton: No. The "probulation" of genetics is, of course, to be concerned with the changes in the gene pools. So to that extent it deals with the whole population. I don't know whether that's a fair answer to the question or not.

Luria: I think the question you are asking is: what is the abstract and what is the normative content of genetics? What are the aspects of genetics that are directed to alter an existing situation and what are the ones directed to understanding it?

Williams: That's part of my question, but I'm trying to get an answer to the question that has been raised about what do we stop. Some here are suggesting we bring to a stop, or bring under greater social control, population genetics. One is not suggesting one stops the genetic counselling. If I've heard some of the geneticists correctly, they are suggesting that in the next generation we are going to be concerned primarily with problems of genetic counselling. The population genetics will have its effect maybe a hundred years or more from now. To sort these out, what does one stop and what does one encourage?

Morton: While population genetics is that branch of genetics which deals with population, population geneticists have not been particularly interested in genetic engineering. The interest on that has come exclusively from molecular biologists, speaking *ex cathedra*.

Hans Jonas: Someone should take up the challenge of the chairman to indicate what might be bad in genetic engineering, and I'll try to do so with my limited knowledge. I take it then that genetic engineering, in the regular sense, would be covered by Section 2, a. and b. in the paper presented this morning by Dr. Davis, namely germ cell alteration — a. Directed alteration by chemical nutrogents of an exposure to naked DNA or to a transforming virus; or b. nuclear transplants from somatic cells to egg cells so that an indefinite replication of one and the same individual can come of it. Did I understand you correctly there? One has to take these strict cases of genetic engineering — rather than those of selective breeding, counselling, abstention from procreation in the case of inherited diseases, and so on — in order to comes to grips with what might be the dangers of genetic engineering. For, after all, it is not without some meaning that the term "engineering" has been transferred now to this area from an entirely different one — namely, from that of mechanical construction and bringing functioning systems about on the basis of blueprints, dealing with inanimate materials.

Now what might be objectionable to that or what dangers lurk there? I divide them into two alternative cases, which curiously enough, though they are alternative, lead to the same negative conclusion. The one is that we do not really know what we are doing there, if we embark on this. That is, our knowledge is not great enough, not only at present, but probably cannot ever possibly be equal to the whole chain of consequences which, by tampering with some part feature of the genetic system, may be set in motion and spread over the whole system. Therefore, instead of producing what the blueprint has specified, we may produce something entirely unforeseeable on a population scale. Now this is the certain humility of ignorance, of limited knowledge, which might stay our hand.

The other alternative is that we do know what we are doing, that our knowledge, if not complete, is at least very extensive and reassuring, in the sense that we can fairly well calculate what the outcome would be. This frightens me almost as much as the first alternative, because it means that we will be able to specify what kind of offspring we and a whole generation and our whole population should produce. I don't think we should be in a position to determine this. One of the greats, speaking of the dignity of man or of the nature of man, said we don't know what the true image of man is, or his essence. We know one thing: one of the great boons of being man is the unpredictability of what human individuals will appear on the scene and what their life, their potentiality, will be. Let's take the extreme case of cloning. If it is effective at all, then it means that we predict precisely what type — not only what type, what individuals — we are going to produce. We have already an executed lifespan of that individual before our eyes. We have not only predetermined the future individuals, but we have already deprived them — since of course they are going to know from whom they come — of an openness or indeterminacy or the wonderful ignorance concerning what the future has in store for them, by this kind of previous determination. On both counts, if we do not know what we set in motion with the genetic intervention of the radical kind, or if we do know, this is the kind of knowledge which we should *not* have and not exercise for the sake of human freedom. We should not destroy nor cause an ultimate effect on certain dimensions in man which should always be potentially at the disposal of each individual who enters new upon the scene of this earth and has something that is unique — has never been before, never something like it — and he may work out his own destiny. These are, in brief, the two objections which I would list.

Raacke: Would the mere possibility of making a carbon copy of somebody change our ideas that are all based on the magnificent uniqueness of man?

Jonas: Oh, yes. We have the power really to change this, namely to destroy it. I argue on the assumption that this is possible. Perhaps it is not possible. I assume on the assurance of many confident biologists that it is possible.

Gross: There is the basic assumption here that for some reason or other seems to be automatically agreed to, namely, that there is something ultimately beautiful and perfect about uniqueness and about being different and about being unable to communicate clearly with each other. I propose the possibility that there might be characteristics in a clone — due to interaction between individuals even though they do have certain similarities — which may produce some rather remarkable things, much better than they are today. I am not convinced from what we have seen at this meeting that the human race has really reached the point of magnificence as the result of individuality.

Todd: Dr. Jonas is arguing that since we don't know — and I think every geneticist would have to agree that we don't — what is going on, we don't want to diminish the polymorphism which has at least brought us to this point. So in approaching the problem like anyone else in the animal husbandry business, one should first and foremost guarantee that he doesn't close any doors. In other words, set aside and rigorously protect the polymorphism that exists. The other side is that we won't know until we do the experiments with humans, whether they be direct intervention or breeding programs and I happen to think the latter are more plausible, what we might be able to produce. Otherwise it remains a mystery to us. But whatever course, we must have that insurance of guaranteeing polymorphism.

DeWolf: There is no evidence that the polymorphism has succeeded or is going to succeed. If we believe John Platt, it won't succeed.

Todd: Polymorphism is a fact. The only arbiter is that we have survived with it, perhaps because of it, to this point.

Davis: I agree with Dr. Jonas. I would re-emphasize even more firmly what I brought out in my talk this morning, that is diversity, the richness of diversity. Maybe this is an expression of taste. It may be just an old-fashioned taste that we have gotten use to, and we justify it because we have had no choice. Let me offer a fairly fundamental biological reason for preferring the preservation of diversity. This is something George Bernard Shaw took up at some length in his play on Methuselah: death is a part of life. Evolution wouldn't exist without death permitting a renewal of life, always in experimentally new combinations. This is surely — according to my old-fashioned taste — part of what makes life so rich. It's even conceivable that a succession of Mozarts would be very boring. The third Mozart wouldn't dare become a modern musician because he was still a continuation of the first Mozart, and yet he would feel that he was a failure if he couldn't feel at home in modern music. I'm quite serious about this.

James Shapiro: I would like to ask you a question very directly. First let me relate a certain story which makes my point. We gave a press conference recently and we talked about genetic engineering. A reporter, after the press conference was over, asked me, "Well, can't you use it to control aggression?" and my answer was that some persons would be very interested to control the aggression of Harvard-Radcliffe SDS. To me that kind of aggression is a very good thing, and therefore one danger in genetic engineering is eliminating that.

A second problem is eliminating genetic variability. Anybody who has read Dobzhansky's books and anything on population genetics realizes that genetic variability is a very important component in the survival of any species. One specific example is that of a clone of identical individuals, say on a large order of the magnitude of thousands and millions. What happens if you have a disease, say a virus infection, to which they are very susceptible? You can wipe out lots of people all at once. That's a bad thing; that's a danger.

The third problem is the whole idea, the whole ideology which is behind genetic engineering and particularly behind cloning. The last social system which really pushed this idea was Nazi Germany, and we have all seen what has happened in Nazi Germany. We all have certain value judgments about that kind of a society based on the idea that political leaders or the forces of the institution know what's best, know what kind of people should exist. From the point of view of natural selection, those societies tend to destroy themselves. So those are the dangers, very grave dangers.

Raacke: Has anybody contemplated genetic engineering on a population scale? I don't think we need to worry about those dangers on a population scale.

Jonas: Why not? We shouldn't get away from that, because what we are trying to say is that is going to become feasible before the other. That is the danger. We are trying to cure a disease, and you are going to create a weapon. This is what we keep repeating, and nobody wants to listen. That's why I insisted this is on the record.

Morrison: But if that's true, then we create a weapon anyhow.

Jonas: Sure, but it's important that people know about this!

Morrison: Yes, I agree. Someone said we should put atomic energy under social control. It is now under the heaviest of social control, but that doesn't make it good.

Jonas: I agree.

DeWolf: We have no right as intellectuals engaged in different kinds of research — whether it be theology, ethics, or science — to depend upon politics to provide the conscience which will direct us in the way to go in our own research. We have a responsibility. I am very much worried about what was called in the days of Hitler, the scientific mercenaries. They had been working under the federal republic, but when Hitler took over he was able to take most of them right along. They worked just as much in his service as in others. This could come true in this country. I am not exempting theologians here. A large number of theologians in Germany also went along with Hitler, though some of them didn't and some scientists didn't. We must within our own communities — the theological community and the scientific community alike — be engaged in the kind of work we are doing here precisely in order to develop our own conscience, our own ethical controls in which we will refuse to develop our study and our discussion in ways that will make us willing tools of any political power structure that may come along and want to direct us, whether it be by giving grants or whatever. At the present time, when the government will give great grants for certain research, that research goes ahead, and maybe that isn't what's needed.

A second point which ties together themes of three of these workshops is that quantity should not be the controlling motif or theme of our works. It must be quality, and carefully selected quality. This came up in connection with population. We are so addicted to the idolatry of larger GNPs, larger populations, larger cities, and so on, that it seems almost to be against progress to be against greater quantities. It came up again in connection with the prolongation of life. The prolongation of human life is not necessarily good; it is a good only when it increases hope and meaning in life, and not when it doesn't. We in the intellectual community need to recognize that a sure quantitative increase in knowledge is not necessarily good, but we too, must make this qualitative distinction before we press further with genetic research or any other. Every scientist or theologian or intellectual must ask himself: is this the thing of which I am capable, which is most needed in order to help promote the highest quality of living for the greatest variety and number of people in our society?

Bresler: Let me follow that and perhaps something that Mr. Green started by asking: how do you shut off the funds? How do you go about that? The laser beam which is used and can be used for genetic manipulation in bio-engineering is also the same one that gives rise to communications and data processing. The second is a technological advance which I understand relates to micro-manipulation, but it also leads to a visual sensitizer which is allowing blind people to at least make out certain forms. Where do you stop the technology? And if you stop technology, you will stop some other things. Who shuts the button off? How do you know when you are dealing with the development of a micro-manipulator that is going to be used for bio-engineering or when you start with the laser beam it will eventually go to genetic engineering? I wonder if Mr. Green or Dr. Goldwater — it's a loaded question — as a government administrator, would comment. How do you turn the button off? How do you stop the funds? Assuming that everybody wants to stop the funds, what do you stop?

William H. Goldwater: Let me speak more as a scientist, than as an administrator. Naturally, I can't isolate one from the other completely. But I submit like you, Dr. Bresler, that it is impossible — I would go that far — to judge what you can turn off in the interests of good or bad, because even the worst of all weapons, the nuclear hydrogen bombs, have themselves in the research had spinoffs that saved more lives than they destroyed. This is important to remember. So far it is turning out to be the only way in which we are going to be able to get energy to support our increasing population without even more hopelessly polluting our atmosphere. There is no question that a nuclear power plant in the neighborhood is much preferable today to a smoke emitting one.

Luria: The argument misses the point that Mr. Green made very fervently. It is not a matter of shutting off the funds — period. It is a matter of creating a timetable which is rational. If the timetable of nuclear energy had been rational, if our scientists had been fortunate to fail in the same way as the Germans failed, we would be much better off. The question is the crash program. The preposterous thing is that the crash program assumes that the goal is overriding. When you talk about space exploration, you find the preposterous adventure of the man-on-the-moon instead of a sensible kind of space science. The question is to evaluate whether certain things should be done within the society in which you live. I personally tried in 1950 to get the *Bulletin of Atomic Scientists* to come out with an appeal to all physicists to refuse to work on the hydrogen bomb. In retrospect, it was certainly too late. But I am still not ashamed of having made that atttempt.

Roger Shinn: I would like to ask a question: how much do we know about the relation between genetics and the identity of man? The reason I ask is that by accident I spend more time among social scientists than among geneticists, and they all emphasize the importance of culture in personality formation, as here I feel we've tended to emphasize the importance of genetics, and I'm not at all competent to settle that particular debate. There is truth on both sides. I do believe, for reasons I can't quite explain, in this mysterious thing we call freedom that somehow or other we all do something with our genetic inheritance and the impact of culture on us. This becomes rather important in some of the contemporary debates. I'm no geneticist but I've followed with great interest the running debate that went on between Herbert Miller and Theodosius Dobzhansky. Particularly interesting were Miller's characterizations that were brought to our attention this morning, of the kind of person he'd want, and granted intelligence, character, health, and so on, he gets to the point of character. He wants a person with loving kindness, concern for other people, but enough aggressivenesss that he be not simply a conformist. I am not sure just how accurately I am reflecting his thought and how much my own. We know we can breed certain animal types that are highly aggressive and certain types that are passive, but is this character quality that we want, simply a balance between these biological natures? Or is there a quality of imagination that enables a Martin Luther King to use a great aggressiveness and persistence in a way that you just don't class as inherited aggressiveness? Dr. Davis, since you touched on this this morning, when you talk about, so far as you can, reducing the qualitative considerations to the quantitative and balancing off these factors of aggressiveness and passiveness, how much are you accounting for human character and how much do we have to say that there are mysteries here of personality we don't really understand?

Davis: The answer, in very general terms, is absolutely clear — that it is a mixture. Which is what Dobzhansky has been saying for many years. Any geneticist knows, because he lives in a culture, that all behavioral traits of human beings not only have a genetic component, but are very much influenced by his cultural exposure. But I am not sure that all students of culture automatically or instinctively or educationally learn that there also are genetic components, and this is one of our large cultural lags today. I am not trying to sell genetics as "the" answer. I am saying that by and large as a society, we are incredibly ignorant of this already well-established part of our problem, and it is a very real part of our problem. I am just predicting, hopefully, that this ignorance will gradually be replaced by knowledge. This isn't any way to downgrade the importance of culture, the importance of education in making people behave as they turn out to behave. This is what I referred to this morning as a kind of sterile polemic that has gone on for decades between nature lovers and nurture lovers. They are touching different parts of the elephant.

What does worry me is the point of view that Mr. Green presented. His concern with research that might lead to cloning, I can understand. Then he suggested that funds be withheld from certain kinds of research, and then at the end of the statement he said something about decreasing funds for genetics. Now I am sure, Mr. Green, you would agree there are obviously very grave dangers to the progress of society and of medicine if we all across the board should decide to cut out funds for genetics. As indicated in my speech this morning, research in genetics is intimately related with research on cancer, and while some people agree that the time has come when we are willing to say that you can no longer be for motherhood, we can still all be for a cure for cancer. So it is extremely dangerous for us — and I am a little bit disturbed that my friend Salvador Luria has leaned in this direction so far — to start drawing the line in terms of which kinds of basic research we must now discourage. We have to draw the lines beyond that at their applications. I agree with you and with Mr. Shapiro in that our present society is technologically applying many scientific discoveries in abominable ways. There are grave dangers that the more power we give them, the worse it will get. The political battle is a very real battle ,but we won't solve it by reducing basic science.

Green: I would be in favor of curtailing the flow of money to any kind of research and development in any kind of a technology which has the kind of staggering potential of the technology that I discussed, including genetic engineering, although obviously I wouldn't be in favor of cutting off all money for all genetic activities. The problem of cancer research is an important one, and let me say how to handle that. To the extent that cancer research would contribute to an undesirable acceleration of those parts of genetic engineering which I regard as of staggering implications, I would not support cancer research.

Morrison: But you don't know.

Todd: It is very difficult to realize how much overlap there is.

Jonas: I want to address myself to the question which Mr. Shinn raised. I have the feeling that we somehow underestimate the mystery of man or are losing sight of this. We are all more or less under the spell of the Cartesian conception of the body machine. Regarding human freedom or the question of desirable and undesirable traits or beneficial or injurious traits, is the saintly man one who is incapable of sinning or whose sinful urges are weaker than those of other men? That is the question to ask the theologians. Is it really the case that by selecting certain desirable traits we produce the kind of personality we have in mind when we speak of the great paradigms of humanity? I doubt it. Or I ask the literary man, was Dostoevski with his epilepsy an acceptable or unacceptable type? Genetically would we have selected him out if we could have diagnosed in the fetal state or human mother that an epileptic would be born? We are being very simplistic in dealing with isolated aspects and features and saying this is good and this is not good, or there will probably be a very unhappy individual produced out of this. Well, Michelangelo was unhappy all his life and he was also a very disagreeable fellow to live with. We have to try for a kind of *mysterium tremendum* in dealing with the rigor of men and the step from animal breeding and animal genetic manipulation to human. There should be an abyss between them.

Shapiro: We started discussing one very important sub-division, the funding of scientific research. In answer to the statement that a lot of useful spinoffs have come from basic research in this country, I think the space program is a perfect example. We have the Vice-President — and I suppose the President, too — saying how many jobs all this is going to create in the spinoff. My personal feeling is if all those billions of dollars were spent in solving the real problems of hunger, overcrowding in the ghettos, poor schools and all that, a great deal more good would have come out of it. If you spend twenty billion dollars a year to help people, you care about people, and that is what we should be doing. So the justification for large funding of basic research in terms of spinoffs is wrong. If you are going to have basic research designed to help people and solve their real problems and not some phony Russian aggression or what have you.

About this problem of cancer research, Dr. Davis and myself and Professor Luria are all in the cancer research business. That should be quite clear to people. Myself, I don't think that we can really justify spending all this money on cancer research. In my view, the solution to cancer is to stop people smoking, polluting the atmosphere, putting additives in food. We live in a myth that basic research can solve all of our problems. Cancer is a serious problem, but a large part of it can be cut down very quickly by cutting pollution. The solution to that problem is political. The dangers Mr. Green has talked about are very real, and they do far outweigh the benefits that come from our cancer research. Most of the people who do cancer research — and this is true in my case — really don't care too much about cancer; they are working on an interesting problem.

Margulis: As someone who gets spinoff from cancer research and also feels that all money should probably be taken away, I agree entirely with you, but I want to address myself to your question, Dr. Jonas. We have gotten to a point where we cannot allow a Dostoevski to come around. We can't afford the survival of children with Down's syndrome (Mongolism). Friends of ours had one the other day and had to give it to an institution, where of course it will be a drain on all resources for the rest of its useless life. We can't afford thalassemia and phenylketonuria. We're keeping alive these children with hereditary disorders, such as phenylketonuria, by our new extensive testing. We have to bring up the basic issue of the normal infant. The normal healthy infant given what he is born with and proper care between the critical ages of zero and five or eight, still has limitations on what he can do, even in the most healthy possible environment. But a normal healthy child, who is mistreated between the ages of zero and five or eight creates a huge, huge, social problem. With all the good will in the world, and we now have plenty of knowledge, I completely agree with Dr. Luria: this is a social and political problem. We have to face this basic issue of which among us is going to leave the children in the next generation. We all can't. There's not enough room.

Todd: To amplify very slightly on what Professor Margulis has said with respect to Dr. Jonas' remarks, he may have confused some of the non-geneticists here by linking creativity and unhappiness or any two other attributes. Professor Margulis makes the point we should wait for the next Dostoevski that doesn't have — I assume it was implicit — epilepsy. You know this will happen. These things don't have to go together. There is such a thing as independent assortment, and we can engineer in that sense to unlink these things. Another thing that is confusing me, is that the issue of cloning humans has been a preconception of this whole session and this morning. Except for methodology, we have been cloning all this century through the production of isogenic strains so that those who think this is something new are perhaps misled.

Jonas: Could you explain?

Todd: The inbreeding, the brother-sister mating of mice or fruit flies or something else approaches this condition of genetic identity. Now perhaps it never reaches it, but in its most practical ramification you end up after many generations with enormous populations which have tissue compatability, display the same kinds of behavioral responses, basically are predictable. In fact, it is through this technique that we understand the genetic basis of such things as aggression in mice or dogs or various physiological phenomena. Doing it from the cell of an individual although it is admittedly a somewhat different approach, leads largely to the same end. I'm suggesting that we are in a position to anticipate some of the ramifications of cloning.

Jonas: But not in man.

Gustafson: It's the time scale.

Margulis: The biologists will agree that the technical problems are trivial compared to the social problems and political problems. Give us a problem and fund it enough, we will solve it. But what are we trying to solve? We have to look at the quality of human life of a limited number of people on the earth. As far as the nature-nurture question which comes up so often with the students, people are born with genes that make them people. All other animals are born with their potential and, given the optimal environmental conditions, they will reach that potential. But no monkey is going to write poetry, because no matter how you influence his environment, he is not going to reach the human potential.

Gustafson: That's another perspective. The most chilling thing said this afternoon is that we couldn't afford, or ought not to permit, another potential Dostoevski to come into existence because one could early discern the epilepsy. This really frightens me. The reason it frightens me is something I tried to say this morning, that this is precisely the kind of place where the argument has to take place. I really adhere very strongly to what Professor Jonas is saying. Are we so sure that the qualities of normality with reference to some biological norm are the kinds of qualities that are going to make life interesting, rich and fulfilling? Isn't it necessary to take certain kinds of risks with reference to other things that we cherish and value? Then we could argue about why we would want to take the risk.

Margulis: I told my doctor just as I was going into delivery: if this kid is abnormal in some obvious way, kill it. But now there is no socially acceptable way of implementing such a decision. Many people are willing to get rid of these very grotesque cases, but this is a social problem.

Asimov: But Dostoevski's epilepsy was not essential to his being Dostoevski, but the Czarist government was. Dostoevski wouldn't have been Dostoevski if he hadn't been brought up under the Czars and hadn't experienced the Siberian exile, etc. We had no hesitation in wanting to see the Czarist system wiped out even if it meant losing Dostoevski.

Luria: That's exactly the political point!

Todd: We weren't saying we aren't going to let Dostoevski be born, because he is an epileptic. We didn't know that. We say we don't want these epileptics to be born.

Luria: The chances of being Dosteovski are completely independent of whether he is epileptic or not. That's the point.

Gustafson: Probably not completely.

Luria: Well, probably not completely, but as far as we know there is now knowledge of the correlation.

Gustafson: That's not true. There is a dark side to Dostoevski as a human character which, I think, it is very hard to argue is not connected in some way with his epilepsy.

Luria: It may be connected in some way, but if you take the total number of people in a category of Dostoevski and you take all of the epileptics, I think that as far as total human resources, there is a gain in not having the latter category.

Gustafson: I agree with the conclusion, but you used the wrong arguments. The sound argument is whether or not you take this risk. You have no certificate that he is going to be Dostoevski. You have a certificate that he is going to have a miserable life. Since we have many people who also make plenty of mistakes, epileptics will come through this fine net that you are going to set up because it never quite works perfectly, tragic people who give us enough of the dark side of life. That is quite clear. But we shouldn't say too easily that there was no connection either. If tragedy disappears from human life, no doubt it will be very much poorer in may ways. Even with the best of our efforts we won't succeed in eliminating it, so I don't worry about it.

Luria: The tragedy of the genetic defects is a tragedy of a very different quality from the human tragedy of Aeschylus or of Sophocles. We shouldn't leave the argument between Mr. Green and Mr. Davis without one more clarification. When you talk about support of research, what you are worried about is the support of technology, of research and development that lead to the technology and the application of technology, and not the support of basic science. Unfortunately, however, once basic findings are made, society is likely to develop and apply the technology. Therefore, while I would agree with both Professor Davis and Mr. Green, we can talk for ages, but we are not going to get anywhere. Because the problem is not support of research, either basic or applied; it is the society in which the support is given. As long as societies are anarchistic, we are not going to have any outcome of this kind of discussion that is practically applicable, except warning the public that the society is likely to lead them to destruction. We are on the way to destruction in a Roman Holiday of nonsense.

Asimov: I'm glad you said that because if it's just the matter of stopping funding, every scientist has enough ingenuity to prove that his own research, whatever it is, is beneficial. I wrote an article recently denouncing chemical biological warfare. The response I got was from a physician colonel in Vietnam, asking me how could I say there was no good in chemical biological warfare when you use chlorine to purify water.

Arthur J. Dyck: One should be worried about the society in which the support is given. This is a very important point. I also worry about those to whom the support is given, in this sense: that they are part of that society, they are part of the woof and fabric of that society. What I see in many of the exchanges that have taken place is precisely what I thought Professor Gustafson was getting at in his adddress: that is, that we are talking about different norms by which we judge how society will be improved by eliminating certain kinds of defects, by getting certain kinds of human beings and not others. Now then, we have come full circle, we are exchanging our various norms. We have said, "Maybe I'm old-fashioned and I'd like to keep this kind of freedom or this kind of openness," and this is a norm. This is saying what I think the human being ought to be like or what I'll go for. So I would hope that those who are getting money would examine and re-examine, and those who are involved in giving money and those who consider themselves critics of the whole process and reflectors upon it, would take Mr. Gustafson's remarks very seriously, especially his opening ones in which he is pointing out that we are all operating with normative conceptions of human beings, and we can't cloak them in scientific terminology and we can't cloak them in political terminology. In the end, there they are, and it behooves us then to ask what these norms are that we are operating with. Why, for instance, it is not self-evident to me that certain genetic defects, so-called genetic defects, are bad. It's not obvious to me that what *looks* like misery to me, in another person *is* misery. I mean the chronic complainers may be very happy, and I detect this in our avowed pessimist. His ability to laugh is really quite remarkable. So really I go with Jonas here, that this is a mystery, and we really want to err on the side of retaining openness, on the side of not deciding hastily what goes and what doesn't go. Perhaps where we just don't know or perhaps even where we think we know, we still have to sort out what we want to live with. We are going to have to have our arguments, our discussions around it. We can't evade this basic question.

Luria: You are missing an important point, however, because what is being said here is that once population pressure does apply, by not making a selection, you are in fact making a selection. It is exactly the same type of thing, if you don't get involved in politics, you are making a political decision. If you choose not to eliminate the person with the birth defect, you are eliminating somebody else because the population pressure is here.

Dyck: I am asking us to reflect on just those things. I don't disagree with that. I'm saying that we must be self-conscious about these normative judgments, including the ones in which we don't take a step. This is also then an implicit or explicit norm. I am pleading that we make them explicit. I am pleading, then, for making this an explicit moral discussion of what is humanly valuable because it's been implicit all the way.

Morrison: What happens in the world is that, gradually, man acquires ability to change random processes into somewhat directed ones. This brings with it heavy responsibility always — weather, food, you name it, whatever is the nature of the human culture. I would say that this also does not mean that he must accept complete responsibility. There is no difficulty at all with introducing a chance procedure in the whole thing. One could go a very long way in the kind of future rational view if you put it that someone whose birth defect was predictable, but not very severe, would have a reduced chance of being born. Someone whose birth defect was very heavy, a microcephalic or something of that sort, even today has almost no chance. You could have a continuous scale.

Margulis: What about Woodie and Arlo Guthrie with their Huntington's Chorea?

Luria: How about all of us with our nearsightedness?

Morrison: That's right. There are plenty of possibilities. Nobody would require perfection. It is just as bad to think of the norm as being defined in some Appolonian way, or by Mr. Miller, or by any other guy. The way it should be done is by a careful, substantial concern for diversity, for a chance for individual preferences, for the right of parents and the like. The law has worked out many such problems.

Dyck: But what you are doing is just what I'm calling for. You are beginning to reflect on some things. You plug in diversity, I would too. But let's just be self-conscious about this. This is also a moral discussion, not only a scientific one, not only a political one. It should be both of those, but it should also be a self-conscious reflection of the kind of things we plug in.

Morrison: But once you admit that, you admit everything. From then on it's a discussion of substantive matters, which we are not prepared to do here, but which we could carry out in a three-week discussion. The question is: do you admit this as a possible moral position, to intervene in this heavy way *against* more diversity? Now mind you, only as a principle — I am not saying to do it in every case, but absolutely not in terms of an idealized model which I regard as absurd.

Dyck: I quite agree.

Edwin T. Mertz: Epilepsy is probably a poor example to use here as an example to explain why someone should not be allowed to live.

Because this is, in most cases, due just to brain lesion and is not inherited. I worked with the Indiana State Hosptials for mentally retarded for over a decade in helping to develop research, bio-chemical research, in ways of curing and preventing brain damage. I have reached the conclusion that the cure of brain damage is essentially impossible, that the only hope we have is for prevention. We are going to have to make decisions in regard to how severe the brain damage can be before we decide that this person wouldn't be a useful member of society. Obviously most Mongoloids are not useful members of society. They are very happy individuals, but certainly all they do is add to the public burden. We estimate that it costs about a half million dollars to keep them in a hospital for life so that this new technique of amniocentesis where they can predict whether or not a child is going to be a Mongoloid, is a terrific advance. It gives the parents a choice. They can make the decision before the event, so if they decide that they want to have this child, then they are going to be prepared to live with him for the rest of their lives. So this is an area that certainly can be developed right now.

Another point that hasn't been touched on at all — it may not be germane to this discussion — but there certainly is evidence enough to indicate that pre-natal and post-natal nutritional deprivation can have marked effect on the development of the brain. This would imply that there probably are children, even in this country, who are born with much lower capabilities than they could have. They can never reach the full IQ that they would otherwise reach because they have not been adequately nourished, or the mother has not been adequately nourished during gestation. This is something that we should certainly apply ourselves to. Mr. Shapiro discussed this morning the matter of the farmer shutting off food supplies. I'm in a school of agriculture and I know that the farmer is not happy about these remarks. He would be more than happy to produce this extra food if the politicians would distribute it to the proper places or teach people to use food properly so that they would be adequately nourished.

We have had some considerable success in improving our food supply by genetic means. Professor Green has given us a lot of things to argue about, and here remarked that maybe we ought to concentrate more on food supplies from non-genetic means. It wouldn't be a good idea to cut off support for research in increasing food supply through genetic means. At the White House Conference one group is recommending ten million dollars a year for support of research that would increase the food supply by genetic means. This is something I don't think that Professor Green would argue with either. But I might point out that I'm considerably optimistic about food. I think that we are going to have man killing himself by pollution long before he starves to death. For example, if we would take the present production of corn in the United States and convert it to the Opaque 2 type of corn, which has almost the value of skim milk protein, our production in one year would be just about enough to take care of the population of this country for two years with no other source of food. I am not sure that we would want to all become long-nosed vegetarians, and just keep a few of our animals in the zoos for the education of our great-grandchildren, but it is a possibility. We could all become vegetarians, but this wouldn't be necessary. Nevertheless, I am saying there is adequate food, that we could produce adequate food. There is no reason why anyone should not reach his full mental capabilities because of lack of food, however this isn't happening now. It isn't the fault of the scientists; it is certainly the fault of our system that we can't get food to people who need it.

Directions

PRESTON N. WILLIAMS

The Task Ahead: A More Open Discussion

The task which confronts me is an almost impossible one. No single person is able without a measure of luck to suggest accurately the most important areas for future conversation between medical and life scientist and ethicist. Any selection by one individual inevitably reflects his bias and ignorance as well as his possible insight. Each reader must trust his own judgment after picking apart the panel and workshop conversation. My conclusion is no attempt to summarize them, but is rather a setting down of one social ethicist's reaction to the whole.

My first reaction is one of awe and appreciation for the achievements of the medical and life sciences. Participation in the conference enables one to know that man is "little less than God," and crowned with glory, honor, and dominion. Too frequently twentieth century man celebrates only his problems and accepts too complacently the marvels of our world and the creations of science. We awake from our apathy only to play childishly with our science, to complain about its cost, dangers, or threats, to blame it for government's and industry's misuse, or to fasten upon it our inattention to the problems of the poor, the aged, and the dying. Seldom if ever do we follow the slow pace of discovery, agonize over the heartbreak and disappointment of the researcher or the difficulty of his problem. Ethicists almost never involve themselves in the process of creative discovery in the laboratory. Their reflection comes after the act of discovery or when the researcher is on the brink of discovery. This is perhaps as it must be, yet the very nature of the ethicist's responsibility suggests he begin with a sense of appreciation for all the labors that have preceeded his own involvement. In the field of medicine and the life sciences the labor and achievement has been astonishing. The universe within has been understood so well that the universe without needs to be reordered.

One of the major tasks ahead for medical and life scientist and ethicist is the task of making more distinct the understanding of the inner world of medicine and biology and the outer world of human societies. The two worlds cannot be made separate because the body is the basic unit in both, but failure to recognize their distinctness will only result in scientists assuming a competence they do not possess and ethicists intervening in processes that should be beyond their right to scrutinize. Much of the hostility and tension that exist between the researcher and the ethicist seems to me to result from this failure to draw lines between the work of scientific inquiry concerning the human organism and the evaluation of man's acts and their consequences. Man may have the right to know all things, but this right is not without its limits. We need to know what these limits are. Those that are set cannot, however, be simply the consequences of what men in some past age have thought to be right and good. They must incorporate the best of what we do not yet fully know. The awkwardness of cooperation between medical and life scientist and ethicist is due not to the ethicist's lack of facts and laboratory experience, but to his reluctance to pioneer in creating new values and to be instructed in this endeavor by scientists. Similarly the scientist must learn from the ethicist a host of facts that are not clearly perceived in the hospital room or research facility. To open oneself to instruction in matters in which one feels oneself to be most expert is a difficult undertaking, but this is precisely what is needed. The scientist must come to know that his undermining of certain orderings of society, for example, the patterns of dying or dating, mating, and child bearing, do not thereby make him capable of alone determining the new patterns in these areas or the possessors of all facts pertinent for construction of the new patterns. The ethicists, on the other hand, must not seek to guard every former definition of the normative even when the facts upon which it was based are no longer acceptable. Scientist and ethicist must learn to respect each other's expertise and the limited nature of their special knowledge while applying that knowledge together with their general intelligence and wisdom to the new complexities facing man. To mutually adopt this posture of humility and honest questing after new truth in respect to man's identity and dignity is an imperative emerging from this conference.

This should not be equated with improvement in communications although that may be a prerequisite. What we need is not simply communication, but a new understanding of "common sense." The rapid explosion of knowledge with its attendant problems for the larger society has made us all cakes half-turned. Ethicist and scientist extrapolate too quickly from expert knowledge about a few things to supposed wisdom about all things. Competence in one area of investigation is used to mask one's shoddy thinking in another. The answer I submit to this pretension of wisdom where there is little wisdom is not to be found in making all persons scientists or ethicists, but rather in admitting our mutual ignorance about much of life and seeking through "common sense" to see a bit farther through the darkness. When one has sifted through all that was said about the population problem and the regulation of behavior one is amply convinced that the fate of mankind cannot be assured by either ethicist or scientist. Neither group is eminent in respect to social worthiness or social responsibility. They were all, however, sensitive, caring souls. Moreover, they appear to be in agreement in urging the necessity of preserving as much freedom as possible for man while seeking to convince man that he must change his attitude toward child-bearing. Technology is needed in order to provide the means, but the crux of the population problem seemed to be the creation of an enlightened communal ethic among a large number of human individuals; scientist and ethicist must cooperate to bring into existence a new "common sense." The experts must not denigrate the intelligence of the masses or seek to dictate to them in the name of science or the good. We must have sufficient faith in the mass of mankind — many of whom are themselves expert in some human activity — to seek to educate them in the knowledge and information necessary for their well-being. Scientist and ethicist alike must then learn to encounter each other and their fellows as humans concerned with abundant living and address each other as men, not expert and laymen. Unless we desire a dictatorship of philosopher-kings, now frequently called meritocracy, this can be our only way. How to elevate the wisdom of the common culture so that men can intelligently think about the options life holds for them is a major problem emerging from the conference.

The general nature of the "population problem" and "human control" serve to recommend the improvement of "common sense" as a major aspect of any biological or ethical solution. Improved common sense would also be helpful in dealing with the problems related to organ transplants and the extension of life. In the conference the misunderstandings between medical researchers and ethicists seemed to be greatest here. The medical researcher seemed to be saying that all ethical problems in this area are fundamentally biological and we shall solve them in our laboratory. If we need ethical assistance we shall secure it from scientific ethicists, that is, other medical doctors or psychiatrists on our staff. In addition they were loath to give credence to any statement seemingly critical of the medical profession. If our conference was at all representative and if the medical reaction was not overly determined by the public reaction to an early phase of heart transplantation, we need to take as a major problem the building of trust between the doctors and the ethicists, especially philosophical and theological ethicist. While it is true that some doctors are themselves exceptionally able humanists and ethicists, it does not seem wise to rely wholly upon the medical profession or a segment thereof for full guidance in respect to organ transplantation and the extension of life. Their experience and knowledge is too parochial; their loyalty is too limited. Trust and then cooperation needs to be built between medical researcher, ethicist, and the general public. The views outlined above about common sense are equally necessary here.

A second task is that of distinguishing between social and individual responsibility. What responsibility does society or the government have for underwriting further exploration in organ transplantation and extension of life? It should be made clear that any responsibility is not determined by the medical profession's conception of the ideal relationship between doctor and patient. In the discussion the medical researchers failed to establish the social and medical necessity of organ transplantation or the extension of life. It was quite clear that society needs to support medical research; it was not made clear why organ transplantation deserves priority. Medicine itself does not appear to be dependent upon it and society has little to gain from its success because the profession did not weigh delivery system research very heavily. We do not seek to deny the doctor's right to do that research which he feels constrained to do by personal or professional conscience. We also accept the notion that the profession is responsible for defining for its own usage proper health care, death, dying and so forth. We seek simply to assert that medical researchers cannot require government or society, without their consent, to subsidize what some medical researchers deem mandatory without first convincing government or society that the research is necessary or desirable. Moreover we question the wisdom of a strategy that seeks to so convince by defining the issue as exclusively biological and open to understanding only by the researchers themselves. Like management, medicine if it is to subsist at the public treasury must submit some of its traditional prerogatives to determination by teams on which the medical profession is one member among several. The problem to be tackled, then, is the nature of public participation in decisions concerning medical research and health care and not the supposed wisdom of doctors or ethicists on certain matters. Public participation will not render insufficient the medical input. Our social history is one in which the regulated manages to preserve sizable control over the regulators, but in the process becomes socially more enlightened. Inclusion of the public will then widen the medical profession's sense of social responsibility and cause it to seek more fully to inform the public about its investment in certain areas of medical research and health care. The time to begin the process is now while the spectacular nature of transplantation has the public open to the new and novel and while neither the medical researchers or the ethicists possesses sufficient knowledge to be called expert on any of the issues involved. Widespread usage of the mass media that touches every aspect of our population would be one of many suitable means for beginning this educational campaign.

The topics of genetic engineering and counseling reinforce the conviction that what is most needed is a rigorous program designed to improve the average layman's understanding of the functioning of his own body. I have no doubt that human evolution has come to supplement natural evolution. Man can and will, in large measure, determine his biological organism and in turn himself. The science of genetics together with immunology will be the areas of greatest promise and danger. In our view the great changes will proceed first from genetics. James Gustafson's query about what is normatively human must therefore be answered, but not by experts alone. The inability of any to know what changes shall flow from genetic intervention suggests that neither medical or life scientist or ethicist should be the new high priest. While the computer and mathematical models prevalent in science predispose us to think in terms of levels of control and to exalt those at the top of the control pyramid, freedom remains a precious commodity and it should be preserved and increased. This can be accomplished only if the general level of intelligence concerning the new behavioral, surgical, and genetic intervention is raised and all men have a greater opportunity to participate in defining the normative. Freedom is a prerequisite for establishing what is sacred and worthwhile about human life and what of human life must therefore be open only to the most deliberate and controlled experimentation. The pressure of population growth and the seductive nature of man's quest after the secrets of life make genetic counseling a necessity and genetic engineering inevitable. Either if done on a large scale will probably increase more than transplantation or life extension the likelihood of human manipulation, especially racial and class injustice and control by a few. Although the risk of danger to human life and to the powerless minorities cannot be completely removed it can be minimized by the institution of a comprehensive program of genetic and medical education. Scientist and ethicist should work to create such a program and to make it readily available to all by means of educational television, secondary schools and all other channels of mass communication. Again, the task is that of increasing the knowledge of the general public in order that they may participate meaningfully in the decision-making process. Genetics is where the inner and outer world meet. Man needs therefore to be kept fully informed and to be enabled to decide what society will sanction as legitimate research and experimentation. The most significant problem emerging from our conference then is how shall we preserve man's right to know. The right belongs to all men, not simply ethicist and the goal is not simply more research in new institutes for life scientist and ethicist, but the communication of information to the mass of mankind. By raising the general level of knowledge and increasing the rational participation of all individuals and groups we shall be best preparing ourselves to save ourselves. Man is "little less than God" and the more rational and informed his decision-making the more man is apt to approach the destiny intended by the Creator.

Spin-Off Projects and Action Programs

The Conference on Identity and Dignity of Man represents an attempt to penetrate the isolationism of physicians, surgeons, and medical leaders grappling with the moral and ethical problems of transplantation and life-saving medical discoveries, to communicate the concerns of the molecular geneticists, genetic engineers, and life scientists pondering the potential impact for society and culture of the key to the genetic code that can provide for regulation of the quality of future generations, to consider the societal and ethical implications of overpopulation, overhunger, and overpollution as related to biotechnological advances, and to bring the isolated but enlightened ethicists and theologians into intellectual contact and future action with their counterparts in science, technology, and medicine. The tendency for scientists and especially physicians to decide these matters among themselves and then to expect the theologians to spread the predetermined word to the people is about as absurd as the course whereby theologians and ethicists per se might establish the limitations on scientific and biotechnological research and medical practices by virtue of preconceived notions on moral and ethical implications. For reasons of semantics, tradition and professional defensiveness among others, the effort to engage in a meaningful interdisciplinary dialogue was achieved successfully only in part, but a significant start was made. The need and desirability for continuity in some format was generally recognized, and the value of the effort was appreciated.

Time and sustained effort are needed to explore controversial issues brought into focus at the Conference but not resolved, such as:

(1) implementation of incentives and rewards not to overproduce
(2) need for the concept of world-wide citizenship in lieu of predominating nationalism as requisite for life without war
(3) implications of the evolutionary concept that the welfare of the species and the group or colony may prevail over that of the individual per se
(4) notion of density dependent ethics

293

(5) concept that man as an individual is not aggressively violent by virtue of biological heritage, as contrasted with frequent cruelties of group behavior

(6) importance of the inheritance of the behavioral patterns implied by the term "love"

(7) search for security as expressed by resurgence of astrology, resort to crutches of drugs and alcohol, wave of anti-intellectualism and anti-science

(8) pros and cons of "genetic manipulation" and cloning with respect to ethics and moral issues

(9) political misuse of science and technology

(10) proposition of the Asimov-model society on the moon as an experiment in living with dignity and anti-pollution

(11) implications and validity of brain death as opposed to heart death

(12) Erroneous semantic trap as in the unfortunate connotation of term "experimentation" as applied to transplantation in contemporary surgery

(13) debate on the resources available to cover the cost of transplantation as opposed to the cost of delivery of health care

(14) who shall decide who shall receive the transplant, who shall conceive the child, what shall be the make-up of the genetic pool, who has the right to die?

(15) overcoming the squeamish, ethical and moral concepts that are associated with abortion, sterilization, the "pill," and population discipline

(16) need for *science* as a background and requisite for theologians.

Deployment of modern media, formation of student activist groups, impact of disciples such as Ralph Nader, and the obvious acute nature of the problems have penetrated the lethargic nature of the general public and made an impression on the vote-getters in our legislative circles locally and nationally. With respect to ecology, the tendencies for overcompensation and faddism are evident to some extent, but we believe that the prognosis is optimistic for sustained and balanced efforts in spite of prevalent pessimism among some extremists. Nevertheless, the basic threat of overpopulation must be curbed and solutions of the relevant cultural, ethical and political problems require the kind of universal statesmanship that tests the validity of the concept that man is capable of preservation of the dignity and identity of life for human or other animal and plant species in the face of the selfish vested interests that have thus far depleted our natural resources and wasted our lives and energy in war as a consequence of the short-sighted nature of the motivating forces of our industrial peers, nationalistic government leaders and heads of state, politicians, pillars of the church and community, and the so-called common man.

Hopefully, the message of the Conference and possible extensions of the dialogue will be fostered by the publication of the proceedings. Several objectives for future undertakings are identified as follows:

(1) addition of a life-scientist and appropriate courses in biological science in the academic programs of schools of theology.

(2) addition of courses in social ethics and orientation to theology to the liberal arts curriculum above and beyond the usual offerings in comparative religion and philosophy.

(3) formation of monthly interdisciplinary discussion groups to keep the dialogue going.

In a broad general sense, the discussions at the Conference and the tenor of the times point to the need for action programs, partly to respond to the needs of society for remedial efforts to contend with overpopulation and relevant problems of hunger, pollution and destruction of natural resources, and partly to dispel the distrust and dangerous anti-science and anti-intellectual attitude that is rampant among the public and reflected by student reaction towards industry, education, and parents. In fact, Dr. Isaac Asimov made the point that the insidious nature of the anti-science attitude of people in general may be the greatest threat of all to civilization as charcterized by the phrase "identity and dignity of man."

As a response to the challenging dialogue indicative of the need for educational reforms and as a sequel to the Conference, we at Boston University have made the following innovative efforts to establish interdisciplinary programs with "relevance" to the needs of society and appeal to the students:

(a) introduction of two new courses in the life sciences for non-science majors without prerequisites, namely, *Brain, Endocrines and Behavior,* concerned with the biological basis and evolution of behavior as determined by information processing and integrative systems with relevance to contemporary problems of crowding, violence, drugs and ecological perturbations; and *Reproduction, Development and Heredity,* concerned with principles, mechanisms and relevance to contemporary problems of population. These two courses will endeavor to generate an understanding of the respective roles of environment and genetics in the determination of the identity and dignity of man.

(b) introduction of a new interdisciplinary academic project in environmental studies, *Arts Environmental Studies Optional Project* (AESOP), consisting of an approach through systems analysis of the parameters of the harbor city formulated as a model for individual and group project work for students from diverse disciplines and departments such as economics, chemistry, biology, sociology, law, political science and others. Lectures, discussion, and field work will involve participation of faculty, students and extramural sponsors and to be followed by a summer practicum for additional credit. This project is in operation at Boston University and the New England Aquarium under sponsorship of the National Endowment for the Humanities and an incentive grant from Arthur D. Little, Inc.

(c) introduction of a new voluntary program of extramural field experience, consisting of the pairing of students with external sponsors for learning experiences outside the classroom with lawyers, doctors, engineers, architects, business managers, educators, urban specialists, government administrators and others.

We have become proponents of the notion of a youth cadre for societal service required of every young man and woman in America at an appropriate period during their secondary school education. A nation-wide compulsory plan of this type would have several objectives such as:

(a) incorporation of the attitudes implied by the cliches of "relevance," "responsibility," and "training" in the educational preparation and maturation of our youth.

(b) provision of an interval for reflection, manual effort, change of pace, and preparation for the future

(c) contribution of youth to the identity and dignity of man through service in capacities that might be described as menial, for a mere subsistence stipend.

The philosophy basic to the notion of the youth cadre for societal service is the generation of responsibility and satisfaction that accrues to the individual from service to others. The pragmatic aspects include the need for inexpensive and continual sources of labor for such chores as mail delivery, milk delivery, street cleaning, garbage removal, truck driving, and many other vital services that nevertheless do not require skilled labor and therefore should not burden the taxpayer with salaries that escalate annually comparable with those for skilled occupations and professions requiring years of experience. We believe that a practical plan can be designed and could be implemented fairly with great advantages to our children as individuals and to society as an entity.